▣ ANIMALS, MEN AND MYTHS ▣

Translated from the German

HARPER & BROTHERS, NEW YORK

ANIMALS, MEN AND MYTHS

An Informative and Entertaining History
of Man and the Animals Around Him by

RICHARD LEWINSOHN

ANIMALS, MEN AND MYTHS

Published in Germany as
Eine Geschichte der Tiere
by Morus

🔲 CONTENTS 🔲

INTRODUCTION by C. W. Ceram   xvii

PART ONE: PREHISTORY

I. ORIGINS   3

Division of Labor – Between Water and Land – New Weapons: Teeth

II. THE AGE OF GIANTS   12

Evolution and Revolution – Limits of Growth – The Art of Flight – Mass Death

III. THE GREAT MIGRATIONS   24

Green Pastures – The Herd Instinct – The Migrations of the Horse – America, Land of Immigrants

IV. THE SUPERANIMAL   32

The Deluge – Before or After Us? – Frontal Assault – Neanderthal Man – Ape Men – The Ancestors of Man – Artificial Claws – Stature and Brain – Transition or Beginning?

PART TWO: ANTIQUITY AND THE MIDDLE AGES

V. HUNTING AND BREEDING LIVESTOCK   57

How Animals Are Domesticated – Cave Art – I think, ergo I become – The Origin of "Capital"

VI. SACRED ANIMALS   71

Metempsychosis – Totem – Tabu – Animal Gods

VII. FABLE AND ZOOLOGY   83

The Heroic Horse – Frogs and Mice – Aesop's Fables – The Sage of Stagira

VIII. MEAT AND CIRCUS GAMES   96

The Kitchen of Lucullus – The Sacrificial Swine – Heroes of the Arena – War Elephants

IX. THE FEUDAL ANIMAL   108

Riders out of the East – The Knight's Charger – Falconry – The Dog Becomes Presentable at Court

PART THREE: THE AGE OF DISCOVERY

X. THE NEW WORLD   125

The Little Rabbits of Porto Santo – Columbus's Eight Pigs – Spanish Centaurs – Puma and Llama – The Land of the Parrots

XI. THE CONQUEST OF THE NORTH   137

The Herring Shortage and the Hanseatic League – Beaver War – Boyar Pelts

XII. REBIRTH OF SUPERSTITION   148

Sea Serpents and Mermen – The Wonder Beasts of the Humanists – Fish Portraits

XIII. MERCHANT TAILORS   163

The Silk Road – Queen Elizabeth's Stockings – Sheep of the Unbelievers – Revolution in Wool

XIV. THE BEAUTIFUL ANIMAL   175

The Medicis' Menagerie – The High School – Bull-fighting – Genealogy of the Bulls

PART FOUR: THE AGE OF IDEAS

XV. BATTLE FOR THE SOUL   191

Speech and Thought – Perception and Apperception – The World under the Microscope – Nature's Clockwork

XVI. EQUALITY OF RIGHTS   204

The First Modern Animal Painter – La Fontaine's Sources – The Creatures of Prometheus – The Bee State

XVII. ORGANIZATION   217

Fixing the Species – Linnaeus, Corrupter of Morals

– Primates, the Aristocratic Class – A Monster Disturbs the System – Buffon the Sceptic

XVIII. THE FIFTH CONTINENT   231

The Discovery of the Kangaroo – The Paradox of the Duckbill – The Bird Paradise

XIX. EXPERIMENTS WITH ANIMALS   242

Animal Magnetism – Galvani's Frog's Leg – The Force of Regeneration – The First Five-Balloon Passengers – Conflict over Vivisection – Animal Protection and Veterinary Science

PART FIVE: THE MACHINE AGE

XX. FEAR OF HUNGER   261

Malthusianism – Potency and Fertility – The Art of Crossbreeding – The Settlement of the Pampas – Frozen Meat

XXI. HORSEPOWER   273

Post Coach and Railway – The Patriarchs of the Thoroughbred – Horse-racing and Betting – Circus and Zoo

XXII. THE DARWINIAN REVOLUTION   289

Schopenhauer's Theory of Descent – The Case of Wallace – The Battle of the Apes at Oxford – Victory of Evolution

XXIII. BATTLE AGAINST SICKNESS   302

The Miracle in the Sheepfold – Mad Dogs – Martyrs of Serum Therapy – Hundreds of Millions with Malaria – Mosquitoes, Flies and Fleas

XXIV. THE INTELLIGENT ANIMAL   317

Feline Aesthetic – Intelligence and Instinct – The First Air-Mail – The Carrier Pigeon's War Memorial – Arithmetical Horses – The Rubicon of Speech

PART SIX: THE AGE OF CHEMISTRY

xxv. NATURAL PROPAGATION AND EUGENICS   335

Mathematics and Heredity – Laboratory-produced Creatures – Genetic Characters at Will – Heredity in East and West – Artificial Insemination

xxvi. SYNTHETICS AND SUBSTITUTES   350

The Origin of Margarine – Artificial Silk and Wool – Textiles from Milk

xxvii. BREEDING RARE ANIMALS   358

Outfoxing the Foxes – Ostrich and Alligator Farms – Japanese Pearl Culture

xxviii. THE POLITICAL ECONOMISTS' RECKONING   368

Bread or Meat – Wartime Slaughtering – Gandhi and the Sacred Cow – The Latifundian Economy – The Big Four of Chicago

xxix. THE ANIMAL'S FUTURE   378

Ecology – The Most Numerous Large Animal – The Bird's Special Privilege – Horses out of Work – Wool without Sheep – Decline in Meat Consumption – The Law of Devitalization – Independence of Man

INDEX   395

🔲 ILLUSTRATIONS 🔲

Figure

1. Animal development   7

2. One of the earliest representations of fossilized Ammonites (Ceruti and Chiocco, Musaeum Calceolarium, 1622)   8

3. Dinosaur, a nineteenth-century reconstruction   15

4. The skeleton of the primitive bird (Archaeopteryx) from the jurassic deposits near Solenhofen—one of the most important discoveries in palaeontology   18

5. The first birds had teeth: Ichthyornis of the Kansas Chalk   21

6. The oldest inhabitant of Montmartre; skull of the Palaeotherium, which Cuvier described in detail at the beginning of the nineteenth century   27

7. Giant salamander. As late as the beginning of the eighteenth century this skeleton was considered to be the remains of a prehistoric man *"Homo diluvii testis."* Ernst Camper and Cuvier corrected this error   37

8. Animals and men in the Quaternary   51

9. Cave picture from Alpera in Spain: woman gathering wild honey   57

10. Wild horse, cave bear, mammoth and cave lion. Drawing from a cave in the South of France (after Hoernes)   58

11. Hunting the wild boar. Dark red rock-painting in the Cueva del Chargo del Agua Amargo (Prov. Teruel)   62

12. Prehistoric hunting scene. Cave picture from East Spain   64

13. Men driving donkeys in ancient Egypt (after Lepsius)   68

14. Gilgamesh battling with lions; on a cylinder seal   72

15. Vulture of Upper Egypt   74

Figure

16. Animals in the life of ancient Egypt. *Top:* Fishermen. *Centre and bottom:* Egyptian herdsmen, cattle and donkeys (from an ancient picture)   80

17. Constellation of Taurus (after Buschik, *Sternenkunde und Erdgeschichte*, 1927)   84

18. Picture of a rider on a Greek drinking vessel   86

19. "The War of the Frogs and the Mice"; a sixteenth-century illustration   87

20. "The Truthful Man, the Liar and the Monkey" (*Aesop's Fables,* the Ulm edition, late Middle Ages)   90

21. "The Lion and the Mouse" (*Aesop's Fables,* the Ulm edition, late Middle Ages)   92

22. Roman animal paintings: mural from the market hall (marcellum) in Pompeii   98

23. Roman animal paintings: donkey and crocodile from Herculaneum   100

24. Garlanding the sacrificial bulls in Greece (British Museum)   102

25. Consulting the oracle. Roman augur inspecting the sacrifice   103

26. Assyrian armoured war dog. Relief from Birs Nimrud   106

27. Chinese war chariot of the Han dynasty, beginning of the Christian era   109

28. Horses of the Steppes (Scythian vase from Certomlyk)   112

29. French caricature of a troubadour (twelfth century)   115

30. The unicorn from the classical *Historia Animalium* by Konrad Gesner (1551)   119

31. Skeleton of the legendary unicorn (after B. Valentini, Musaeum Museorum, Frankfurt-on-Main, 1704)   120

32. Inn sign of the Fox Inn, Huntingdon, England   121

33. Conquest of the Aztecs by the horsemen of Cortés   131

34. Pre-Columbian drinking vessel of the Incas (Museo Nacional, Lima)   133

35. Stranded whale (after Olaus Magnus, 1532)   138

Figure

36. A great problem: providing England with fish (Angler, 1496)   141

37. Indians stag-hunting. In order to approach the animals unnoticed they have clad themselves in deerskins (illustration, about 1570)   143

38. Polar expedition of the Dutchman Barents (about 1596)   146

39. Fabulous snake from the *Buch der Weisheit der alten Weisen* (1483)   151

40. The sea serpent is immortal. The Daedalus Sea Serpent, which was "sighted" 1848   152

41. Young dragon (after Petrus Bellonius, 1553)   155

42. Fossil fish (Aldrovandi, Musaeum Metallicum, 1648)   160

43. Winding silk, from a Chinese picture of the eighteenth century   166

44. The first magnified picture of a piece of silk, taken and drawn by Robert Hooke (1665)   169

45. Dürer's rhinoceros (1515)   176

46. Picture of a triumphal procession of the Renaissance period (Francesco Colonna, Poliphili Hypnerotomachia)   177

47. Bull-baiting with dogs. Spanish woodcut of the eighteenth century   182

48. Bullfight in Peru, from El Toro (Instituto de Arte Peruano)   184

49. An animal-fight in the "Jägerhof" at Dresden (copper engraving, 1746)   187

50. The first illustration of microscopic fossils (Aldrovandi, Musaeum Metallicum, 1648)   198

51. Jacques de Vaucanson's mechanical duck, which picked up grain, digested and expelled it   200

52. Illustration of La Fontaine's fable—"The Stork and the Fox"   209

53. A drawing by Grandville: the queen bee takes the salute   212

Figure

54. Two horses talking. Illustration by Grandville for Swift's *Gulliver's Travels*   213

55. National assembly of the horses. Illustration by Grandville for Swift's *Gulliver's Travels*   214

56. Man with Kangaroo. Rock painting from Northwest Australia   233

57. Duckbill or platypus. After an old illustration   235

58. The extinct giant bird Moa which lived in New Zealand probably looked like this   238

59. Dodo. A sketch by the Dutchman Roelandt Savery, who was one of the last to see the bird and who reproduced it in a drawing   240

60. "The Great Steam-duck." American imaginary drawing of a jetplane (1841)   251

61. Veterinary surgeons and their remedies: syringes for enemas, apparatus for opening the mouth, etc. (copper engraving, 1701)   257

62. Three sheep with one head (engraving of the seventeenth century)   265

63. A caricature of new machinery: a "beardshaving mill" shaving a dozen men at the same time (about 1754)   274

64. An engine patented in England in 1829; it was meant to be driven by one harnessed horse   275

65. Patent "Impulsoria" (1850), one of the last attempts to prevent the replacement of horse power by steam power   279

66. The defeat of the horses is complete: mechanical tramway disguised as horse carriage   280

67. The superseded cart horses are compelled to earn their living in this melancholy way (caricature of 1834)   283

68. Heraldic menagerie. Political animal caricature, about the middle of the nineteenth century, by Grandville   286

69. "A Runaway War-horse" by Adolph von Menzel (1840)   290

Figure

70. Mechanical money box "Mad Dog," from the period when Pasteur undertook his experiments in fighting hydrophobia. If one pulls the button the dog snatches the coin from the stooping boy   308

71. Dogs' heads from Lavater's *Physiognomische Fragmente zur Beförderung der Menschenkenntnis und Menschenliebe*   321

72. "Three Little Wolves" by Walt Disney   328

73. Apparatus for experimenting on the colour sensitivity of animals (R—red; G—green; the animal in B is meant to find its way to A)   331

74. Chromosomes of the Fruit-fly (*Drosophila melanogaster*), on which innumerable modern experiments in heredity have been made   340

75. The eternal stork legend. Illustration by Theodor Hosemann of Hans Andersen's fairy tale "The Storks" (1851)   343

76. Dance of the Mock Turtle and the Gryphon (from Lewis Carroll's *Alice in Wonderland*)   359

77. Pen drawing by an unknown artist of the nineteenth century (The Metropolitan Museum of Art, New York)   363

78. Baluchitherium, the largest extinct mammal, giants of the present day and man (drawing by H. Ziska)   383

79. Prairie horses. Copper engraving from Catlin, *North American Indians* (London, 1845)   387

80. Transition from animal to vegetable and mineral matter   392

PLATES

facing page

Georges Cuvier, the "Napoleon of Palaeontology." His theory of cataclysms was the greatest obstacle in the way of the theory of evolution   46

D'Orbigny, Cuvier's most influential pupil, who proclaimed the theory of twenty-seven successive creations   46

Gabriel von Marx: "The Ape Man of Java" (Haeckel Museum in Jena)   47 *facing page*

Cave painting from Altamira, North Spain   78

Prehistoric picture of a herd. Hodein Magoll, Nubian
    Desert   79

Animals shown in relief on a silver cup from Gudestrup in
    Jutland (National Museum, Copenhagen)   82

Egyptian bed, eighteenth dynasty. Painted wood. Hittite
    lion of a Royal palace; from the Karatepe, in the south-
    eastern part of modern Turkey   83

Roman watchdog. Mosaic from Pompeii   106

Stallion from the Erechtheum on the Acropolis in Athens   110

Horseman from the west frieze of the Parthenon, fifth
    century B.C.   110

Knight on armoured horse, statue on the grave of Mastino
    II Scaliger in Verona, fourteenth century   111

Silkworm cultivation in Japan, from a coloured woodcut
    by the Japanese master Utamaro   111

Albertus Magnus, Bishop of Regensburg (1193–1280)   150

The French potter Palissy was one of the first to explain
    correctly the nature of fossils   150

"The Peaceable Kingdom," painting by Edward Hicks
    (1780–1849); The Metropolitan Museum of Art, New
    York)   151

Game of polo at the Mogul's court, Indian miniature of
    the eighteenth century (Berliner Staatl. Sammlung)   166

"Bullfight" by Goya   166

Capriole of the Spanish Riding School in Vienna   167

Has an animal a soul? René Descartes "no," Gottfried Wil-
    helm Leibniz "yes"   222

Hawking. Engraving, seventeenth century   222

Animal picture by P. Potter, Holland, seventeenth century   222

Buffon, Linné's adversary, was a forerunner of the evolu-
    tionists   223

Carl Linné, the great classifier of the animal kingdom   223

"Old Brehm," father of the well-known naturalist   223 *facing page*

Village circus, about 1820   278

"Dancing Bear," lithograph by Otto Speckter   278

The victors over horses: James Watt, Gottlieb Daimler   279

The theory of evolution in the nineteenth century. Etienne
   Geoffroy Saint-Hilaire, Charles Darwin   294

The ape problem   295

Village street as seen by man   334

The same street seen through the eye of a fly (after
   Uexküll and Brock)   334

Carrier pigeon as cameraman and the picture which the
   camera took between the wing-tips   334

The animal in philately   335

French courting card   335

American poster advertising a remedy against hog cholera 335

Gaucho on the Argentine pampas   382

The holy ram, early Ptolemaic period   382

The sheep as a domestic animal; merino ram   382

Wonderfully trained animals shown on an English variety
   stage   383

The Elephant of Notre-Dame, Paris   383

🔲 INTRODUCTION 🔲

by C. W. Ceram

ANIMALS have made history no less than men. Animals were gods to the ancients, but they also fed men and clothed them. By the labor of animals the face of the land was first conquered and then reshaped, and with animals whole wars were won. Animal and man—here is an epic of friendship and enmity which has been set forth in the earliest myths and songs and in the religions of all peoples. In the last century technological advances appeared to be relegating all animals to an insignificant role in man's life; but then a last and most terrible beast was recognized, one that had invisibly won more battles than the war-elephants which Hannibal took across the Alps. And a new kind of hunting began: microbe hunting.

There are many books on animals. This book seems to me one of the most fascinating because it deals with the animals of the earth, air and water not only as zoological objects, but also as social beings. There have been special investigations of this subject by ecologists interested in the relatively new "science of organic communities." But hitherto there has been no book that has treated—so comprehensively, and with such mastery of subject-matter extending through millions of years—the history of animals, the history of the earth and the concurrent history of mankind.

Naturally, a zoologist could not undertake such a task. A book of this sort had to be the work of a sociologist—which is what Lewinsohn is—of an authority on the old and new forms of society. Coupled with this, the author had to possess a sovereign knowledge of the zoological science of our time. Such a many-sided intellect is rare. But it is even rarer for someone completely at home in two sciences to manifest a talent for brilliant writing, a sense of humor that enables him with deadly certainty to put his finger on the comical elements in the most solemn scientific disputes, and a dramatic sense that instantly organizes the driest theoretical conflict into a drama of the mind. It is the sheerest delight to follow where he leads us through the animal kingdoms, the realms of extinct and living beasts, and to observe with him the ponderous and helpless primordial giants, the deadly little mites that have only recently become visible, the venerable creatures of fable and the hard-working domesticated animals.

To me, one of the most intriguing chapters is the one in which the animals figure as objects of the scientist's studies, that is to say, play their part in the dramatic development of modern thought. Here the great Buffon is ranged against Linnaeus the classifier, Darwin against the cultivated laymen of his time, Robert Koch against the whole world. This makes exciting reading indeed.

No less exciting are the author's forecasts. What may be the future of animal life on a globe whose very geological structure man is shaping, exploiting, controlling? A vital question for the century in which man has launched the most inhumane of wars and has simultaneously—for the first time in fifty thousand years— founded societies for the prevention of cruelty to animals. In dealing with this enigma, Lewinsohn has some arresting things to say of human as well as animal nature.

This history of animals is more than fascinating reading, however. It is also highly useful. It is one of those books that fill a gaping void, a want whose existence we were not even aware of until the book was written. Such books instantly become the staples of our cultural heritage. That, I am confident, will be the destiny of this book.

PREHISTORY

🔲 I 🔲

Origins

MOST modern biologists believe that life originated thousands of millions of years ago when the fiery mass of the earth cooled and hardened. All living matter contains carbon, oxygen and hydrogen. These elements were present in the dense clouds of water vapour and carbon dioxide that once enveloped the young earth. Some sort of agent was needed to start the process of changing these inorganic substances into organic matter and possibly this agent was found in the sun's ultra-violet rays, then much more powerful than they are today. We can only speculate about the nature of the earliest life.

The first living creatures we actually know of were water-dwellers. Traces of them have been found in the rocks of North America and northern Europe, embedded in strata that were deposited by the seas in which these organisms lived. Their forms are so similar to present-day marine animals that there can be no doubt that they were inhabitants of the seas.

From this fact a good many biologists have concluded that organic life originated in the waters of the earth. Their argument seems logical. The raw surface of the land was still too hot to permit life while the waters were already cooled off sufficiently for proteins, of which all life is composed, to survive. If we care to speculate along Darwinian lines we might say that even if life originated on dry land, water was its necessary refuge. It had to flee to the water or be burned to death. Hence the water-dwelling animals would be the survivors in the struggle for existence.

This much seems certain—that the more highly differentiated

3

animals found conditions in the water more congenial than conditions on dry land. We do not know what the first living beings were like but the oldest marine animals of which we have a fossil record were already quite highly developed.

DIVISION OF LABOUR

The development of multicellular living beings out of unicellular creatures is something of a mystery from the evolutionary point of view. The usual theory is that colonies of like individuals developed first. Since there were no physiological differences among them, they formed what is known as homogeneous tissue. Later, each of these individual cells took over special functions; thus differentiation of the cells came into being. This is charmingly anthropomorphic reasoning by analogy—quite common in evolutionary theory. It assumes that nature imitates man and operates by the same principles of division of labour as a modern factory—or at least a primitive African village. Obviously, such analogies are not scientific explanations.

In speaking of differentiation we are already weighting the answer to the problem in a particular direction and excluding other possible solutions. Most theories of evolution are based upon the idea that complexity has developed out of originally simple organisms. But this does not necessarily mean that the more complex organisms were formed by the splitting up of simple original units. They might also have developed by the synthesis of various elements.

Empedocles, the first Greek thinker to deal with this problem, conceived of the evolutionary process in strictly synthetic terms. First, he argued, the parts must have been present; then a whole developed out of them. But this argument sets considerable difficulties. In order to present the principle vividly, Empedocles used curious images which incidentally reveal close observation of the lower animals. First, he said, hair, eyes, arms and fingers evolved; later the various parts joined together, but quite imperfectly at first. Some living creatures had eyes in their arms, the head attached to the legs, and ears on their hands instead of fingers. Such malformed creatures could not survive, however. It required an infinite number of combinations before organisms capable of survival were formed.

At bottom this theory is nothing less than the Darwinian principle of natural selection. Nature, that is, had to experiment for a long time before she found the proper way to produce organs and organisms capable of withstanding the struggle for existence. Improvements could be made only by better combinations. Lamarck and his school, on the other hand, wanted to explain evolution by adjustment to the environment; but this explanation presupposes an innate capacity for adjustment—which is precisely what the non-fit would lack. And the Lamarckian theory does not in the least account for original differentiation—for there can be no doubt that in homogeneous tissue all the cells can perform the functions of reproduction as well as feeding.

Differentiation, therefore, must have started by the joining together of various cells. We must assume that some cells whose reproductive abilities were meagre or totally atrophied joined with cells having stronger reproductive powers. The former would then take care of feeding and the latter of reproduction. It is not even certain that both came from the same mother-cell. Possibly the multicellular creatures which first achieved this separation of functions came into being from a joining of cells of different origins.

At any rate, it seems illogical to suppose that no other forms of effective synthesis took place until the copulation of bisexual organisms developed. Even though evolution as a whole may not have followed one single principle, it may be assumed that in all phases of evolution synthesis was a crucial factor.

BETWEEN WATER AND LAND

By the beginning of the Palaeozoic era, as the geologists call it, a great variety of metazoa or multicellular animals existed side by side with the unicellular protozoa. The land was still inhospitable to them, and all lived in the seas. A few algae had taken a firm grip upon underwater rocks and were beginning to reach slender tips out above the surface of the sea. These varieties of seaweed were the first life to lend colour to the primordial world. By taking in the sun's energy as it filtered down through the water and turning it into chlorophyll, they became green on the surface, blue farther down, brown still farther down, and at the sea bottom, where they received only a faint shimmer of sunlight, their colour was red.

Sponges, corals and jellyfish were the predominant animals. Sponges and polyps, many zoologists believe, were the ancestors of all higher animals. But soon—that is to say after millions of years—the trilobites appeared. These are the palaeontologists' showpiece, for every natural history museum possesses a large collection of their fossils. The young look like oval shellfish with the arch of the shell rather flattened. In later stages the three lobes which have given them their name become more defined; transverse segments appear; and in maturity they strongly resemble crabs with recognizable limbs. In spite of their armour they were extraordinarily flexible and could roll up into a ball like a hedgehog. Their habits have been the subject of much speculation. Some were bold hunters capable of swooping swiftly down upon other animals; others were peaceable vegetarians content to live on seaweed. Presumably they preferred living in mud flats and shoal waters. Guessing at their mode of life, we can give our imagination full play. We are, it must be remembered, still in the Cambrian Age—fifty million years ago according to the older geologists; 500 million years ago by the physicists' radioactive calendar.

The first students of the history of rocks and their relationship to the fossils embedded in them (and thus presumably of the same age as the rocks) were English scientists. Accordingly, some geological periods of the Palaeozoic bear English or Celtic names —the Cambrian, for example, is named after the Cambrian Mountains of southern Wales. But that is no reason to think that the

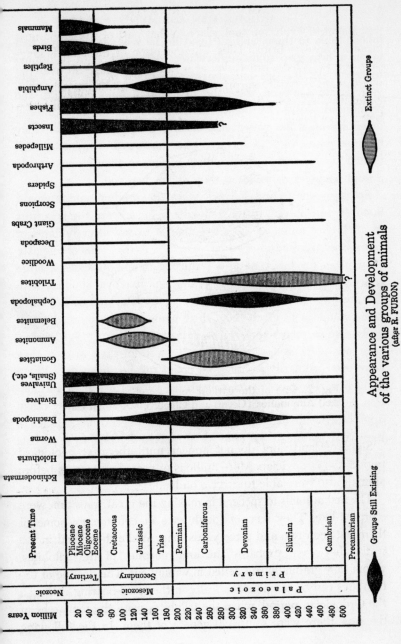

Appearance and Development
of the various groups of animals
(after R. FURON)

Fig. 1

Groups Still Existing   Extinct Groups

first stages of evolution took place in that part of the globe now occupied by the British Isles. The evolution of the animal kingdom seems to have proceeded at a fairly even pace all over the world. This is hardly surprising, since the earliest animals were water-dwellers. In all ages water has fostered communication better than land.

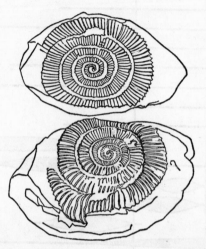

Fig. 2. One of the earliest representations of fossilized Ammonites (Ceruti and Chiocco, Musaeum Calceolarium, 1622)

Signs of land flora do not appear until the next geological period, the Ordovician. More millions of years had to pass before animals also were able to survive on land.

The first animals to succeed in making the great transition were scorpion-like. They were a tough race of conquerors, some of them between two and three yards long. While they lived in the water they were probably the arch enemies of the trilobites, whom they gradually succeeded in wiping out. The decline of the trilobites can be traced statistically in the fossil-bearing rocks. In the Ordovician period, when the trilobites were the monarchs of the seas, there were some 120 genera of them. In the following period, the Silurian, the great sea spiders ruled the waves and only some thirty-five genera of trilobites were left. Perhaps the increasing scarcity of available prey in the ocean was the reason the more adaptable animals went on land. But we must not take too rationalistic a view of mass migrations in the animal kingdom. Hunger has never been the sole motive for emigration.

NEW WEAPONS: TEETH

While life was spreading out on land there appeared in the waters a new type of creature. Nature seemed to have taken a dramatic leap, for this new animal was vastly different from all others. Many of the more primitive animals wore stout armour as a shield against the outer world; hinged shells, thickened skins or spines afforded them protection. As far as outward appearances went, the new animals were not nearly so well equipped for the struggle for life. All they had for covering was a smooth layer of thin scales. But inside their bodies they had a flexible framework of bone which gave them great strength without impairing their mobility. Although they paid no special attention to other life and preferred to feed on one another, they soon became the masters of the seas.

External armour disappeared more and more. In the oldest fishes, the ostracoderms, the fore part of the body is still encased in a hard shell. Others were plated with a kind of tortoise shell on the sides. In later species even such defences were dropped, for these fishes were equipped more for offence than defence, and they carried accordingly better offensive weapons than any that had previously existed. In addition to skeletons and powerful muscles they had movable jawbones and teeth. Something new had come into the world: a creature that could bite. The appearance of teeth was a sign of tremendous progress, the beginning of a new chapter in evolution. Henceforth the creature with the strongest teeth had the best chances of survival in the struggle for existence.

The age in which fishes were the most highly developed

creatures fell within the period known to geologists as the Devonian—after the ancient red sandstone in the county of Devon. At this period the seashores here and there were already covered with vegetation but the borderline between sea and land was still not well defined. Between the two elements lay a wide muddy plain where animal life developed very slowly. Only a few of the creatures that were washed to land by the tides were able to breathe. Some transitional types living today show how water animals became land-dwellers. The lungfishes dig their way into the mud. Their swim-bladders function as lungs and enable them to live through the summers when the mud dries out.

In about the middle of the Devonian—about 300 million years ago by radioactive measurement—tall ferns and conifers began a period of enormous growth. A sudden change in climate must have stimulated this efflorescence. Tropical heat spread over the polar regions; Greenland and Spitzbergen experienced equatorial temperatures. There followed vast floods which toppled over and rotted the first great virgin forests of the earth. When the water level sank again, similar vegetation shot up even more luxuriantly. For twenty million years this alternation of growth, flooding and decay continued. The sunken forests piled up in enormous layers —and became coal. The tremendous stocks of coal which for the past two centuries have provided men with their principal source of power were, in the main, produced during that primeval era known as the Carboniferous—the age of coal formation.

For all the vast upheavals and destruction of the Carboniferous Age, it was on the whole not unfavourable to the evolution of animal life. In the towering trees insects practised leaps and their first attempts at flight. Flying was difficult; the greatest problem for flying insects seems to have been the furling of wings after they had once been spread out.

The other great novelties were the amphibians and the reptiles. The theory of amphibian descent from fishes was as good as proved when Scandinavian scientists found several well-preserved

skeletons of the Ichtyostega—which smply means "fish-amphib-
ian"—in Devonian strata of Mount Celsius in eastern Greenland.
It was a creature with four short, stumpy legs, on each of which
were five toes apparently webbed for swimming, a head more
like that of an amphibian than a fish, but a distinctly fish-like tail.

The reptiles held their own even when the hothouse atmosphere of the Carboniferous was followed by the cooler climate
of the Permian period (named, by way of exception, after the
Russian province of Perm where its characteristic red shale and
sandstone formations are found). The Permian is the last major
division of the Palaeozoic era. Again vast changes in the surface
of the earth took place. Vast parts of the globe were covered with
ice. The cold wave—for reasons not yet adequately explained—
even struck as far as present-day tropical regions.

The Permian was not an age of rapid evolutionary development. Nevertheless, palaeontology records some newcomers of
historic interest. Permian cotylosaurians, bulky reptiles which still
crawled about clumsily on four feet, seem to have been the
ancestors of all higher forms of life. Or at any rate they seem to
have been in the direct line of the cold-blooded forebears of the
human race. Evolutionary theory is a bit vague about this, as it
so often is.

🔲 II 🔲

The Age of Giants

MEN'S view of the past depends largely upon the circumstances of the present. In the Napoleonic age, when Europe was being turned topsy-turvy and whole systems were being levelled and rebuilt within a few years, the most learned and dogmatic zoologist in France—Georges Cuvier—quite naturally applied the geological theory of catastrophes to the animal world. He argued that in the course of the tremendous upheavals which changed the face of the globe during prehistoric times all organic life had been repeatedly wiped out.

During the eighteen-thirties, on the other hand, the British geologist Charles Lyell tried to show that the great changes in the surface of the earth had been wrought slowly by the small, cumulative effects of water, fire and earthquakes. He rejected the theory of rude shocks and revolutionary changes, and maintained that the history of the earth had followed evolutionary lines. In effect, Lyell was extending to geology the political and social history of England, for during the past hundred and fifty years England had not experienced a revolution. On the whole her tremendous industrial development had taken place peacefully, without bloodshed or violent upheavals. Why should not Nature herself have adopted the same mode of gradual growth and progress?

Peaceful development did not, of course, totally exclude struggle. Progress, in fact, depended upon competition; the law of life was the "struggle for existence." Many would fall in this struggle, it was true. That was regrettable, but inevitable—for, as

Pastor Malthus had shown, there simply was not enough food to go around. Many would die, yet it was absurd to think that all together, fit as well as unfit, would be wiped out every so often, as the catastrophe theory held. Instead of alternations of doom and creation, Lyell saw the processes of death and life going on simultaneously—and on the whole he thought the forces of creation predominated over the forces of destruction. In quality, if not in quantity, life made steady advances.

EVOLUTION AND REVOLUTION

Lyell's epoch-making book, *The Principles of Geology*, prepared the ground. A quarter of a century later Charles Robert Darwin reluctantly yielded to persuasion and published his *Origin of Species*. In this work he applied to the organic world Lyell's basic principle that minute gradual changes could lead to the same results as violent revolutions. Darwin presented such a wealth of impressive evidence that Cuvier's catastrophe theory seemed to be conclusively refuted. Moreover, the very internal weaknesses of the catastrophe theory speeded the acceptance of Darwin's doctrine of gradual evolution. Cuvier had counted on only three great global upheavals and therefore conjectured only four distinct and separate creations of life, but later geological and palaeontological research had discovered more and more such revolutions. According to d'Orbigny, one of Cuvier's disciples, there had been at least twenty-six catastrophes—and consequently twenty-seven creations.

The clumsiness of such a theory is obvious. Darwinian doctrine had the advantage of simplicity and elegance. Even if there had been innumerable successive creations it was more convenient to consider them as a continuous series, as the human eye transforms the successive pictures in a strip of film into a single unbroken picture of motion. But whether the theory of evolution has greater inherent probability than the theory of catastrophes is another question entirely. The idea that all created life has been repeatedly destroyed appeals to our minds just as it did to our forefathers' in Napoleonic times. The knotty question in Cuvier's theory is the matter of periodic re-creation after each global catastrophe. Did Nature have to start all over again and create the most primitive living creatures anew? That is implausible, since conditions for the origin of life after Cuvier's upheavals were in no way like the conditions of a newly cooled earth's crust.

Even so, the catastrophe theory is still within the bounds of possibility. It has one great advantage over the Darwinian theory. Both theories take note, of course, of the breaks and sudden innovations in the natural line of descent. The Darwinists attribute these discrepancies to our ignorance; we have not yet found the intermediate stages, they say. The Cuvierists are more realistic and less speculative in that they take the gaps as they find them and blame Nature for them, not the state of our knowledge.

The history of life on earth seems to prove that on the whole, in spite of their weaker external armour, the newer and more complex forms of life withstood the periods of stress better than the older forms. The latter would probably have died out anyway; the disastrous weather and the global upheavals only hastened their passing.

Limits of Growth

The true victors in this fearful struggle for existence were the reptiles. Their success has been attributed to the fact that they were egg-laying animals whose young therefore had a better chance to survive. But this is a feeble explanation, since the eggshell is only a temporary protection. Once the shell was broken the young reptiles were just as vulnerable to the drought and cold as all other animals. All we can say definitely is that in the Darwinian sense reptiles were the "fittest."

The Mesozoic reptiles were very different in form from their primitive ancestors of the Carboniferous, and they continued to change with a rapidity rare among the higher animals. They grew taller and larger; their hind legs became solid pillars capable of supporting very heavy bodies.

Even after a hundred million years the remains of the dinosaurs, the most imposing members of the tribe, can fill us with wonder. We are altogether too easily impressed by sheer size. While we take it for granted that animals can be one thousand

Fig. 3. Dinosaur, a nineteenth-century reconstruction

and even one million times smaller than ourselves, we are awestruck to think that any could have grown so big that they would have towered over a three-storey building; but if for a moment we stop thinking of man as the measure of all things, what amazes us in the animal kingdom is not gigantism but the comparatively limited size to which animals grow. Among the prehistoric reptiles, among fish (the sharks of the Tertiary) and among mammals, evolution produced none larger than about one hundred feet. On the other hand, there seems to be no limit of smallness in the organic world; beyond every microscopic form of life still smaller forms are constantly being discovered. Among higher plants, incidentally, the maximum size does not greatly exceed that of animals. However, among the lowest forms of plant life, the algae, for example, specimens six hundred feet long occur.

One of the few fairly certain laws of evolution is that within each branch of the animal kingdom smaller forms appear first. Size then gradually increases until it becomes stabilized at a certain point. Although there are some examples of decline from a maximum size, this does not happen as a rule, which does not imply that the larger forms of life are those best fitted to survive.

The giant lizards survived "only" for some thirty to fifty million years, and some zoologists have taken their excessive size as the reason for this relatively brief span of life. It is argued that they were very sluggish mentally as well as physically and could not react fast enough to danger. In a sixty-foot Diplodocus, for example, the transmission of an impulse from the brain to the end of the tail and back again is supposed to have taken about a second. Such arguments sound reasonable, but must be taken with several grains of salt. There is no reason to deduce, from the smallness of a dinosaur's head, that its nervous system was rudimentary, for in addition to the tiny brain in the head it possessed a second and much larger nerve centre in the lower part of the spinal column. The movements of the hind legs and tail were probably controlled from this nearer centre. These great reptiles were sufficiently well co-ordinated to clear paths for themselves by knocking down the branches of trees with their fore legs; and they probably used their claws to reach out after prey.

Palaeontologists have given these Mesozoic giants ferocious-sounding names which have made them even more awe-inspiring. There is the Tyrannosaurus, one of the largest known reptiles, a flesh-eater who stood twenty feet high on his two hind legs. Beside him the huge Titanosaurus looked like a dwarf. Both the tyrannical and the titanic reptiles had trouble in keeping their bellies filled, however. Some of them had such poor teeth that they were unable to grind up the tougher plants. Probably they browsed on the soft underwater vegetation of shallow lakes.

About the middle of the Mesozoic, during the Jurassic period, some great reptiles migrated back into the water. This step backwards may have been prompted by their difficulty in finding food enough on land—for as a general principle atavism facilitates adjustment. For a time the fish-lizards or ichthyosaurians were the rulers of the water; they were immeasurably stronger and more agile than the crocodiles, which took the same path. Toward the end of the Mesozoic, however, both crocodiles and fish-lizards fell victim to a third variety of reptile which also returned to the water. This was the mosasaurian, a creature that could expand its mouth like a snake and whose gullet was big enough to swallow any animal.

THE ART OF FLIGHT

The migration of reptiles back into the water was, in the context of geological time, a mere episode which made little permanent impression upon the evolution of the animal kingdom. But the lizards performed an even greater feat than their readaptation to life in the water. They learned how to fly. The doctrine that birds are descended from reptiles is nowadays one of the commonplaces of zoology. But in 1861, two years after Darwin first published his *Origin of Species,* it created a tremendous stir in the scientific world when Hermann von Meyer and A. Wagner first announced the finding of the Archaeopteryx, the fossil of a bird with unmistakable reptilian characteristics.

The find was made in a quarry at Solenhofen in southwest Germany. This quarry was a well-known and highly profitable source for a type of chalky slate much used in lithography. Now it had another claim to distinction—it contained fossils. Remains of primordial plants and animals had been pressed into the stone like flowers in a herbarium. The quarry workers were aware of

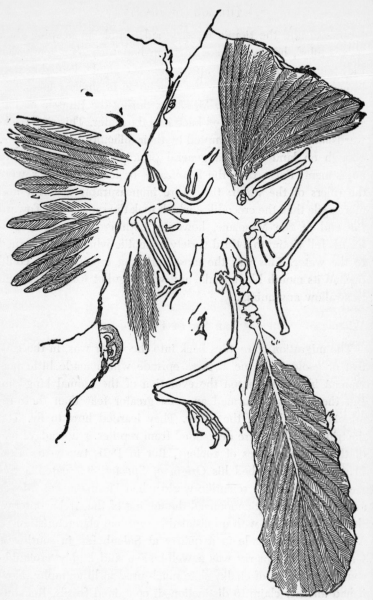

Fig. 4. The skeleton of the primitive bird (Archaeopteryx) from the jurassic deposits near Solenhofen—one of the most important discoveries of palaeontology

18

this and looked out for fossils—they had learned that there were always enthusiasts willing to pay for these imprints in the stone.

This time something really unusual had been chipped out. There was first of all the imprint of a feather. That in itself was a significant find, since the prevailing view among geologists and zoologists held that birds had not existed until the Tertiary period. The Jurassic stone of the quarry was much older than that.

The Solenhofen feather alone would have been enough to shake to its foundations the whole theory of the origin of birds. But on 15 August 1861, before the scientists could even begin worrying and disputing about the feather, the imprint of an entire bird, bones, claws and feathers, was discovered in the same quarry. The limbs had been wrenched apart by the pressure of the stone, but the structure of the whole was easily seen. The bird must have been about the size of a pullet. The zoologist Wagner, to whom the find was brought, did not allow the long, wide feathers to lead him astray. He recognized the essential fact —that in spite of its feathering the creature's tail was as long as the entire body and composed of twenty vertebrae; that, in other words, it very much resembled the tail of a lizard. He also saw that the wings had had movable claws.

Wagner was so amazed that he named the animal after the fabulous gryphon, calling it "Gryphosaurus." The gryphon of Greek mythology had the head and wings of an eagle, the ears of a horse, the body of a lion and the fins of a fish. Although the prehistoric bird of Solenhofen was not quite so fantastic as all that, a rather pedantic scientist like Wagner could not help but find it bizarre. To ease his conscience and to avoid the embarrassing question of whether there had been birds before the Tertiary, Wagner classified the animal as a saurian.

In all probability Wagner was not altogether overjoyed at this world-shaking find, for he was a stubborn opponent of the theory of evolution. However, fate saved Wagner—a fine scholar in his own narrower field—from having his own name linked forever with this fossil monster, for, before he could write out his description in final form, he died.

First publication on the Solenhofen find was thus left to a lesser-known but more daring scientist, Hermann von Meyer. Meyer put forward the simple and blunt argument that an animal with feathers was a bird. Dropping the reptilian classification and the mythological allusion, he called the monster "Archaeopteryx," the primordial bird.

Although his paper appeared on the back pages of a geological journal, the news spread like wildfire among naturalists all over the world. Sir Richard Owen, the British anatomist, took a special interest in the case. Like Wagner, Owen was an outspoken opponent of Darwinism, but he had long differed with his colleagues in holding that birds had existed before the Tertiary. Here was a striking bit of evidence for his view and he made the best of it. His paper, "On the Archaeopteryx von Meyer," was a masterpiece of exact description and ingenious interpretation. Owen pointed out many details that had escaped the first observers, and like Meyer he concluded that the animal must be classified as a bird, not as a lizard, although it had many characteristics in common with the saurians.

Owen could, of course, see that the find helped to substantiate the Darwinian theory. But he was too arrogant and jealous a personality to change his mind over a thing like that. On the contrary, he became more anti-Darwinist than ever.

In 1872 a second bird fossil was discovered in the Solenhofen quarry, close to the site of the first. This one was somewhat smaller than the first and sufficiently different in detail for the zoologists to consider it another species. It was given the name "Archaeornis," which also means "primordial bird." This second specimen was even more detailed than the first. The bird's head was well preserved and it could be seen that the beak contained small, sharp teeth. This was no longer so surprising, for meanwhile two large, toothed waterfowl had been found in Kansas, also in Mesozoic layers. It was one more proof that birds had descended from reptiles.

Darwin himself was surprised and delighted by the Solenhofen finds. In a later edition of his book the *Origin of Species* he added a few sentences about "this strange bird, the Archaeop-

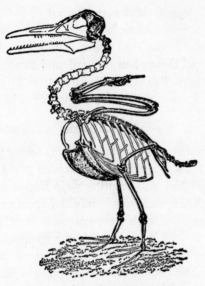

Fig. 5. The first birds had teeth: Ichthyornis of the
Kansas Chalk

teryx" and concluded his comments with an ironic reference to his opponents (and perhaps to himself): "Hardly any recent discovery shows more forcibly than this how little we as yet know of the former inhabitants of the world."

His scepticism was well founded. Although this time a real transitional form had turned up, scientists immediately began looking for a "missing link" between the Archaeopteryx and the reptiles. Theories were ten a penny. Most scientists assumed that the "pre-avis," the ancestor of all birds, had been a four-legged reptile which crawled about on trees and like the first flying insects let itself fall from branch to branch. From parachuting in this fashion, it was thought, the reptile's limbs gradually developed the knack of keeping the body in balance on long horizontal leaps as well as on vertical drops, and finally it learned how to fly upward like a true bird.

A more recent theory holds that the ancestors of the birds were agile, two-legged dinosaurs. The art of flying, it is argued, did not develop from gliding but from running. As they ran, the first flying creatures made vigorous flapping motions with their fore legs to propel themselves forward, and these in time became real flying motions. The whole question is still unsettled—as, for that matter, is the question of the origin of feathers.

Mass Death

While this momentous development was taking place, a change of apparently far less significance was also going on. Some animals that looked like small reptiles were beginning to grow hair on their skins. Their skeletons hardly differed from those of true reptiles, although the teeth were not quite reptilian. If palaeontologists had not had living animals for comparison they would hardly have deduced from the fossil skeletons of these animals that a fundamental change had taken place within their bodies. For some retained the eggs within their bodies until the young were fully developed; others sheltered the young after birth in a half-open pouch.

A third group of animals developed an organ for nourishing the embryo. This "placenta"—so called from the Greek word "cake," which is what it looks like—would then be expelled as the afterbirth but even after the young were born the parents continued to feed them, for all these novel creatures had mammary glands which produced a liquid rich in proteins. The young took this liquid by sucking.

We must not think, however, that earlier types of animals had not taken care of their young. The eggs of big reptiles which an American expedition found in Mongolia were as carefully arranged as Easter eggs on a candy counter. They had obviously been buried in the ground so that no other animal would step on them or eat them. But in the new type of animal, the mammal, the relationship between parents and children was undoubtedly much closer. Learning by imitation, by the transmission of experience, had been introduced.

Perhaps the greater security the mammals provided for their young before and after birth helped them to survive the new great upheavals which began at the end of the Cretaceous period. Perhaps—explanations of this sort are always highly questionable. We have already mentioned the theory that the first reptiles so well withstood the terrible test of the Ice Age towards the end of the Palaeozoic because their young were born protected by the hard shell of an egg. But this time, although the cold was less fierce than it had been then, the eggshell did not help. The thick-skinned reptiles died out completely—the clumsy, heavily armoured ones and the swift-moving dinosaurs as well. They and all their brood vanished, and their cousins which had taken refuge in the waters were also soon to become extinct.

Had the big saurians died of "gigantism," that is, of a disproportion between the brain and the mass of the body caused by glandular disturbances? Glandular disturbances had not kept them from living for many millions of years. And this explanation certainly does not hold for the simultaneous extinction of many small creatures, such as the delicately spiralled ammonites which had peopled the seas of the Mesozoic.

Violent causes must be sought to account for their sudden (geologically speaking) death. But how many diseases of the living man show up in the human skeleton? We can scarcely hope to deduce, from pathological traces in a few fossils, the causes of mass death. Though it may seem illogical, the facts insist that great terrestrial catastrophes decisively influenced the course of evolution and account for the zigzag development that so little accords with the theory of gradual change.

III

The Great Migrations

THERE is really no point in saying that the animals of the Palaeozoic and Mesozoic lived in America, Europe or Asia just because their fossil remains have been found in the rocks of those continents. The surface of the earth was still subject to violent shifts. Continents bobbed up out of the waves and sank beneath them again; volcanic upheavals overturned layers of earth. Perhaps there were horizontal as well as vertical displacements; the geographer Wegener has explained the ice ages by assuming that whole continents shifted round.

About the middle of the Mesozoic the relationships of land and sea were only remotely similar to what they are today. Three wide continents embraced the globe like slack belts. The largest continuous land mass had formed in the northern hemisphere. It extended across North America, Greenland, Iceland, northern Europe and Siberia. In the antarctic regions was a smaller land mass. A third continent, Gondwana Land, stretched from Brazil across central Africa all the way to India. For a time this central continent in the southern hemisphere reached out to Australia and Tasmania. Probably a southeastern bridge extended to the antarctic land mass.

Towards the end of the Mesozoic the crust of the earth once again stirred. Extensive lands rose out of the ocean on the site of present-day Europe. France and England grew together. But in other parts of the world the seas triumphed. The land bridge between India and Australia sank. Henceforth Australia would remain an isolated island continent with its own distinctive flora

24

and fauna. In the west also great upheavals took place. A land
bridge between the northern and southern continents was flooded
by what is now the Caribbean Sea.

Each of these upheavals meant death for innumerable creatures, possibly for whole species of animals. But in the Eocene,
the second epoch of what, geologically speaking, are modern
times, a change took place all over the land surface which
opened up new opportunities for animal life. The earth became
covered with grasses. Hitherto vegetation during warm periods
had consisted of vast virgin forests, during cold spells of dry,
stunted, woody undergrowth. Thick forests were obstacles;
underbrush provided no nourishment. Now even the larger animals could move about freely and eat their fill. For now there
was pasture.

GREEN PASTURES

The reason for the division of the animal kingdom into meat-
eaters and plant-eaters remains highly mysterious. But it is clear
that the herbivores now had the better chances to survive—
provided they were fast on their feet and, when a pasture was
grazed off or the grass withered in the sun, able to find other
feeding grounds.

Small mammals throve on grass forage. In other respects also
the Eocene was a fortunate time for mammals. Few of the large
animals that might have threatened them were left on earth. The
saurians were extinct: the age of giants had been followed by an
age of dwarfs; but this did not last long, for the mammals themselves grew in size and intelligence. Most of them were better
proportioned than the Mesozoic reptiles; they were not so overdeveloped in the lower half of the body as the saurians had been.

There were exceptions to this rule. Australian animals continued to display the short fore legs and scantily developed brain
of the saurians. Presumably their ancestors could not defend
themselves against the more robust placental-type mammals and
retreated to the extreme southeast of Gondwana Land. The isola-

tion of Australia saved these species from extinction, whereas the pouched animals that withdrew to the other end of the Gondwana continent—South America—were almost completely exterminated.

Among the mammals, however, such tragedies were relatively rare. The great majority of them were vegetarians, and in the favourable pastureland environment they grew so big and strong that they were by no means easy prey for the carnivores. Some, in fact, grew to be monsters. The Baluchitherium, whose skeleton was found in Mongolia, was a twenty-foot giant with a rhinoceros-like body and the long, thin head of a tapir. In weight and probably in strength it surpassed even the biggest saurians. But the mammalian giants proved to be even less fit for survival than the giant lizards. Most types died out by the late Tertiary—probably from diseases caused by micro-organisms.

The elephants proved to be the most enduring of the very big mammals. By the last epoch of the Tertiary and the beginning of the Quaternary they had spread over the whole world except for Australia, which was no longer connected by a land bridge to any of the continents. They owed their superiority to their intelligence, not their tusks. As a general rule Nature is a poor producer of armament. Like all armament manufacturers she has a tendency to go in for overproduction until the principle of armament has been carried to absurdity. The mastodons' teeth stuck ten feet out of the jaw like hay forks. In other species these external teeth were curved like tubas and were quite useless as weapons. They were little more than ornaments, like the jagged bony structure on the back of the Stegosaurus which looked like the rampart of a mediaeval castle but left the animal's body quite unprotected.

The armament of the smaller grazing animals probably contributed no more to their survival. Their horns would do for fighting one another over feeding grounds or mates but did not help them to defend themselves against meat-eating predatory animals.

THE HERD INSTINCT

The weakness of individual herbivorous animals led them to gather in herds for mutual defence. Such is the explanation of rationalistic evolutionists. The theory fails to explain why some of the most savage carnivores—wolves and hyenas—also formed packs. A likelier hypothesis is that the herd instinct—present at all stages of evolution but much more in evidence among mammals than among the Mesozoic reptiles—is a consequence of migratory life rather than of the need for defence; that is, animals herd because they formed the habit of herding while wandering about in search of food or safety.

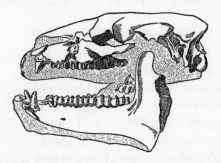

Fig. 6. The oldest inhabitant of Montmartre; skull of the Pallaeotherium, which Cuvier described in detail at the beginning of the nineteenth century

The Tertiary was the age of great migrations in the animal kingdom. Like the later migrations among the nations of men, these mass movements of animals were caused by environmental pressures. The upheavals which threw up the Alps, the Pyrenees, the Apennines and the Atlas Mountains, which wrenched North and South America apart and fused them together again, which shattered and restored the land bridge from Africa to Asia, which drowned thousands of islands and formed thousands of new ones —placed all animal life in peril of sudden death. However, these tremendous cataclysms—earthquakes, floods and volcanic eruptions—were often preceded by warning signs that it was time to move elsewhere.

The rise of mountain chains changed the landscape and climate for hundreds of miles in all directions. When the Alps shot up towards the clouds, the Mediterranean dried out, leaving behind a region of lakes and swamps where the antelope grazed. During the Eocene a salt lake covered the area where Paris now stands. It was a far from pleasant place, but fossils show that on the shores of this lake many mammals found an exile's refuge. Other mammals fled to the region of lakes and forest that existed where we now have the English Channel. That was only a temporary asylum, for at the end of the Pliocene the ocean once more poured in to separate the British Isles from the Continent.

THE MIGRATIONS OF THE HORSE

In all ages isolated herds wandered across vast stretches of country, but in the Tertiary the roaming flocks gathered into great migrations of whole species which moved in a particular direction across the globe. Some of these mass migrations can be traced stage by stage. We are best informed about the paths followed by the ancestors of the horse. These animals of the early Tertiary, which zoologists have classed among the Equidae, were very different from our contemporary horses.

Scientists are in fair agreement on the line of descent. About a dozen fossil types are known; arranged in order they give the impression of an evolutionary succession almost without missing links. The first ancestor, however, has not yet been found. Supposedly the forefather of all horses had five toes on all four feet, like the ancestors of other mammals. Its scion, the Eohippus, which was not much bigger than a cat, had only four toes on the fore feet and three on the hind feet—a sign of progress, for in the equine family advances are measured by the atrophy of the toes. Thus the modern one-toed horse represents the peak of evolution. It walks on the nail of its middle toe—the only one left. This overdeveloped toenail is the horse's hoof.

The evolution of hoofed horses took some forty million years. It is pretty well agreed that horses originated in America. The oldest of the Equidae have been found in Eocene strata in the American northwest. At a somewhat later period, however, a large number of horse-like animals appears to have roamed the European part of the northern land mass. In France and England numerous equine fossils have been found, most of them three-toed. Their legs are slender; later varieties are taller and more powerful in body. One variety, the Palaeotherium, found on the hill of Montmartre in Paris, was as big as a rhinoceros. In Europe, however, the cataclysmic geological changes were hard on the older horses. By the beginning of the Oligocene—the second period of the Tertiary—they had already died out in Europe.

In their American homeland the Equidae remained one of the dominant families. They were well proportioned and the number of their teeth diminished—a sign of advance in mammals. They swarmed over the prairies of North America in great herds, and when the connection between North and South America was restored they spread out over the southern continent as well. Other herds crossed from Alaska to Siberia over the land bridge now sunk beneath the Bering Sea. They wandered all the way across Asia and reached Europe for the second time on the eve of the great Pleistocene Ice Age. Their passage through the broad northern steppes of Asia and Europe had inured them to all the buffetings of bad weather and created a type that could withstand the coldest temperatures. But in America, this time, they died out. They vanished completely from both North and South America; no memory of them was left by the time the Spanish conquistadors introduced horses into America.

The evolution of the camel followed similar lines. In the beginning these were not subtropical animals of the desert. They also originated in North America and during the later part of the Tertiary also spread out in two directions—towards South America and towards Asia. Although their heavy coats seemingly gave them better protection against cold than the horses had had, they were much more sensitive to low temperatures. In the east they established themselves in central Asia, and from there passed to North Africa in historic times. In South America a dwarf variety, the llama, outlived its larger cousins. In their North American homeland the camels died out at the beginning of the Pleistocene Ice Age.

AMERICA, LAND OF IMMIGRANTS

Once again the question arises: What caused the mass death of these animals? This time it cannot be attributed to pathological overgrowth, as in the case of the great reptiles. The horses and camels of North America were not, at the time they vanished, clumsy giants. Neither were they degenerate dwarfs like those curious lilliputian elephants which retreated from the Pliocene floods to islands in the Mediterranean, where they died out— perhaps because of their isolation.

If the horses and camels had died out in Europe, we might guess they had died by violence as the first victims of an unusually treacherous and destructive new animal—man. But this ruthless murderer—"the most devastating of all placentals," the American palaeontologist W. K. Gregory has called him—had not yet entered the western hemisphere. There remains only the disease theory; it must be assumed that these large grazing animals, who appeared to be very well fitted for survival, were wiped out by an epidemic. Perhaps the germs of the epidemic were the same micro-organisms which concurrently attacked many of the most highly evolved mammals in Europe and Asia and completely exterminated some species.

Where this world-wide epidemic came from or how it spread remains a mystery. Unless we assume that new kinds of microbes arose simultaneously in various parts of the world, or that existing types suddenly became virulent (which is quite possible), we must imagine the germs or their carriers, possibly insects, following the same path of migration as the larger animals— across the land bridge from Alaska to Siberia.

In spite of the cosmopolitan traits that migration imposed upon the animals, regional differences nevertheless became more marked. Climate and vegetation do not sufficiently explain the specialization and the rhythm of evolution. Inner motive forces did not everywhere have the same strength or tend in the same directions. That undoubtedly was always true; but with higher development of organisms the differences, the special weaknesses and special advantages, stood out.

The most amazing phenomenon was the evolutionary lag in the Americas compared with the eastern hemisphere. North America, which during long prehistoric epochs had displayed a livelier creativity in originating and perfecting various types of fauna, seemed to have grown weary. It took no part at all in the development of the highest animals—the anthropoids and man. America became a land of immigrants.

回 IV 回

The Superanimal

IN 1716 a London pharmacist and antiquarian named Conyers discovered in the gravel of a former river bed near the city an assortment of elephant bones. Close by the bones he found a crudely chipped pointed stone. His announcement of the find was greeted by gales of laughter. In London coffee houses people joked about the African pachyderm that had strayed along the Thames. Probably, some wits suggested, it had run away from a circus and died a miserable death when English food didn't agree with it. Perhaps, others jested, it was a true-blue ancient Briton. After all, hadn't giants and dragons once roamed the British Isles? Why not an elephant, too?

A historically minded friend of the pharmacist, a Mr. Bagford, suggested a reasonable explanation. "The elephant bones go back to the time of the Emperor Claudius," he said. "The Roman army brought elephants across the Channel to help them conquer the Britons. But the early inhabitants of our country fought bravely, and one of them killed the elephant, whose bones you found, with a sharpened stone."

This seemed to make sense to the pharmacist. He placed the elephant bones and the stone in a curiosity cabinet and labelled them: "Find from Roman times."

Professional scientists paid no attention at all to this incident. Nor were they much more interested when, almost a hundred years later, a similar find was made, also in southern England. This time the bones of various extinct animals, mingled with chipped stones, were found some thirteen feet underground. The

32

finder, one John Frere, was a more tenacious type than the pharmacist had been. He persisted and persisted, and finally succeeded in having his finds published in an archaeological journal. In his paper he argued that the men who had chipped the stones must have lived at the same time as the fossilized animals.

THE DELUGE—BEFORE OF AFTER US?

During the first decades of the nineteenth century other finds of similar nature were made in England, in various parts of France, in Belgium and in the Rhine Valley. But these, too, were ignored or discredited by professional scientists. The scientists argued that the fossil animals and the worked stones must date from different periods, for all that they had been found on the same sites. The tools and weapons had to be later than the fossils, for man could not possibly have lived at the same time as the elephants, rhinos, hyenas and other animals that had become extinct in western Europe many thousands of years ago. All these fossils were "antediluvial," while *Homo sapiens* dated strictly from the "postdiluvial" period.

This was the prevailing scientific view and, except for a few nonconformists, no zoologist, anthropologist or geologist dared to challenge it. To their credit it must be said that the attitude of the scientists in the field towards these new finds—most of which had been made by dilettanti—was not based solely on intellectual arrogance. Their unwillingness to admit new facts was self-defence, defence of recently acquired knowledge. Old sciences are moderate and tolerant, young sciences dogmatic. Palaeontology was still a very young science at the beginning of the nineteenth century. Ever since the days of the Greeks there had been a few perceptive men from time to time who recognized the true nature of fossils. But only in the past generation or two had it come to be generally accepted—in the face of vigorous opposition—that fossils were the remains of animals and plants from very remote times, not chance natural formations. With infinite pains the accumulated material had been sifted and arranged in chronological order—and now the scientists were being asked to abandon all their hard-won gains because a few amateurs were raising a fuss! As yet no fossilized human bones nor even a fossil monkey had been found. Were the scientists to sacrifice their existing theories on account of a few chipped stones of uncertain age found on a dubious site improbably mingled with dubious fossils?

The supreme authority on fossils was the Frenchman Georges Cuvier. Cuvier was born in 1769 in Montbéliard, near the Swiss border, at that time a part of the Duchy of Württemberg. The son of an army officer, he first studied natural science at the German university of Stuttgart. He emigrated to France, however, and observed there all the violent changes of the Revolution—although he himself was unaffected. During the Reign of Terror he was a private tutor in Normandy. At the age of twenty-six he went to Paris, where he was entrusted with the Chair of Natural History at the École Centrale du Panthéon. He also became, young as he was, a member of the Institut de France. By the time he was thirty-three he had been appointed professor of comparative anatomy at the Museum, then the foremost centre in the world for the study of natural science.

His arrogance kept pace with the growth of his influence. He quarrelled with the friends who had given him backing and ruled his field like a despot. This he was able to do because even his opponents recognized his genius. His insistence on the subordination of single organs to the organic whole, and on the correlation of forms, was based upon conscientious observation and comparative studies conducted with the greatest precision. But at bottom Cuvier was an intuitive scientist. For him the whole was not the sum of its parts; he had the vision to reconstruct an entire animal when he had only a small part of it to work with. Methodologically that was a dangerous approach; but Cuvier applied this questionable method with the imagination of an artist and with an amazing sureness. Before Cuvier, fossils had been mere bones. Cuvier made them animals, living creatures, though they might have been extinct for millions of years.

His passion for unity extended beyond the reconstruction of individual organisms. He saw entire geological epochs as forming units—but he went no further. As he saw it, the flora and fauna of each epoch were distinct. It was illogical to suppose otherwise, and what was illogical was not scientific. The last great geological upheaval had been the Diluvium. Cuvier did not conceive of it as a simple flood in the Biblical sense, but rather as a tremendous cataclysm in which entire countries and mountain chains had been overturned, with a resultant destruction of all life in those places. He granted the possibility that some contemporary species, and perhaps even man, might have existed before this catastrophe; that there might have been some survivors in un-affected parts of the world. But none, he maintained, would have lived where they are living today.

These few sentences in which Cuvier left a loophole in his own theory have often been cited as proof of his caution and tolerance. In point of fact they are alien to the whole spirit of his work. As far as Cuvier was concerned, there really was no bridge between the antediluvial and the postdiluvial worlds. Noah's Ark was sheer myth. If continuity there was, it had been preserved by immigration from nebulous and unspecified regions —and there was no fossil evidence for it.

With a smug delight in exposing the errors of others, Cuvier examined a number of supposed human fossils and proved them all to have been anything but human. One batch was in reality elephant bones, another the remains of a whale, a third the bones of a reptile. His most famous revelation was his exposure of a collection of bones that had been labelled by the Swiss scientist Scheuchzer, "*Homo diluvii testis*"—"the human witness of the Deluge." Cuvier showed that the bones were sections from the skeleton of a giant salamander!

After so many vain attempts to show that the human race was

older than the Deluge, how could anyone believe that stone weapons were really antediluvial?

FRONTAL ASSAULT

The initial attack on Cuvier's chronology and cosmology began the year after his death. In 1833 a Belgian physician, P. C. Schmerling, published an extremely thorough study in two volumes of fossils found in a cave near Liége, Belgium. A whole menagerie of fossils had been discovered—the remains of a rhinoceros, a bear, a hyena and a horse. Along with them were stones and bones obviously worked by human hands.

The main frontal assault came from France itself. Its commander was a clever amateur in palaeontology named Boucher de Perthes. He was chief of customs in Abbeville on the Somme. Since the port was small and its shipping trade far from brisk, de Perthes had plenty of time on his hands. At different periods of his life he had written plays and gone in for social reform— aid to the poor and the emancipation of women. Lately he had turned to the study of prehistory and had dug a number of stone tools out of the alluvial flats on the shores of the Somme. He waged a fierce fight to have these tools recognized by science as "antediluvial," which, of course, involved recognizing the makers as antediluvial also.

Since he was the son of a reputable botanist, Boucher de Perthes had little difficulty in getting into touch with authoritative scientists in Paris. The Academy of Sciences decided to send a commission to Abbeville to examine the finds. Only one member of the commission actually undertook the journey, however —and was not convinced. Boucher de Perthes's wild claims and amateurish blunders had the effect of alienating even the most open-minded scientists. His tragi-comic one-man battle to prove the existence of antediluvian man went on for twenty years—but it ended in victory. Slowly but surely the specialists in prehistory came to see that Cuvier's rigid dividing line was untenable. Man and mammoth had been contemporaries, which meant that

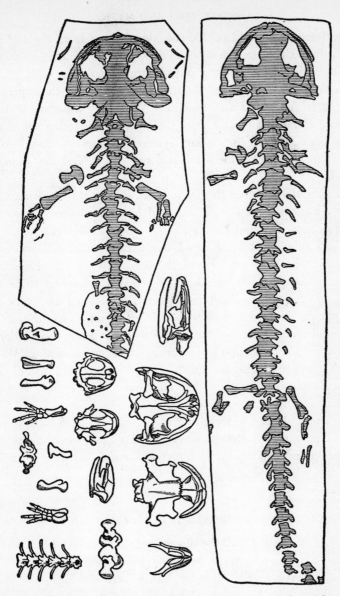

Fig. 7. Giant salamander. As late as the beginning of the eighteenth century this skeleton was considered to be the remains of a prehistoric man "*Homo diluvii testis.*" Ernst Camper and Cuvier corrected this error

henceforth man could not be considered apart from the rest of the animal kingdom. Scientists plunged into an intensive study of the anatomy and physiology of prehistoric man.

What was the nature of the men who had made those primitive tools? What did they look like? Were they members of the species *Homo sapiens,* or were their bodies altogether different from ours? For the time being laymen and scientists could only speculate wildly, for the earth had not yet yielded any human fossils.

During the eighteen-thirties a fossil anthropoid ape—presumably an ancestor of the gibbon—had been discovered in southwest France. The find knocked another hole in Cuvier's system—he had ruled that apes could never have inhabited western Europe. The man who found the ape skeleton was Edouard Lartet, a lawyer who later became one of the leading students of the Dordogne cave culture. After his sensational discovery of the ape, he devoted himself with burning eagerness to the search for fossil human remains; but he continued to probe the Tertiary formation where the ape had turned up and found nothing. After much toilsome digging he gave up—but continued to insist, along with Boucher de Perthes, that man must have existed in the Tertiary.

Others continued to search for many years. In 1848 came news from Spain that a strange, very flat skull had been found in Gibraltar and might possibly represent some extinct type of man, but the reports were vague and the discovery attracted little attention.

Neanderthal Man

A new era began with the discovery in the region of the lower Rhine in Germany. Some workmen found human bones in a limestone cave in the Neander Valley between Elberfeld and Düsseldorf. The bones were embedded in six feet of clay—an indication that the burial site was very ancient. The workmen might well have carted the bones off to the kiln along with the lime; but fortunately a teacher from a technical school in Elberfeld, Johann Carl Fuhlrott, got wind of the find. He arrived just in time to save the bones. While he was about it, he went over the site carefully and assembled almost an entire skeleton. Only the top of the skull was left, but the upper arm and thigh bones were perfectly preserved, most of the lower arm bones, the collar bone, parts of the shoulder blades and pelvis and fragments of the ribs.

Fuhlrott was not a great anthropologist but he had a good all-round knowledge of the natural sciences. In his youth he had written a thesis on the classification systems used by French botanists. He had also dabbled in zoology and had a really remarkable knowledge of the geology of the region where he lived and worked. He knew that the substructure of the cave where the skeleton had been found was ancient Devonian limestone but the layer of clay in which the bones had been embedded was "diluvial"—to use the term common in his day. Since the diluvial was post-Tertiary, it was obvious that Tertiary man had not yet been found.

The structure of the bones differed in many respects from that of contemporary man. In fact the skeleton rather resembled that of an anthropoid ape. The skull was extremely flat, the forehead low and receding, and there were heavy ridges over the eyes. The odd curvature of the thigh bone and the shape of the pelvis also suggested anthropoids. Probably the Neanderthal man had walked with a heavy, shuffling gait, the upper part of the body bent far forward.

Fuhlrott did not want to be caught out. He went to work with the greatest care, familiarizing himself with the pertinent literature and consulting specialists before he announced his find. His report was published in 1859—a good three years after the discovery. Although the publication appeared in an obscure provincial journal, it created a tremendous sensation. Everybody began talking about the Neanderthal man. And all Fuhlrott's scrupulousness was of no use. Before he knew what had happened he found himself embroiled in a furious controversy. Innumerable questions were raised. How old was the skeleton? Had Neanderthal man known the use of fire? What sort of manual skills had he had? (The bones of the hands had not been found.) In view of his flat head and low brow, could he have made weapons and tools?

For the scientists, the key question was how to classify him. Could Neanderthal man be considered a member of the species *Homo sapiens*—in spite of all differences? Or was he too ape-like to deserve such an honour? Many zoologists and anthropologists decided that he was a type of pre-man. Among these was Schaaffhausen, whose label *"Homo primogenius"* remained fashionable for quite a while. But then the famous Rudolf Virchow, the foremost pathologist of his day, protested against this classification. He declared that the peculiar characteristics of Neanderthal man, especially the beetling brows, were only the marks of disease. By sheer chance a man severely deformed by a bone disease had been found; such misshapen bones also occurred in contemporary human beings. They were no justification for classifying Neanderthal man as a new species.

Virchow's prestige was such that for several decades many persons accepted this view, but in the long run it could not be maintained. By the time of the First World War the characteristic bones of seventeen Neanderthal-type men had been found in widely scattered places all over the world and it was hardly likely that all had suffered from bone diseases. However, Virchow's opponents had to make concessions too. They had held that the Neanderthal era dated back a hundred thousand years or more. This view has had to be abandoned. The modern estimate is that Neanderthal man was much more recent—that he lived no more than twenty-five to thirty thousand years ago. It appears certain that he co-existed with *Homo sapiens.* Measurements of Neanderthal man's skull have shown that his brain was as large as modern man's. And everything else we can deduce about his nature and abilities indicates that he was truly a type of man, not semi-human.

APE MEN

Darwin's *Origin of Species* came out just as the debates over Neanderthal man were getting under way. Inevitably, early Darwinian enthusiasts promptly rushed to the conclusion that the Neanderthal man had a definite place in the human line of descent. They hailed him as a direct descendant of the anthropoid apes and a direct ancestor of *Homo sapiens*. Darwin himself was, as usual, more cautious. In his book he did not commit himself on man's ancestry. His adviser and apostle, Thomas Huxley, bravely tackled the problem, employing all his vast knowledge of zoology in the attempt to solve it; but his final conclusions did not differ widely from those of Linnaeus, who a century earlier had already assigned both men and apes to the order of Primates. Huxley ultimately went no further than the observation that man was more closely related to the most highly developed apes than the higher apes were to the lower apes.

The first scientist to take the plunge and draw up a genealogical tree for man was Ernst Haeckel. He published his line of descent in his book, *General Morphology*—six years before Darwin himself publicly clarified his own position in his *The Descent of Man*. Even today many scientists feel that Haeckel's theory is correct in essentials. Modern man, Haeckel argued, did not descend directly either from Neanderthal man or from any contemporary types of anthropoid apes. Rather, all had a single common ancestor—the *Dryopithecus*, a tree-dwelling ape of the late Tertiary. Only the scantiest fossil remains of this ape existed and, since this was going pretty far back, Haeckel tried to make the kinship more credible by introducing a theoretical intermediate ancestor into the line of descent. This ancestor, a primitive and entirely animal-like pre-man or super-animal, supposedly lived in the Pliocene. Haeckel even gave it a name: *Pithecanthropus*, the ape-man.

For many years *Pithecanthropus* had no existence outside Darwinian writings. But then suddenly Haeckel's working hypothesis —or shall we call it stopgap?—was confirmed. In 1891–92 a young Dutch army doctor named Eugène Dubois found on the island of Java the remains of a creature which conformed to Haeckel's specifications. Near Trinil in central Java he came across a remarkable back tooth and a skull unlike any fossil human skulls hitherto found. After a long search he found two more molars and a thigh bone just fifteen yards from the site of his first finds. For the time being that was all. It took a great deal of imagination to reconstruct a whole body out of these paltry fragments.

Nevertheless, some facts were indisputable. The skull was extremely flat, but less massive than that of Neanderthal man. It resembled that of a chimpanzee but with room for a larger brain. The teeth also were half human, half ape-like. The thigh bone, however, hardly differed from that of present-day man. Assuming that it was part of the same skeleton, the primitive Java man could probably walk erect, and in this respect was superior to Neanderthal man; but the shape of the skull, the extremely receding forehead and the comparatively "smooth" brain, without strong convolutions—as shown by the markings inside the skull— placed the Java man far below his European rival on the evolutionary ladder. Moreover, the layer of earth in which he had been found was older than the clay covering of Neanderthal man.

Dubois was a man of resolution. As far as he was concerned, the case was crystal clear. The bones he had found must all have belonged to the same creature, and this creature was the long-sought missing link between ape and man. It was neither an ape nor a man, but an ape-man—none other than Haeckel's brilliantly predicted *Pithecanthropus*. Since the thigh bone was so well shaped, Dubois added the epithet "erectus"—the ape man who walked upright. And as *Pithecanthropus erectus* the Javanese man took his place in the prehistory of mankind.

THE SUPERANIMAL 43

When Dubois published his discovery, he started a tremendous furor among educated laymen as well as scientists. All the arguments for and against the descent of man from apes, which had apparently long since been settled, were raked up anew. The specialists were particularly aroused by the old question of the existence of Tertiary man. Dubois had boldly asserted that the layer in which he found the ape-man was from the Pliocene, that is, the latest period of the Tertiary. Reputable geologists thought otherwise. A sea of ink was also spilled over the question of whether the thigh bone and skull came from the same individual. Dubois complicated matters for the specialists by keeping his finds under lock and key, after briefly exhibiting them in 1894. Not until 1923 did other anthropologists have the chance to study the bones carefully. They are now in the museum of the University of Leyden in Holland.

These later studies indicated that the bones were shaped more like human bones than the first hasty descriptions had suggested. New finds made in Java shortly before the Second World War have strengthened the view that *Pithecanthropus erectus* was a member of the human race. His dates have had to be moved ahead also. Geologists are now generally agreed that the Java sites all belong to the Pleistocene epoch, that is, to the Quaternary and not the Tertiary. Nevertheless it is widely recognized that the bones of Java represent a very early and primitive type of human being—an "ape man" in the popular if not in the strictly scientific sense.

Competition for the title of "first man" has meanwhile become very keen. Manlike fossils have been found in many places in the eastern hemisphere. Science now possesses a whole collection of perfectly preserved Neanderthal skeletons, of children as well as of adults. Remains of older prehistoric human beings are still scanty; but there are enough of them to have given rise to the most diverse theories of species and classification. There is, for example, the *Maueranthropus*, found in 1907 in the village of Mauer, near Heidelberg, Germany. All he left of himself to puzzle posterity was his jawbone. Among others are the Bushman type found in the Transvaal (1913), who was possibly a forerunner of the Australian Negro, and Rhodesian man (1921), an African contemporary of Neanderthal man. Later finds, such as the Steinheim skull (1933), the *Africanthropus*, found in 1935 in East Africa and in Swanscombe on the Thames, have helped to fill out the branches of the human family tree and have stimulated brief flurries of public interest and prolonged controversies among the scientists.

The most significant find of recent decades was undoubtedly *Sinanthropus pekinensis*. Since 1926 some twenty-five more or less well-preserved skulls of this type of early man have come to light. Originally *Sinanthropus* was found embedded in early Pleistocene layers of stone in a cave near Peking. It is closely related to *Pithecanthropus* of Java. A common home in Tibet, Africa and other places has been conjectured for both of these specimens of early man, but so far all speculation on that subject remains in the realm of pure fantasy.

THE ANCESTORS OF MAN

It seems likely that the human species did not develop simultaneously all over the world. In the Americas no human or anthropoid fossils have as yet been found, in spite of diligent searches. About a hundred years ago the Danish geologist Wilhelm Lund thought he had found petrified human skulls along with animal fossils in the limestone caves of Lagoa Santa, on the Minas Gerais Plateau in the interior of Brazil. Here, apparently, was evidence for primitive man in America since the Pleistocene. But closer examination of the finds did not bear out this view. The Americas were probably populated at a late period by men who crossed over from Siberia via the Aleutian Islands.

The skulls and leg bones of early man which have been found in Europe, Asia and Africa do not definitely answer the question of who were the direct ancestors of *Homo sapiens*. A number of anthropologists have attempted to draw up parallel lines of descent. Hermann Klaatsch holds that Neanderthal man and contemporary African Negroes shared a common ancestor with the gorilla and the chimpanzee, whereas Mongolians and Europeans are cousins of the orang-utan. The idea that Neanderthal man was an ancestor of any of the present races of mankind has been abandoned. It is now generally assumed that he was the last link in a chain and that with his passing one branch of the superanimal became prematurely extinct.

A good many anthropologists go further than Klaatsch in dismissing intermediate stages without suggesting alternatives. Anthropoid apes also are now no longer recognized as ancestors of *Homo sapiens*. Whether the lower apes belong at all in the human family tree is once more the subject of lively discussion. At present the lemurs, another branch of the Primates, are the favourites of the specialists. F. Wood Jones and his followers believe the tarsiers to be man's ancestors. Tarsiers are charming, vivacious animals of the lemur family. The only living species of tarsier is the *Tarsius spectrum,* which is found hopping about in the trees of Borneo. The most striking feature of the tarsier is his long tail, but his high standing among zoologists is due chiefly to his having a yellow spot on his retina, like man and the anthropoid apes. This enables him to form stereoscopic images and see the world three-dimensionally.

That is certainly a laudable attribute, and if the tarsier of the Eocene or the as yet undiscovered pre-tarsier of the Cretaceous —for never, never let it be thought that man has descended from the contemporary type of tarsier—also possessed the yellow spot, man can well pride himself on having such gifted forebears. But men probably won't. If the theory ever becomes popular, the phrase "Man comes from the lemurs" will probably acquire the same embarrassing overtones as the phrase "Man comes from monkeys." Undoubtedly that phrase is partly responsible for the way even scientists have more and more shied away from the far more obvious theory of man's descent from anthropoids. Although very few scientists nowadays reject flatly the theory of evolution, they are still reluctant to see the transition from animal to man right before their eyes. Putting the transition back as far in the past as possible makes the whole theory less painful to man's self-esteem; and at the same time the principle of the thing is preserved intact.

One group of biologists, who in principle agree with the concept of evolution but give it a wry twist, have restored the anthropoid apes to their place of honour. But they have done so in a way that sounds like mockery to the orthodox Darwinist. Evolution, they argue, need not necessarily mean progress. Retrogression is quite frequent in nature, as is the third possibility, stagnation, the persistence and transmission through heredity of embryonic and infantile traits. This is in effect turning Haeckel's biogenetic law upside down. Haeckel postulated that an embryo goes through all the stages passed by its fully grown ancestors but rapidly outgrows these to become an adult. In cases of stagnation, the adult form will be similar to an ancestral embryonic stage. The phenomenon is so common among lower animals— insects and salamanders, for example—that scientists have given it a special name. It is called "neoteny"—prolongation of youth.

The Dutch anatomist Bolk has had the courage to ascribe this type of infantilism to man. According to Bolk, *Homo sapiens* in many respects resembles the foetus of an ape. Man has stagnated at this particular ancestral stage. And Bolk's theory has won quite a following. The French biologist Jean Rostand has called it "ingenious," and one of the most famous biologists of our time, Lucien Cuénot, has taken up the theory and put it even more bluntly than Bolk himself: "Man can be considered a gorilla foetus whose development and growth have been greatly retarded. He has retained his infantile characteristics and reaches sexual maturity very late. The chimpanzee and the gorilla have progressed beyond the human stage by specializing as acrobats —the chimpanzee more so than the gorilla. In other words, man appears to be a neotene descended from some unknown anthro-

Georges Cuvier, the "Napoleon of Palaeontology." His theory of cataclysms was the greatest obstacle in the way of the theory of evolution

D'Orbigny, Cuvier's most influential pupil, who proclaimed the theory of twenty-seven successive creations

Gabriel von Marx: "The Ape Man of Java" (Haeckel Museum in Jena)

poid which was probably close kin to the present-day gorilla
and chimpanzee."

ARTIFICIAL CLAWS

Even if the theory of descent were to be entirely abandoned,
the question of man's origin would still remain. An even sharper
line would have to be drawn between man and animal and it
would be necessary to say definitely: From this point on *Homo
sapiens* begins. By now there are so many transitional types that
the choice would be very difficult. Zoologists are inclined to see
the crucial departure in some detail of bone structure or the like,
such as man's ability to oppose his thumb to his other fingers, or
the absence of protruding eyeteeth. Such differences hardly seem
conclusive enough to decide so large an issue. Much has been
made of certain psychological traits—for example, that men alone
can laugh and cry—but Köhler's and others' celebrated experiments with chimpanzees strongly suggest that these abilities are
not uniquely human. In any case psychological tests cannot very
well be applied to fossils. The same difficulty holds for speech as
a criterion. Peking man or Neanderthal man may or may not have
been able to speak—there is no way in which we can possibly
know.

There is, however, a crucial cultural test which must be considered *the* test. From the human standpoint, the greatest event
in the history of the Primates was the discovery—by some few of
them—of the art of making tools. Not only using them, but making them! Even anthropoid apes can throw sticks and stones at
their enemies, but man alone takes materials and works them for
specific purposes.

Neanderthal man has been called *Homo faber*—"man the
smith." The label is false, since he could not forge anything. But
he was able to chip stones, and probably he was not the first to
practise this craft. Near the cave of Chou Kou Tien, where the
first traces of Peking man were found, a veritable arsenal of tools
was turned up—enough, obviously, to equip an entire tribe. There

were some two thousand flaked quartz stones, smoke-blackened deer antlers, and the ruins of a huge fireplace.

One of the foremost authorities on French Stone Age caves, Abbé Breuil, has concluded from these finds that *Sinanthropus pekinensis* understood the art of making fire and fabricating tools. Yet Peking man may not have been the first to accomplish these feats. English scientists have claimed this honour for their own countrymen, for crudely chipped stones have been found in East Anglia in Pliocene layers, which must therefore be much older than the tools of Peking man. The Java *Pithecanthropus* has not yet been entered in the competition for the producer of the first tools, though he was possibly quite capable of shaping stones. However, until proof that he actually did so is found, either the primitive inhabitants of England, or Peking man, will have to be accorded the distinction of first toolmaker and therefore first true human.

The oldest tools are weapons—man was attempting to provide himself with claws. He could make fire once he had learned the principle that sparks resulted from things being struck or rapidly rubbed together and that he could produce such sparks from the flints that lay about on the ground, but he could not always stop to build a fire for defence. For emergencies, and for attacking animals stronger than himself, he needed a new type of weapon. Nature had equipped him very poorly for battle at close quarters. Nature appears habitually to have made such mistakes. We have seen that powerful armoured animals were ill-suited to the struggle for existence because they were too clumsy or because their armour shielded the wrong places, leaving vital organs unprotected, but man was in even a worse case. He was vulnerable from head to foot. He lacked speed or protective coloration. He was powerless to escape enemies by flying into the air or diving deep under water.

Besides his poor defensive armament, he was poorly equipped for attack. His teeth were blunt compared with those of most flesh-eating animals. He could not open his jaws wide. His gullet was inelastic, his limbs relatively feeble. Like the oldest reptiles, he had five fingers or toes on each of his four limbs, but the nails were stunted. He could grasp things with his hands, but his feet were not even adapted to climbing rapidly. As weapons, any donkey's hoofs were superior.

STATURE AND BRAIN

The first human beings were neither giants nor dwarfs. The block-like skull of the Neanderthal man might lead to the impression that he had been a monstrous brute, and childish "reconstructions" of his face fortified such a picture. Actually, he had been about five feet five inches tall. His older cousins, Peking man and the ape man of Java, were somewhat smaller, while his supposed contemporary, Rhodesian man, attained the height of six feet one inch. Later Cro-Magnon man, who had all the characteristics of present-day *Homo sapiens,* ranged from five feet eight inches to a little over six feet, but contemporaneously with him a smaller type of the human species lived in what is now France—a type only about five feet two inches tall. On the whole, then, early man averaged out to about the same size as contemporary man, but in relation to his environment he was smaller, since the animals he had to fight were huge by present standards.

Man's sole superiority consisted in that remarkable, gelatinous, grayish-white mass called the brain. We have no knowledge, of course, of the nature and workings of the brain in early man, but from the structure of the skull, the weight of the brain inside has been deduced, and from the remains of skeletons the total weight of bodies has been calculated. From the relation between brain weight and body weight, intelligence has then been estimated. In modern man the proportion between brain weight and total body weight is as 1:50. In the gorilla it is 1:200; in smaller anthropoids, 1:90. For the Javanese *Pithecanthropus erectus* it has been estimated at 1:70. On the face of it, such a scale of brain weight to body weight seems highly significant and revealing.

So logical did it seem to be that nineteenth-century anthropologists made the construction of such "cranial indices" a
favourite hobby. But the index has its quirks. In birds, which are
not distinguished by excessive intelligence, the proportion is 1:35
—a good deal better than the 1:50 proportion of man. And in
new-born human babies the proportion is 1:6. By the cranial
index, babies should be eight times more intelligent than adults.

Nevertheless, there seems to be some significance in the fact
that the most primitive human beings, the first toolmakers, had
room in their skulls for about one thousand cubic centimetres of
brain, whereas chimpanzees must get along with six hundred
cubic centimetres.

In any case, even in the earliest stages of mankind it was quality rather than quantity that counted. The decisive step marking
the transition from animal to man was taken when an animal
transcended his own body, so to speak. The use of tools not only
increased his skills; it brought objects beyond his reach under
his physical control. Tools lengthened his arm, multiplied his
strength, provided him with claws more deadly than the sharpest
of animal claws.

The use of artificial limbs left deep traces in man's nervous
system. At a very early date the sense of touch was shifted outward. Man has taken this extension of one of his senses so much
for granted that no one ever realized how strange it really is.
Only recently have physiologists noted that when we touch an
object with a stick, for instance, we actually feel the resistance
outside our bodies, not in the tips of our fingers where they are
in contact with the stick. Tools seem to lengthen our nerve fibres.
All finer technical work depends upon this astonishing faculty
of the human nervous system.

The first toolmakers were interested only in the simplest operations—stabbing, drilling, scraping, cutting. Theirs was toolmaking
for hunters; the implements were meant to help in the killing,
skinning and roasting of animals. The most important operation
was stabbing—the bear or mammoth couldn't be cooked until it

Geological periods			strata and climates	fauna	archaeology	Types of Fossil Men
Quaternary	holocene	(present)	Recent alluvial deposits. Peat	Present-day species	Metals { Iron, Bronze, Copper	Homo sapiens
Quaternary	Pleistocene	upper	Upper strata of caves. Younger loess. Cold and dry climate. Steppes and tundras. Post-glacial	Steppe fauna Reindeer period Tundra fauna	Neolithic Azilian (early neolithic) Palaeolithic, younger: Magdalenian	Chancelade man
Quaternary	Pleistocene	middle	Lower cave deposits. Older loess. Cold and damp climate. Glaciation	Mammoth (Elephas primigenius) Rhinoceros Tichorhinus	Palaeolithic, younger: Solutrean Aurignacian	Cro-Magnon man Grimaldi man
Quaternary	Pleistocene	lower	Oldest cave deposits. Terrace deposits. Great interglacial. Mild climate	Hippopotamus Elephas antiquus	Palaeolithic, older: Mousterian Acheulean Chellean	Homo neanderthalensis Homo Dawsoni Homo heidelbergensis
Quaternary	Pleistocene	lower	Glaciation	Rhinoceros Mercki		
Tertiary	Pliocene		Plateau deposits Long interglacial period	Southern elephant Rhinoceros etruseus		
Tertiary	Pliocene		Severe glaciation	Equus stenonis		

Fig. 8. Animals and men in the Quaternary

was caught. The earliest tools were pointed for killing four-footed opponents—and no doubt two-legged rivals also.

TRANSITION OR BEGINNING?

This does not necessarily mean that the first men were far wilder, greedier and more cruel than later specimens of the human race. Even if they were, they had better reason to be. The human species arose in an epoch of fearful stress. Even though human beginnings may extend back to the more temperate Pliocene times, toolmaking man is, after all, a product of the Pleistocene, the great Ice Age. It must be remembered that the Ice Age was not a period of unbroken cold. There was at least one, and perhaps there were two or three, interglacial periods during which the average temperature in Europe was probably not much lower that it is today. But the age of Neanderthal man, known in archaeological chronology as the period of Mousterian culture, coincided with intense cold. Human beings and animals fled to caves to escape the cold and the advancing glaciers.

Within these shelters some of the most frightful dramas of prehistory took place. The animals and men who had been thrown together by common hardship were probably far from aggressive, but hunger impelled them to attack one another. There is no evidence that man was always the attacker, nor that the lions, hyenas and bears always fell upon him so that he was forced in self-defence to kill them with his pointed stones. Probably chance decided who was the attacker and who the defender. The outcome of these battles was equally a matter of chance. Sometimes the man ate, sometimes he was eaten. At times these struggles seem to have ended with all the participants dying from their wounds.

Such is the picture suggested by all the caves of this era. Human and animal bones lie side by side. Along with human bones are the remains of bears, hyenas, reindeer, aurochs and even lions. In some caves traces of lavish victory feasts have been found. In Pasly, for example, the bones of a mammoth, a cave bear and a giant stag were found buried under ashes. Cave paintings support this picture of man fighting his environment and winning. The struggle was fought with unequal weapons; against nature's claws and teeth were set the weapons created by brain and hand—wedge-shaped stones, axes, spears. The maker of those weapons could be master of nature.

The super-animal was not simply a new species of Primate; he was destined to transform the whole world. Let us not be deceived by the theory of gradual evolution—this was a tremendous development. It was not a transition, but the beginning of something entirely new. An event of enormous importance had taken place, a revolution in the history of the earth. Within a very short time, geologically speaking, the super-animal would gain control of the surface of the earth and all life upon it. He would change the world to suit his own ends. If in previous ages creation and destruction had had only causes and no aims, now the aims, the conscious will of a single species, would become world law.

PART TWO

ANTIQUITY AND THE MIDDLE AGES

Hunting and Breeding Livestock

MAN gained control of the animal kingdom by extermination and domestication. The first method consisted of hunting and its ostensibly more peaceful variant, fishing; the second of taking and keeping in captivity animals either useful or pleasurable to man.

Between these basic tyrannies was a third which proved fateful for several animal species. This was raising animals for slaughter. For a long time only mammals were bred for this purpose but

Fig. 9. Cave picture from Alpera in Spain: woman
gathering wild honey

later fish and fowl, reptiles, amphibians and even invertebrates were added to the list. Species doomed to this lot usually escape extinction, but individuals pay for it by a shortening of the life span.

It seems certain that human beings were taming and breeding animals for thousands of years before they abandoned hunting as their chief occupation. It was known long before Stone Age weapons and cave paintings were found as proof that hunting was mankind's oldest vocation. On the other hand, whether animals were first tamed with the idea in mind of letting them live or whether they were raised with the intention of killing them at a given time is a question still disputed. Some analogies from the

Fig. 10. Wild horse, cave bear, mammoth and cave lion. Drawing from a cave in the South of France (after Hoernes)

history of primitive customs support the first thesis. According to the early Brazilian chronicler, Padre Fernão Cardim, the Tupi Indians kept parrots, armadillos and pigs for their amusement long before they knew anything about breeding animals for slaughter.

Since it has become fashionable to make introverted dreamers out of primitive people and to give a metaphysical twist to all their doings, attempts have been made to trace back the practice of domesticating animals to the totem animal cult. Even if there is some truth in this interpretation, there is no direct connection between totemism and the breeding of livestock for slaughter.

All archaeological finds indicate that *Homo sapiens*, even in prehistoric days, was materialistic and highly practical. At the same time, his matter-of-factness did not prevent him from liking amusing and ornamental things nor from having great artistic gifts. He seems to have liked to make fun of his own kind but in general took animals seriously. In prehistoric cave paintings only clumsy, long-haired giants such as the mammoths and the rhinoceroses have an air of caricature. The nimble, smart animals like the horse, reindeer, red deer, goat or bison are obviously the ones that primitive man liked best, even though he hunted them. No wonder, then, that he wanted to possess them, to enjoy seeing them alive about him, as well as to have their carcasses hanging up by the hearth fire. Aesthetic pleasure and the lust for power, the two chief motives for domesticating, no doubt went hand in hand with the idea that it would be a good thing to have a reserve of meat for the days or weeks when hunting was poor. Domestication, however, was no easy matter. Killing was easier than taming, and raising animals took more time than the perfecting of weapons.

How Animals Are Domesticated

In order to bind animals to man, not only the temperament of the animals, but that of human beings as well, had to be changed. To be sure, the people of the later Quaternary should not be thought of as savage wild men. Human beings able to fashion tools and weapons out of stone, to carve figures and make coloured drawings, were certainly capable of concentrated, continuous work. Yet there is still a difference between handling lifeless material and domesticating living creatures ever ready to resist or run away. Rearing animals required a different kind of patience. It took foresight applied over a long period, effort without an immediate prospect of success.

Prehistoric man must have experienced a great many failures before he learned how to keep wild animals penned in the open. The wooden fence marked the beginning of the concentration camp, and the cord was the first shackle. In this connection, however, no one knows just how much the use of wood was understood in the Old Stone Age—whether, for example, human beings at this level knew how to erect a palisade. Illogical as it may seem, architecture is the youngest of the plastic arts. Technical experience in this field was completely lacking when sculpture and painting were already flourishing.

As for the other "binding medium" between man and animal—the cord, the lasso for capturing, the line for holding fast—it, too, was a relatively late invention. There is no evidence that palaeolithic folk were able to braid fibre or other material. They might have been able to tether small animals with vines or lianas, but this method would not have worked with big ones. The only secure fastening was by thongs of hide, and to make these fast or lengthen them new skills were needed; the art of making knots—one of the very greatest primitive inventions—appears not to have been learned until the Neolithic, i.e., the Late Stone Age.

Probably it was climatic change that gave animal husbandry its decisive impetus. After the glacial ice had melted and the earth became everywhere covered with green, both men and animals began to behave more peacefully and the hunter was able to turn to the herdsman's life. Unfortunately, this idyllic version is contradicted by palaeontological and archaeological finds. The end of the last Ice Age, which dates back about twenty thousand years, actually signalled no deep change in the relationships between man and animal. Plant life changed very slowly, in keeping with the very gradual softening of the climate. According to estimates made on the basis of loess deposits in deglaciated zones, a sub-arctic climate prevailed in the greater part of the north temperate zone until the sixth century B.C. (The Stockholm region is assumed to have been still completely under ice ten thousand years ago.)

Animal movements, however, are not strictly regulated by the thermometer. Though climate may be one of the factors determining animal migration, it is none the less an uncertain signpost.

Four-footed, warm-blooded creatures move about slowly, and never in a straight line. They have no real idea of where they should go to find a suitable climate. They have not had thousands of years of experience, like the birds, and the temperature sense of birds themselves does not seem to be as highly developed as was once supposed. Trans-equatorial bird migrations show that the need for warmth cannot be the only motive for long flights during the nesting season. Nor can the "long waves" in bird migration, that is, the great movements occurring at intervals of nine to twelve years, be explained in terms of heat and cold. Plainly birds have their own geopolitics, the fundamental laws of which are still but little known.

The animal population of Europe during the Quaternary glacial period was more or less like that of modern Africa, with the addition of some animals that had wandered in from the north at the beginning of the cold wave. As the cold ebbed the climatic zones became more sharply differentiated. Animal migrations proceeded in two directions, north and south. The bear, bison and elk withdrew to the north. The giants with woolly winter coats, the mammoth and the rhinoceros, also sought colder regions. This attempt to settle in a northern climate turned out badly for them. Both species perished on the Siberian steppes. In 1902 a frozen mammoth was found with flesh, skin, and hair as perfectly preserved as if some zoologist had packed the beast in ice for future study. The last migrants to northern regions were the reindeer. They remained populous in middle and southern Europe until the Neolithic age.

CAVE ART

We know the animals of the Stone Age not only through fossils, but even more intimately through artistic representations made by the very people who hunted them. Some of these primitive sculptures and cave paintings of Palaeolithic man rank among the most expressive artistic works of mankind. Never have animal movements been more aptly recorded—the characteristic element in springing, in headlong flight, in the death agonies of the wounded beast. The colours have mostly been damaged by the dampness of the walls, and their effect is handicapped by bad lighting. Actually, as seen today, they are not as impressive as the fine-toned copies of them made by that artistically gifted archaeologist, the Abbé Breuil, who worked from the cave paintings of Dordogne and northern Spain. The mere fact that Stone Age people undertook such tasks borders on the incredible. They used earth colours on the walls of narrow passageways and holes in the rock, working by the light of a miserable oil lamp with a floating wick, sometimes so cramped for room they could not stand upright.

Fig. 11. Hunting the wild boar. Dark red rock painting in the Cueva del Chargo del Agua Amargo (Prov. Teruel)

The age of these animal drawings was hotly disputed many years after their discovery in 1879. It did not seem possible that prehistoric man could have done such good work; also, the fact that the first finds were accidental made for distrust. Had a competent archaeologist first stumbled on the drawings, they might at once have been accepted as genuine but, as it happened, the credit for their discovery belongs to a twelve-year-old Spanish girl, the daughter of a Don Marcelinos Sautuola. The child found them in a cave near the village of Santillana del Mar in the mountains of northern Spain. While Don Marcelinos himself was searching the area for old bones and stone implements, the girl went alone into the low cave, a light in her hand. Suddenly she shouted: *"Toros! Toros!"* She had found the wall paintings of Altamira. The animals were not bulls, but leaping bison and galloping horses drawn in black and red.

At first the experts refused to believe that wild men, whose greatest accomplishment was supposed to have been chipping stones, could have created such works of art. Not until sixteen years later, when similar paintings were discovered in the cave of La Mouthe in southern France, was the authenticity of these prehistoric animal pictures finally established. Since then monochrome and polychrome frescoes, as well as reliefs and sculptures in the round from this same epoch, have been located in various parts of the world. As yet, however, no one can say with certainty in just what region of the world Stone Age art originated.

With this wealth of material the racial question raised by the initial discovery was cleared up. Not so long ago the experts were sure that Palaeolithic art sprang from the highly developed Cro-Magnon "master race," a people very likely of North African extraction. These Cro-Magnon people came after the gorilla-like Neanderthal man, that is after they had extirpated him. However, later investigations showed that Cro-Magnon man—so named after the place in Dordogne where the first skull of this race was found—actually achieved nothing in the artistic line but modest carvings in stone. The great art of the Magdalenian period, to which the famous cave paintings of southern France and northern Spain belong, was probably the work of the Chancelade race. These people were named after the village of Chancelade in Dordogne where their mortal remains were first discovered. In habit and origin, however, the Chancelade race were basically different from their somewhat older neighbours on French soil. They were a small people, very like Mongolians in bone structure, so that it is generally assumed that they migrated into Europe from the far east.

The artistic abilities of the Chancelade race accord well with their "Mongolian" physical characteristics. There is a striking similarity between Magdalenian and east Asiatic animal pictures, though at least twelve thousand, and possibly between fifteen and twenty thousand, years separate the two art forms. In Chinese drawings isolated animals are often depicted either at rest or in the act of springing, with no landscape nor even a trace of vegetation as background. This same bareness is typical of Palaeolithic

Fig. 12. Prehistoric hunting scene. Cave picture from
East Spain

art. Here the world consists of nothing but men and animals, hunters and hunted. Everything between them—trees, bushes, rivers, mountains—is inessential and consequently does not belong in the imaginary space seen by the artist's eye.

In the large group drawings, too, as for instance in the wall paintings of the Roble Grotto at Morella la Vella in eastern Spain or in the paintings found, in 1940, in the cave of Lascaux at Montignac in Dordogne, no vegetation is shown, nothing but people and animals. In part the paintings show very naturalistic fighting and hunting scenes. In part, too, they are contrived combinations expressive of the artist's pleasure in bringing together as many different kinds of animals as possible. In the Lascaux frescoes, a herd of young horses is shown within a frame of deer heads, together with cows, bulls, bears, lions, a rhinoceros and a buffalo which has just killed a man with a bird's head. The scene is remarkable not only for its zoological diversity but for the fact that an animal is represented as victorious over man. Usually man portrays himself as the conqueror, in Palaeolithic as well as in later times.

I Think, Ergo I Become

Although many of the animals in cave paintings look peaceful enough, this does not mean that they had been tamed. The hunting dog who accompanied primitive man on his raids and hunting trips is supposed to have been the first animal to be domesticated. Yet at first the dog may have been only a camp follower, who in fact did as he pleased about joining the hunt and who was tolerated because he helped to bring down the quarry. Altogether, it was more a matter of sharing booty than a relationship between master and servant.

It is hard to say which species of dog deserves the fame of being man's first companion. Despite much research the prehistory of the dog has not been clarified. An older canine relative has been discovered in the gypsum of Montmartre but in later geological strata the ancestral line is less certain. Some authorities claim that the present canine race descends from at least two ancestral types: the fox-like jackal of the tropics and the wolf of the north. Others suppose that the domestic dog comes from the wolf alone, and still others point to the similarity between the Dinocyon, a dog of the late Tertiary, and the bear family. All that has been definitely established is that by the Middle Stone Age there were dogs hardly distinguishable from those of today.

But the larger question is, at what point did domestication

begin? The usual answer is that only animals born in captivity can be considered truly domesticated. Otherwise they have been individually trained or have become attached to man by chance, in either case altering the characteristics of the species. How the change came about physiologically remains a mystery. The inheritance of acquired characteristics, a phenomenon which would best accord with lay logic, is contradicted by countless experiments.

August Weismann, the famous nineteenth-century biologist, held the theory that heredity is centred exclusively in the germ cell and that changes in other body cells have no effect on posterity. This idea, however, offers no really satisfactory explanation—indeed, rather tends to obscure the problem all the more. In fact, it brings to mind exogenous theories which argue that terrestrial life originated on other planets but do not tell how. Inevitably the question arises as to how a change came about in the germ cell in the first place. Under what conditions can outside influences induce changes in the germ cells? Or does everything go its own straight and immutable way as the adherents of orthogenesis claim? Weismann does not answer these queries.

If we deny the possibility of mutation wrought by external influence, there is no way of explaining how a whole series of wild animals came to be domesticated in such a relatively short period, that is, during the few thousand years of the Late Stone Age. It would be too miraculous altogether to suppose that the requisite mutations, the sudden genetic changes, postulated by the Dutch botanist Hugo de Vries and his genetic school, should have all piled up during this one period. Taming often involves subjugation by force and the use of crude physical means but tameness is a psychological phenomenon. Enduring results are attained when fear, or a comfortable life, has led to complete submission; when the will to freedom which makes the creature "wild" has been suppressed for good. To achieve true subjugation a psychic impress must be made with a physical correlate—in Semon's terminology, an engram.

It must be assumed that originally a change occurs in the brain, one lasting enough to bring about a correspondingly changed psychophysical disposition in the progeny. In many cases this remoulding, which we call domestication, is successfully accomplished in one generation, but in many other instances several generations must pass before subjugation has enduring effects. In either event the nervous system plays the decisive role. Only when the central nervous system has been adequately conditioned by the taming process is the stage set for heritability. The thinking organ has to capitulate before the animal consciously abandons freedom in favour of a slave existence with the help of the chromosomes or heredity-controlling parts of the germ cell.

The brain, therefore, is a powerful factor in heredity. The Cartesian maxim of *cogito, ergo sum*—"I think, therefore I am"—in evolutionary context becomes *cogito, ergo fio*—"I think, therefore I become." The process of "reflection," of weighing the relative advantages and disadvantages in an external situation, by virtue of repetition and familiarity develops into a very quick reaction, a reaction as automatic in its way as the "wild" animal's when he resists, runs away or attacks. In principle there is no difference between the two kinds of response. It is wrong to call the first artificial and inbred by training, the second natural and instinctive. Actually the so-called instinctive behaviour of an untamed animal is the result of ancestral experience. The animal's ancestors reacted in a certain way to external dangers and stimuli, until this characteristic behaviour became constitutional by way of the genetic elements in the germ cell.

This does not mean that physical changes can be produced at will through the thinking process. A four-legged animal cannot be made into a six-legged one nor a trained flea into an elephant. All in all the physical as well as the psychic changes brought about by domestication or by artificial crossing are not so very great. Animal breeders and experimental geneticists agree in observing that whatever changes are possible can be quite quickly achieved. Then a fixed state ensues, exactly that form of heredity which has led to the belief in the permanence of the species.

THE ORIGIN OF "CAPITAL"

The specific variations produced by domestication may be small in a zoological sense but they are enormous from the sociological point of view, for they have effected deep-reaching transformations in the history of both human beings and animals.

Where and how domestication was accomplished is uncertain, and when prehistoric beginnings do not have adequate documentation, the usual thing is to remove them to central Asia. Short-

Fig. 13. Men driving donkeys in ancient Egypt (after Lepsius)

horned cattle are supposed to have been introduced into Europe from central Asia at a time when the older longhorned *Bos primigenius* was still running wild. *Bos primigenius* was not tamed until later, and then with poor success, for by the Middle Ages this well-built type of cattle had died out. In all probability the domestic pig, an animal much smaller than the wild pigs of the Palaeolithic shown in cave paintings, also came from central Asia. The domestic sheep, remains of which have been found among the Neolithic lake-dweller settlements of the Alpine lakes, likewise is supposed to have been of central Asiatic origin. The donkey of Mediterranean lands is regarded as the descendant of the wild ass of western Asia, which apparently put up a long resistance to being made into a draught animal. Among the large animals of the temperate zone, however, the horse took the longest to tame. The first to be raised in captivity is also assumed to have been of Asiatic stock, although in the hunting period of the Palaeolithic great herds of wild horses ranged all over Europe as well.

Be that as it may, domestication was a great achievement. The human beings who accomplished it must have had good level heads and common sense. At about this time they also turned to agriculture, initially to gathering the seed grain of grasses growing wild in river regions. They learned how to prepare meal, also how to sow some of the wild seed to ensure new crops. All this may have been an accidental discovery, but soon man used his wits to devise implements enabling him to introduce plan and purpose into his production of food. The development of an agriculture was man's first creative act in the scientific field not attended by destruction, for man had yet to contribute anything to animal husbandry.

After primitive man could more easily satisfy his dietary needs, he began to share his grain crop with the animals when the pasturage was burnt up by drought or covered with snow. The fodder crib was an important factor in attaching half-tamed beasts to man, but feed alone did not overcome their resistance. Breeders must have observed at an early date that wildness is connected with sex and that male animals are more recalcitrant than females. As yet, however, they knew nothing about the art of castration. The only other recourse was to butcher the bulls, stallions and rams when they defied their masters, sparing only enough to keep up the stock. This sort of selection was the first procedure in stock-breeding to go beyond mere confinement. It led to an inequality in numbers between the sexes but did not affect the increase of the herds, since a single bull could impregnate many cows.

The concept of property arose from the power of disposal over the herds and was older and stronger than the property concept

based on ownership of land, for arable land was plentiful, tamed
animals scarce. Land spells production, cattle spell consumer
goods; only consumable property has tangible worth. In still
older times Palaeolithic hunters no doubt quarrelled over the
division of their prey. The cave paintings of the Roble Grotto
show how fierce these disputes could be. There may have been
arguments now and then over the right to a rich hunting ground
or a good watering place where animals came down to drink, but
such privileges were not comparable with dominion over a herd
of tamed animals on whom the whole clan could live with far less
effort than if they hunted for food.

Animals were the first form of capital. The word "capital" stems
from the Latin "capita," relating to the head count of cattle by
which a man's wealth was measured; but the concept is surely
much older than this. For a hundred years economists have been
arguing whether land was originally held in common or individually. So far as herds are concerned it is certain that in primitive
societies no one but the patriarchal or tribal head had the right to
slaughter cattle as he wished or to use them for barter.

Communal possession, however, much more than individual
possession, tended to stir up strife between different economic
groups. One clan would be rich in cattle, another poor; one might
own a fat pasture, the other a lean one. If the poorer clan got
hold of better weapons—and weapons underwent tremendous improvement during the Late Stone Age—the richer clan did not
long enjoy its property. Only in pastoral poetry were these
shepherd folk peace-loving. In reality they were not far behind
hunters in rapacity and belligerence. No zoo-sociological catch
phrase is more questionable than the one which defines man as a
domesticated animal. Man is one of the very few mammals who
will kill his own kind without the provocation of extreme hunger.
Up to the present all attempts to train him out of this habit have
been in vain.

◫ VI ◫

Sacred Animals

MAN had exterminated a good part of the animal world before he became uneasy about his own mastery in killing. Fear is as old as greed, but better hidden. Like modern man, primitive man was able to interpret the psychic life of animals only by drawing analogies between the animals' behaviour and his own. Where external similarities are limited, or if human beings become psychologically complicated, the possibilities of understanding by analogy practically cease. Explanations of animal behaviour then incline to slip into the realm of anthropomorphic fable, as when the poultry farmer speaks of geese "holding trial." When the geese gabble among themselves, they are supposed to be arguing the case. Then, after having condemned the defendant to death, they fall on him and pull him to pieces, that is, "execute" him.

Considering the close social connection, at least after the late Palaeolithic, among members of the same clan, it is highly probable that primitive man projected his own customs and concepts of justice into the animal world. Man on this level, though he did not regard animals as equals, felt a strong affinity with them. The affinity was evident in all forms of behaviour expressing the will to live: in the search for food, in attacking, in self-defence, in fleeing from danger. The similarity, moreover, was apparent in whole groups of animals, not only in individuals, just as in man. When one animal stormed forward, the others raced with him; when one ran away, the others fled too. Often the animals' sense of community seemed to be even more clearly revealed, as when one of their kind, for instance, was threatened by man or by some other kind of animal, whereupon they came to his assistance.

Mutual help and revenge are most intimately bound up in the human spirit. Must it not be the same with the animals? And will they not take revenge if man kills some of them, even as men of the same clan take revenge when one of them is killed or carried off into captivity?

Fig. 14. Gilgamesh battling with lions; on a cylinder seal

Fear of animal revenge is the great *leitmotiv* resounding in all the social and cultural prescripts lumped under totem and tabu. This theme was later carried over into higher social forms. We can detect its reverberations in the rites and myths of the old cultures and it still echoes on in our own time. Transposed into the moral sphere, this fear of revenge is called the conscience. Sometimes it takes a curious, almost commercial, form as when man tries to buy himself immunity from the consequences of his sins against the animal world by not only sparing certain animals but by showing them the respect and honours due to a divinity as well. After having sacrificed whole species of animals, man preserves others to ensure his soul's salvation, for the worst feature of the retributive menace is the fact that it continues after death. During man's lifetime he may be the conqueror, he thinks, but

after death the animals may get the upper hand and even make
him like themselves so that if he ever came to earth again it
would be in some ugly animal form.

METEMPSYCHOSIS

The idea that man can revert to an animal state is very old
and is found on intellectual levels high and low in many regions
of the earth. Some anthropologists see in this a kind of primitive
Darwinism—a belief in human descent from the animal. There is,
however, a great difference between primitive and scientific ideas
of evolution. The primitive holds that evolution is reversible; the
scientist that it is not. Paleontologists have formulated the "law
of irreversibility." This law states that if an organ becomes physiologically useless, if a species degenerates into dwarf forms, the
loss can never be made good; nor does the mutation theory, despite its emphasis on sudden changes and exceptions from the
rule, usually admit of developmental reversal.

Nature is not regarded very optimistically among earlier civili-
zations, or, at least, primitive optimism is of a different kind.
Great transformations are not excluded as they have been by
natural science for the past two thousand years. To the primitive
or non-scientific mind evolution does not mean a more or less
rectilinear upward movement, but rather a movement back and
forth. In this context the principle that what once has existed
can come again—a principle that modern man admits as applicable only to political history—is made to apply to the natural
world. It is a kind of cyclical thinking.

The cyclical idea was most purely expressed in ancient Egypt,
perhaps because the regularity of the Nile floods and the cosmic
order observed in star-gazing fixed in people's minds a belief in
periodicity. In any case, from the ancient Egyptian point of view
the material world remained strictly unchanged; only its inhabitants were mutable. Immediately after death the human soul
entered into an animal and thereafter migrated successively
through all the creatures of land, water and air until, three thou-

sands years later, it again returned to a human body. Even so, it
did not remain long in human guise. When the new person died,
the transmigration through the animal kingdom was repeated,
and so through all eternity.

This pattern is called "metempsychosis," the transmigration of
souls. It has the character of an inevitable natural law, according to which there is scarcely any difference between man and
animal, since both the human and the animal state are but stations on an eternal circle. Metempsychosis may have originated

Fig. 15. Vulture of Upper Egypt

as a sectarian concept, since it ill accords with the older Egyptian
notion of life after death. In the sixth century B.C. the doctrine of
metempsychosis spread far and wide through the east and the
west. Through Pythagoras and his school it penetrated the Greek
world in an entirely metaphysical form, and in India, through
Gautama Buddha, became a source of moral metaphor which his
disciples, however, took literally.

According to Buddhistic teaching, animals stand far below
man (the veneration of the cow came at a much later time).
Thus the transmigration of the soul through the animal kingdom
becomes a frightful punishment, which Buddha uses to threaten
evildoers, pleasure-seekers and all those of short-sighted outlook.
Anyone who behaves like an animal during his lifetime will sink
after death to the animal level. Such is the thought that the
"Illuminated One" tried to hammer into his followers. As Buddha

developed this idea with poetic eloquence, he introduced a very peculiar division of the animal world according to typical behaviour. Here are some sentences from this discourse:

"Monks, there are animalized beings who eat grass; they wet the grass with their slaver, and chew grass between their teeth. What are they, monks, these animalized beings that eat grass? Horses, cattle, donkeys, goats, antelopes, and whatever other kind of animalized beings that eat grass. Any such fool, monks, who has loved his food in earlier days, who at that time did evil deeds, upon the decomposition of the body after death will return to the community of those beings who live as grass-eaters."

"Monks, there are animalized beings that eat dung; when they smell the dung-smell from far off, they hasten thither, (saying): 'There shall we refresh ourselves.' What are they, monks, these animalized beings that eat dung? Chickens, pigs, dogs, jackals, and whatever other kind of animalized beings that eat dung."

And so it continues, in psalmodic form. There are animalized beings that are born in the dark, live in the dark and die in the dark: the beetles, moths and wood lice. There are others that are born, live and die in water: fishes, turtles and crocodiles. Then there are still other animalized beings that are born in filth, live in filth and die in filth, and those that are born, live and die in rotten fish or in spoiled food or in pools and puddles. Each enumeration follows the same menacing formula: foolish men who do wicked deeds will become such and such creatures. Buddha makes it clear that he considers it wrong to imagine animals live well in their own way. "If I wanted, monks," he says, "in many ways to expound to you the things of the animal world, words could not comprehend, monks, how deep-reaching are the sufferings of animality."

TOTEM

The idea that human beings can be punished by degrading them to animal status is common throughout both the eastern and western worlds. Greek mythology is studded with incidents telling of the transformation of rebellious humans into cattle, pigs, dolphins and the like. Ovid's *Metamorphoses* offers a whole selection. In many cases, to be sure, the change occurs as the result of divine caprice or because the god, in a clement mood, wants to rescue the victim from some great danger. All these Greek legends nevertheless take man's superiority for granted.

On early levels of civilization, however, man is aware that animals very obviously have many useful qualities lacking in himself, and this awareness tends to qualify his sense of mastery. Weapons, of course, can make up for the fact that some animals are superior to man in physical strength, but it is harder to compensate, say, for superior manœuvrability, and a great many animals are fleeter and more agile than man. Even when man has partly succeeded in making up for this disadvantage by taming speedy animals, still other animal qualities remain to evoke wonder and envy. Fishes, for example, swim better than man, and the flight of birds, in particular, reminds him of his own imperfection. Of course he has bow and arrows to hunt with, even in the air, but the carrying-power of this weapon is not great. Man is indeed a bungler, compared with the birds.

Jealousy and the lust for power gnaw at him. His feeling of inferiority is reflected in social organization and cult forms. The goal, despite all masking and beating about the bush, is plain: man wants to appropriate the animal qualities he lacks. He wants to add them to his own to increase his power. He would like to make them a part of himself, so that he and his clansmen, none other, may have the resultant advantages.

In the beginning was guile. Or perhaps it was only playfulness, the age-old delight in pretending to be someone else, in "dressing up" to look different and fool others, which first led cave-dwellers to wear the heads of slain animals as a disguise. Topped with a bear or deer head, they could give their camp-fellows a wonderful scare and animals might be thrown off their guard if someone crept up close to them in their own guise. It is a simple hunter's trick. No magical interpretation or resort to psychological profundities is needed to evolve it. When the game was repeated and also resulted in a surprisingly large bag, the disguise became an emblem, a mascot, believed in as anything is believed in when it ensures success. As other members of the clan followed suit, the animal head developed into a collective symbol. Thus the luck-bringing animal became the totem of the clan.

This kind of animal symbolism existed as far back as Palaeolithic times. In the cave paintings at Lascaux, paintings believed to be several thousand years older than the frescoes at Altamira, the artist, as we have already noted, drew a man with a bird head shown lifeless after an encounter with a large animal. Outside the scene of battle proper huddles a real bird, mourning his dead "half-brother." This bird was probably the clan symbol of the painter's and the dead man's clan.

Once an animal had become the totem, the "mascot," of a clan, even failures could no longer do him any harm. We know how stubbornly loyal people can be to the flag under which they have lost a war, so naturally a luck-bringing animal was never harmed. The totem animal was not only *tabu*, sacred in the sense of being untouchable except during religious ceremonies, but *mana* as well, that is, productive of extraordinary strength, unusual quickness and skill, and useful talents.

Primitive man was no altruist or apostle of nature. Once he had something that seemed to ensure his physical superiority or well-being, he was loath to part with it. The totem was exclusively the property of his clan, to be shared with no other. In order to make this exclusive right plausible to himself and others, primitive man invented an ancestral line. Family connection, consanguinity, genealogy, then as now were deemed the best proof of social legitimacy. Once the totem animal had been made the ancestor of the clan, all other relationships explained themselves. The clan's "forefather" could not be hunted, killed or eaten, except in the course of ceremonial rites intended symbolically to strengthen the group.

The primitive explanation of man's supposed descent from the totem animal is in most cases not very clear. In American Indian and African legends, all beings are described as having originally belonged to the same family. Sometimes, though seldom, his belief in a common past condensed into a definite picture of man's animal ancestry, e.g., in the pretty Indian legend in which a swan is portrayed as having sired all living creatures. From this swan, in a most remarkable fashion, came a magpie, a wolf and a coot. One day the magpie proposed to the wolf that they should get some earth, so that the coot might have something solid to stand on. The earth was found, and while the wolf sang and shook a rattle, the magpie poured water over the earth. Thus land and sea came into being and the magpie himself, the wisest of animals, turned into an Indian.

In many totem communities, however, there was apparently no idea at all of the clan's genealogical relationship to the totem animal. In many cases a plant or even an inanimate object served as totem. All generalizations in this field have proved to be inadequate.

TABU

The relationship between totem and tabu, moreover, is not so close or so binding as was earlier believed. At least the supposition that all animals on the tabu list are sacred to the folk or religious communities in question is erroneous. Frazer, who tried to force his great collection of material into a couple of small drawers, among other things made the assertion that the pig must have been a sacred animal to the Jews, since they would neither kill nor eat it. This would logically imply that all animals which for some reason or other were neither eaten nor exterminated must originally have been sacred.

The fact that the ban on eating pork among Jews, Syrians and Arabs—among the last two long before Mohammed—was actually an hygienic measure is perfectly obvious to anyone who has ever lived in a hot climate. It is generally known that meat-poisoning and intestinal disurbances, even in these days of vastly improved

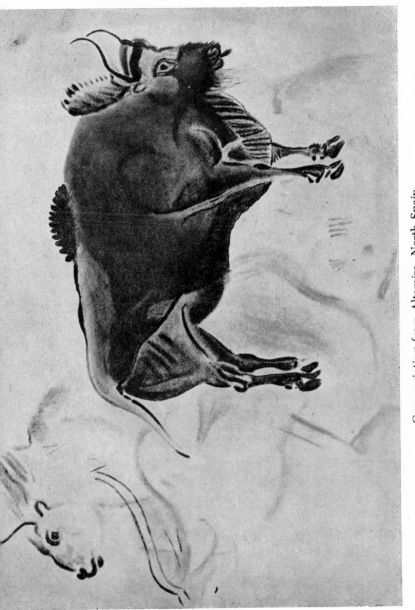

Cave painting from Altamira, North Spain

Prehistoric picture of a herd, Hodein Magoll, Nubian Desert

food-conserving methods, come more often from eating pork than from any other kind of meat. Moreover, among nomadic people pigs are harder to look after than grazing animals and are therefore less desirable.

In fact, economic and hygienic attitudes in the middle east vary from land to land and tribe to tribe. Whereas camel meat is one of the most important Arab foods, among the Jews it is considered unclean, although they, too, use the camel as a beast of burden and in no way regard it as sacred. It is quite possible that an epidemic or some other chance event originally gave rise to the Jewish tabu on camel meat. Even in modern times the camel is identified with disease, in the sense, at least, that he is supposed to attract plagues, thus preserving human beings from them. This would be ample reason for careful people to make sure they did not eat his flesh. In the Old Testament similar properties are attributed to birds, which are described as being used to cleanse people of leprosy.

That such procedures seem absurd to us today does not alter the fact that in their time they were considered effective sanitary measures and not religious rites. In the Bible the highly complicated bird ritual for leprosy is sharply distinguished from the scapegoat sacrifice next outlined. It is also a mistake to explain such matters on magical grounds—so far as magic is understood as involving supernatural influence—or yet as evidence for the "mystic mentality of the primitives," to use Adolphe Lods's phrase. For that matter, where in modern medicine is one to draw a line between the mystic and the rational?

Animal Gods

Even more obscure than totem or tabu are the peculiar animal cults of antiquity, particularly the Egyptian cults. The sociologists have certainly offered many interpretations of these cults, but leading Egyptologists are more sceptical and openly admit that they know nothing at all about the origin and symbolism of the animal gods. The existence in pre-dynastic Egypt of totem organizations that resembled those found among the Australian Negroes and the North American Indians still does not explain how such cult forms developed and flourished in the advanced Pharaonic culture.

The inhabitants of Egypt were hunters and fishermen long after the Mesopotamian peoples had turned to agriculture, but at the zenith of its history Egypt was an agricultural land, one where raising livestock was of only secondary importance. Ani-

Fig. 16. Animals in the life of ancient Egypt. *Top:* Fishermen. *Centre and bottom:* Egyptian herdsmen, cattle and donkeys (from an ancient picture)

mals were used mostly to draw ploughs and raise water from the wells. The question of slaughtering was not of paramount concern, and in some districts oxen may have been allowed to die a natural death. In any case, it was an easy step to the deification of living animals. Nevertheless, although Apis, the sacred bull, came to enjoy great popularity in all quarters as he advanced from local to imperial status, at no time was the practice of yoking oxen abandoned, nor that of burdening them with the heaviest kind of toil.

In fact animal gods, even in the very oldest religious myths, had become so symbolic that all they had left in common with earthly creatures was their form. Heaven was the belly of a cow, the sun either a falcon with glowing eyes or a great scarab, and the moon an ibis. The creator-gods of Elephantine, Sebek and Khnemu were represented as a crocodile and a ram respectively. Isis, one of the later divinities, was given the head of a cow and often, too, was shown with stylized cow horns on a human head; or again as a woman, with nothing emblematic of animality, standing under the giant cow, Hathor, in whom she was personified.

For a time the animal-god cult was supplanted, to some degree, by the custom of deifying the pharaohs and by the symbolic ascendancy of the sun-god in the human semblance of Ra, whose only animal characteristic was decorative horns, but during the last pre-Christian millennium the cult experienced a renaissance, bound up with mystery rites imported from other lands. Not until this juncture, when Egypt was in political and artistic decline and the old significance of the animal symbols had patently dimmed, were animals of divine connotation deified in daily usage. Now not only cats and poisonous snakes but cows and fishes also became sacred and untouchable. Anyone who harmed them did so on pain of death. If the situation actually was as it was described by Herodotus and other Greek writers, the Egyptians must virtually have become vegetarians.

Foreign conquerors fostered this development, for superstitious people are easier to rule. So long as Egypt supplied grain, these conquerors did not care what happened to the animals. Even in Alexandria, which was more of a Greek than an Egyptian city and where the favoured cult was that of Adonis and Aphrodite, a riot is said to have broken out because a Roman soldier killed a cat.

However, the strangest animal monuments in Egypt are not the stone and bronze gods which give museum visitors the creeps, but the great pyramids at the edge of the Libyan desert. The

Egyptians themselves were unaware of the fact that when they built the pyramids in honour of the pharaohs they were piling up millions and tens of millions of protozoa. Modern palaeontologists have discovered that the limestone of the pyramids of Gizeh consists almost entirely of fossil nummulites.

Animals shown in relief on a silver cup from Gudestrup in Jutland
(National Museum, Copenhagen)

Egyptian bed, eighteenth dynasty. Painted wood

Hittite lion of a royal palace; from the Karatepe, in the southeastern part of modern Turkey

Fable and Zoology

A LONG time passed before men found out that animals would carry them as well as inanimate burdens on their backs. Now and then, perhaps, some herdsman might have ridden an ox or a donkey but there is no evidence that animals were widely ridden before the rise of the near eastern kingdoms that marked the end of the prehistoric era.

The earliest signs of this development come from Mesopotamia but even there it seems that animal-drawn vehicles were in use fully a thousand years before the art of riding was born. On one of the oldest sculptures from the near east, the Vulture stele in the Louvre—so called because in one of the reliefs vultures are shown flying over the corpses of fallen warriors—a Sumerian king leads his troop in a chariot. Unfortunately the part of the stone showing how the harness was hitched is missing. Riding horses are first mentioned in historical record in the time of Hammurabi, about 2000 B.C.

The Semitic folk who forced their way into Mesopotamia from the west in about the middle of the third millennium and created the Babylonian kingdom may have been mounted and this may well have accounted for their conquest. However, some authorities believe the Kassites, conquerors of Babylonia c. 1800 B.C., brought horses with them from the Sarmatian flatlands. Still others claim that Mongolian tribesmen were the first horsemen. But all this is merely hypothesis. The only certainty is that the Babylonians had definitely mastered the horse, first using him for military purposes as a draught animal, later for riding.

The domesticated horse was brought to Egypt from Syria by the Hyksos, the "shepherd kings" of antiquity. After the Eighteenth Dynasty, about the middle of the second millennium, horse-drawn vehicles replaced litters as transport among the Egyptian upper class, but in desert sand and in the marshy ground of the Nile valley horses did not do so well. The Egyptians were apparently never great riders. Even the donkey was used almost entirely as a beast of burden in the kingdom of the pharaohs. As for the camel, he did not come into Egypt until Roman times.

THE HEROIC HORSE

The great equestrian period began in Greece where the horse became the favourite animal of gods and men. The Greeks recognized his beauty, which appealed to them more than his utility. They loved the horse for the very reason that he was not com-

Fig. 17. Constellation of Taurus (after Buschik, *Sternenkunde und Erdgeschichte*, 1927)

pletely tame, the least submissive of agricultural animals. Every young horse had to be broken in. He was an individual, he loved freedom even as man did, and yet he was man's friend and ally if handled properly.

In Greece the horse was not a beast of everyday use, being too costly and too difficult to manage for simple peasants. He belonged to the heroic side of life. A myriad legends were built about him and all of them, despite the variety of the Greek imagination, played on the same theme: the horse was a symbol of perfect motion. The Greeks sensed a musical element in the movements of the horse. To them he was of godly origin, sprung from the union of two great divinities, Poseidon and Demeter. The first horse was called Arion, and later a great musician was to bear the same name. Horses were sacred to Poseidon, the god of the sea. In Greek myth they symbolize the foaming waves, the ever restless flood. To the Greek mind horses were more than mere earthbound animals; they belonged in an imaginary space. They drew Poseidon's car over the ocean, they lifted themselves on mighty pinions into the air. Pegasus was one of these, sprung from the head of Medusa. Before becoming allied with the Muses he bore the poets up into the realms of fantasy.

In the *Theogony* of Hesiod, Pegasus is described as a spirited war horse who brings Zeus thunder and lightning.

In Homer's verse and thereafter the horse was an adjunct of the great heroes of ancient Greece. The greatest warriors rode on wonder beasts given to them by the gods. Most of these horses had wings, and many were able to talk. From his father, Peleus, Achilles inherited the immortal steeds Balios and Zanthos, a gift from Poseidon. Alexander the Great tried to equal the Homeric model. If his Bucephalus was not a divine horse, Alexander made sure he received the highest mortal honours, founding the city of Bucephala to mark the spot where his war horse died of old age after having carried his master all the way to India.

Horses used in sporting contests were equally esteemed in Greece; about them, too, were garlanded the laurels of legendary fame. The first horse race—chariots were used, races on horseback not being common in Greece—was a contest of love, according to Diodorus. King Oinomaos of Pisa, near Olympia, announced that he would give the hand of his daughter, Hippodamia—"the steed-tamer"—to the man who could beat him in a chariot race. This was a dangerous enterprise, however, since Oinomaos had winged

horses and whoever lost forfeited his life. After thirteen con-
testants had lost their lives in trying to win Hippodamia, a young
Lydian named Pelops decided to try his luck. Poseidon, who was
in league with him, lent him his own winged horses. Even so this
help might not have been enough had not feminine guile come
into play. Pelops had already secretly won Hippodamia's love,

Fig. 18. Picture of a rider on a Greek drinking vessel

and she persuaded her father's driver to loosen one of the chariot's
wheels. Hardly had the race begun when the chariot collapsed,
and Oinomaos was killed in the crash. The ancients assure us that
this was the first chariot race in Olympia, long before Herakles,
at the behest of Zeus, laid down strict rules for the Olympic
games.

A more realistic picture of horse racing in early Greek times
is given in the twenty-third book of the *Iliad*, antiquity's oldest
and most magnificent piece of sporting news. The race is arranged by Achilles on the plain of Troy in honour of his fallen
friend, Patroclus. Five of the greatest Greek charioteers take part,
among them Menelaus himself. Yet it is not Menelaus, but a
much lesser character, Diomedes, who wins the first prize of a
woman well-experienced in the domestic arts, and a great bronze
tripod.

FROGS AND MICE

The Greeks loved pathos, and when it came to horses they were particularly lavish in their use of high-flown language. But they knew, too, that from the sublime to the ridiculous is but a step and voiced only scorn for the heroic posturings of the would-be great. For this they sought their similes in the animal

Fig. 19. "The War of the Frogs and the Mice"; a sixteenth-century illustration

world, though perhaps not always with justification, for an anthropomorphic animal psychology—the interpretation of animal nature in terms of human analogy—is always a ticklish thing. The Greek poets, however, went about their satirizing with so much wit and such ingenious thrusts that they created some of the most wonderful banter in world literature.

One of the first of these satires was a "Batrachomyomachy," a "war between the frogs and the mice." For a long time this

Batrachomyomachy was held to be the oldest of all animal poems and attributed to Homer. However, it is not very likely that Homer poked fun at himself and the war of the frogs and the mice is obviously a parody of the *Iliad*. Plutarch surmised that the poet was a brother of Queen Artemisia of Caria, who fought on the Persian side in the battle of Salamis. According to this belief the parody would have been written about four hundred years after the *Iliad* itself. Modern philologists feel that the satire may possibly fall in a still later period.

The two parties in this mock Trojan War are the frog-people and the mice-people. As in the model, the *casus belli* is an abduction: the mouse Pricharpax is carried off by the frog-king, Physignathos. On the ensuing journey across the water the frog-king, frightened by a snake, ducks under, and the mouse riding on his back drowns. The mice then declare war on the frogs. As in the *Iliad*, the gods take sides in the conflict below. At first Zeus is warmly disposed towards the mice. As supreme arbiter, however, he must maintain a show of neutrality, so he tries to persuade Athena to favour the mice, pointing out that they are indefatigable visitors to her temples. Athena turns down this unreasonable request; the mice, she says, have eaten up her robes! On the other hand she will not intervene for the frogs, since they disturb her night's rest with their croaking.

Amid the thunderings of Zeus the two parties fall on each other. There are frightful duels, and, as in Homer, heroes deliver long discourses before they go into battle. The terrible mouse Meridarpax gives his opponent some dismaying blows but Zeus, after vacillating, finally intercedes for the frogs! At the crucial moment he sends the crabs to their aid. The crabs nip off the mice's legs and tails. Thus the war ends in a victory for the frogs.

Unlike the Trojan War, which went on for ten years, this war of the frogs and mice lasts but a day. The comic effect is gained by reducing everything to a ridiculously small scale. This would indicate that the satire might have been written by an eastern Greek for the Persians, since the Persians thought the Greeks west of the Aegean Sea were a small people, until they learned better at Salamis.

This was not the last time the Greeks used animals to satirize political conflicts. The device was refined in the comedies of Aristophanes. His very titles—*The Wasps, The Frogs, The Birds* —bespeak his fondness for transplanting human characteristics into the animal kingdom. Aristophanes' comedies are not animal dramas in the strict sense of the word. The actors do not come onto the stage dressed as animals, as in Rostand's *Chanticleer* or in *The Insect Play*, a world-wide success of the 1920s by Josef and Karel Capek, the Czech dramatists. In Aristophanes the principals are always human beings or gods in human guise.

In *The Wasps*, a satire on the Athenian courts, the heroes of the title are confined to the chorus. In *The Frogs*, a brilliant piece of mockery directed against Euripides and his admirers, once again the animals form a chorus, but this time one that sings lovely songs—"a chorus that really hits you in the middle." The famous frog chorus "Brekekekex, koax, koax" is the first phonetic imitation of animal sounds. In *The Birds* the animals have an even more important part. Two adventurous Athenians invade the kingdom of the birds, there proposing to found a Cloud-Cuckoo-Land. This was a satire on the irresponsible Athenian foreign policy which soon afterwards led to catastrophe in Sicily.

In assigning animals to dramatic roles, the first thought was to amuse the public. The very idea of animals acting like human beings was sure to evoke laughter, and when the animals took sharp digs at important personages as well, the applause was uproarious. Moreover the censors, and even free Athens had them, could not very easily object, since the poet, so to speak, could hardly be held responsible for what animals might say.

Aesop's Fables

Even though animals in dramatic and epic poetry were as a rule only used as a device to characterize and caricature human beings, nevertheless this usage fixed people's ideas of what animals are like. Animals acquired character by this process of making them analogous to definite human types, types to which in actual fact they bore nothing more than some external resemblance in shape or movement. Animals came to be measured and evaluated by human standards; they became moral creatures. Relatively quicker or slower reactions were interpreted as intelligence or stupidity. Animals were labelled brave or cowardly, diligent or lazy. Not only domestic animals, but those of wood and heath, of water and air, were issued character references.

Fig. 20. "The Truthful Man, the Liar and the Monkey" (*Aesop's Fables*, the Ulm edition, late Middle Ages)

This fixation of animal character as a composite pieced together from human and animal traits can be observed in its formative stage in the writings of Simonides of Amorgos. This poet originally hailed from Samos and is believed, by some, to have lived in the first half of the seventh century B.C., by others, early in the sixth century B.C. In his bitter satire on women, Simonides presents a whole catalogue of female types. Each of these types has an animal ancestry, which accounts both for good points—the few that women have—and their much more numerous defects. Slovenly women stem from a "long-haired sow"; peevish women who think they know everything from a "crafty fox"; and mean, spying women from a "bitch." Easygoing, passive women are descended from a female donkey; and those without charm from a weasel, "that unhappy and lamentable race." Even worse off are the ugly women. They are of ape extraction, "the greatest plague that Zeus has given man for companion."

There are also some less repulsive representatives of the weaker sex in Simonides, those who show, as it were, a better animal pedigree. Proud and cultivated women come from a mare with a beautiful mane, and good mothers and housewives from a bee. The poet esteems the horse and the bee most highly. This classification was to become routine in the literature.

Simonides' imitator, Phocylides, was a famous countryman and somewhat younger contemporary of Thales of Miletus. He simplified the female line of descent. According to him the female sex has four sources; noble and beautiful women are descended from a horse; industrious housewives from a bee; dirty, but basically goodhearted, women from a sow; and violent, unmanageable termagants from a bitch. The most surprising thing to us is the Greeks' contempt for the dog, but actually the dog was held in low regard all through antiquity. To this day the female dog, in English at least, retains the bad mark given it by the Greek poets.

Once an animal's character had been established, it was possible to make a hundred and one combinations for the reader's or play-goer's edification. The specific form of moralizing among animals is the fable, which itself has contributed much to popular acceptance of alleged animal characteristics.

The fable is a short anecdote of practical moral application in which several animals are played off against each other. As a rule these animals have the gift of human speech and in other respects also behave more like people than animals. But the make-believe evokes and maintains suspense. The reader listens more readily when an ant speaks than if a schoolmaster were expounding the same sort of wisdom. Basically the fable involves a distortion of nature, and because of the stereotyping of the animal character, curtails what the human eye sees. However, since great poets have made use of this literary form, some significant works of art have come of it.

In all folk-poetry there are attempts to write fables but really striking examples of high literary quality are not very numerous. Writers still consistently borrow stock themes from older or foreign literatures. The greatest mine of fable is the region of Greece, though many of the Greek fables themselves were imports from eastern lands. The Reynard-the-Fox fable stems from Babylon and others are supposed to have come from India.

Fig. 21. "The Lion and the Mouse" (*Aesop's Fables*, the Ulm edition, late Middle Ages)

So closely is Greek fable linked with the name of Aesop that the two are virtually synonymous. Aesop lived in the first half of the sixth century B.C., a contemporary of Solon and of King Croesus who brought him to his court. Actually many of the animal fables which were still circulating as Aesopian during the Middle Ages probably derived from both earlier and later times. Aesop's fables simply became a prototype; therefore anything good in the fable line could have been originated by no one else.

Aesop's fame doubtless rests not only on the quality of his work but on his powerful personality as well. He was the Socrates of the pre-Socratic sages—physically malformed, cynical, rough, sarcastic, dogmatic. At the same time he had a heart of gold and was always on the side of the underdog. Far superior in intellect to his opponents, he was a man with an inflexible sense of justice. Such traits did not make for being liked in ancient times any more than they do today. In isolated cases they might lead to power, but more often they led to a violent death.

After Aesop had risen from slavery to be ambassador to Lydia and enjoy international fame, he felt strong enough to criticize the most powerful and yet most decadent institution in Greece, the Delphic oracle. He publicly accused the priests of Apollo's temple of greed and venality. The priests took Aesop's denunciations in silence. But when he rashly went to Delphi, they smuggled a golden bowl into his baggage and upon his departure had his effects searched. They then accused Aesop of having purloined the bowl from the temple treasure. He was sentenced to die, and thrown from a cliff. This was the end of the man who gave so many animals a character—a character which for the past two and a half thousand years has impressed itself on the memory of children before they have even laid eyes on the animals themselves.

THE SAGE OF STAGIRA

Thanks to Aesop, animals were morally classified before they were ever arranged in a system based on physical characteristics. The first scientific classification was also a product of the Greek mind. Previous achievements in the zoological field in Babylonia, Palestine and India had been relatively modest, compared with those in other branches of knowledge. There are supposed to have been animal doctors in Babylonia but their treatments must have been highly empirical.

In Greece Empedocles and Diogenes of Appolonia were the first, a hundred years after Aesop, to show a scientific interest in the origins and relationships of the animal world; but still another century passed before anyone went beyond guesswork and scattered observation and created the general framework without which can be no real science. The man who fashioned this structure was Aristotle, the sage of Stagira. Though only a small section of his total works is devoted to zoology, none the less Aristotle's *Natural History* is a basic work, one of those which bring a science into being at a single stroke, an achievement which makes everything that has gone before shrink to mere precursor status. The fact that Aristotle's *Natural History* contains a whole series of factual mistakes in no way alters its greatness.

Aristotle was a deductive thinker: first the general, then the particular; but before he went to work he amassed so much of the raw material of knowledge that his logic did not do too much violence to the facts. In the Aristotelian system, as previously in the Democritean, the animal kingdom is divided up into two main groupings: animals with blood, and those without. This means, in effect, vertebrates and invertebrates respectively. In the vertebrate subdivisions of this system, reproduction is the criterion, as it is in modern classification. There are animals which bring their young into the world alive, others which lay eggs, and intermediately a third class, in which the young crawl out of the egg inside the womb. The invertebrate subdivision, which includes cephalopods, crustacea, mollusca and insects, is based more on anatomical differences in the external skeleton.

Over five hundred animals are cited in the Aristotelian zoology, many of which are precisely described, fifty plainly on the basis of dissection. According to tradition, Alexander the Great and his court-philosopher, Callisthenes, supplied Aristotle with animals and plants collected during the eastern campaigns, in the interests of widening the scope of natural history. Although Humboldt and Cuvier doubt this story, and although many moderns are of the opinion that Aristotle depended more on the observations of others than on his own, his results, after all, are what count. Even pure collecting can open new paths, since it changes mere quantity, in Hegel's phrase, into quality.

Aristotle's biological observations show that he was more than a collector and classifier. He opened up new worlds. He saw reproduction as the essence of the organic. He related function and *organ* structure. He tried to bridge the gap between the organic and the inorganic. These feats alone compensate a thousand times over for his errors in counting ribs and teeth.

Most astonishing of all are his insights into embryology. In Aristotle's day there was still disagreement on the question of whether the mother had any share in the actual reproduction of the offspring, either in animals or in man. The prevailing view was that the male seed alone supplied the formative element and that the female body was nothing but a container and a source of nourishment. The significance of the ovum as yet was completely unknown. Aristotle was the first to describe the origin of a hen's egg. Thereafter it was known that young are not only brought into the world by the mother but descend from her as well, and that genesis is bisexual. Of course, this was only an hypothesis in Aristotle's day. The relationship between mother and child could not be proved without the microscope. No matter: this was one of those great intuitive insights that carried science further than the most careful experiments.

▣ VIII ▣

Meat and Circus Games

JUVENAL's formula *panem et circenses*—"bread and circuses"—was a way of expressing contempt for the proletariat of ancient Rome. It was very apt. The masses have never asked for much more than cheap bread or free bread for the poor. Not that they have ever preferred bread, but had they demanded meat instead no one would have been able to fulfil their wish. Already in antiquity the supply of livestock was simply not large enough to support a meat diet in the large urban centres.

So it has remained to this day. Except for those who live in thinly settled cattle-rearing regions, the poorer population all over the world lives mainly on products of the soil rather than on meat. Even in prosperous countries, where the very poorest have their daily bread, only a small segment of the population has its daily meat. The great majority must do without, not because they are vegetarians but because meat costs too much. Breeding animals for slaughter has become geared to the needs of "normal" meat consumption, which in effect means an inadequate consumption limited by income. Whenever special circumstances increase demand serious difficulties arise. For example, in time of war a few million men, many of them recruited from the poorer classes, become soldiers, and are richly provided with a meat diet. At the same time workers in war industries are paid higher wages. When this happens, even a country as rich in fodder and livestock as the United States must ration meat. The experience of the Second World War reminded all those who

96

might have forgotten that even in our times meat is a semi-luxury.

The history of human diet shows there has been no basic change in this regard since mankind first became sedentary and learned how to till the soil. Seemingly the earth cannot feed both mankind and livestock at the same time. Because of this discrepancy, agricultural products that nourish man directly have first call. Bread comes before meat. But the proprietary and ruling classes, great consumers of meat that they are, insist that their tables shall be abundantly provided with animal products. To meet this demand, grain-growing lands may be turned into pasture or an excessively high percentage of the grain harvest may be turned into stock feed. This process may continue until neither the urban poor nor the farmers themselves have enough grain for bread, whereupon bread riots ensue. Then adjustments in an opposite direction have to be made, by means of land reform or by conquest of new grain-producing regions.

The Kitchen of Lucullus

The class wars of antiquity were an expression of this latent conflict between bread and meat. This conflict first appeared in the Greek city-states, especially in Sparta, which after the fourth century B.C. became a latifundian country of great pastoral estates. Yet articulate though the Greeks may have been on a high intellectual level, the phenomena of ordinary daily life are but weakly and incidentally reflected in their literature. Social questions were much more thoroughly and eloquently aired in Rome. In Roman politics we hear about bread all the time. Bread was the issue in the revolts of the Gracchi. Maintenance of the bread supply was the chief problem of Roman rulers in imperial times. Yet the revels of the upper class which the Roman poets and sociologists never tired of describing were marked by a consumption of meat never equalled before or since in abundance or variety.

Lucius Licinius Lucullus, a contemporary of Julius Caesar,

was one of the most lavish among gourmands. His banquets assured him a more enduring fame than his exploits as field commander in the war against Mithridates. Yet actually he was more than a frivolous glutton. Lucullus' house was a meeting place for artists and philosophers, and at his richly decked table the most profound metaphysical problems were discussed. Though the anecdotes about his extravagance and generosity are endless, not much is known about the culinary creations that immortalized his name. His lasting service to mankind was his importation of the cherry into Europe, an incident in his military campaigns in Asia Minor. The cherry was named after Cerasus on the southern shore of the Black Sea, where Lucullus was first delighted by the new fruit.

Fig. 22. Roman animal paintings: mural from the market hall (marcellum) in Pompeii

Roman gourmets for the most part were omnivorous, that is, they tried everything that showed promise of being pleasing to the palate. Roman cooks had to prepare delightful dishes out of the most bizarre raw materials and sometimes they succeeded, sometimes not. The *haute cuisine* of the Romans was experimental as it is today among true gourmets. In order to select the best, everything had to be tasted. The rarer, the more exotic, the more expensive the different kinds of meat and garnishings, the more they were welcome. Specialists were sent out into the most distant provinces of the empire and even to foreign lands to get rare fowl, exceptional kinds of fish and shellfish, and the varieties of game and domestic animals in greatest demand. Roman annals tell of guinea hens from North Africa, pheasants from the Caspian Sea, peacocks from Media—at first they had been only decorative—sheatfish and cormorants from the Nile, oysters from the Hellespont, and many other rarities.

Yet even in matters of luxury the Romans were a rational people. Because the importation of exotic animals was a terribly expensive and unreliable process, the well-to-do began to raise them themselves in order to have a sure supply. As a result several European animal species were transplanted, and many which might otherwise have been exterminated by hunters, fishermen and trappers were saved from extinction.

The first man-made oyster bed was started in about 100 B.C. Sergius Orata is said to have been the pioneer in oyster culture. Soon afterwards artificial ponds—*piscinae*—were dug for the breeding of fresh-water fish. Eventually every aristocratic country villa had to have at least a container for moray. Lucullus introduced an even more startling novelty. He had a basin for salt-water fish constructed by his seashore villa, fed with salt water from the ocean brought in through a conduit. This method, however, was soon surpassed when lagoons were created by the construction of jetties in shallow waters so as to have fresh fish at any time straight from the sea.

Since hunting did not produce enough game, wild animal preserves were laid out. This innovation came from the east, and had been known to the younger Scipio Africanus. In Italy the first experiment of this sort consisted of putting up fences to pen in rabbits. The name *leporarium*—"rabbit farm"—was later applied to parks for larger game laid out during the days of Lucullus. Quintius Fulvius Lupinus is remembered as the inventor of the forest-prison, an institution that for two thousand years thereafter continued to be a feature of all princely estates.

Though all this effort served only the pleasure of the upper class, the culinary cult undoubtedly contributed in a general way to the improvement of animal husbandry. Since the rich Romans who prized good meat were mostly owners of large estates, they vied with each other in seeing who could produce the best beef cattle. Cicero and a number of other Roman writers are agreed

that during the oldest Roman period cattle were regarded as aids
to man in the cultivation of the soil, and that on this account
slaughtering was forbidden on pain of death. The fact that
butchering has always been looked upon as a low occupation
may be a dim echo of this prohibition. On the other hand it is
an established fact that beef, and also veal, lamb, pork and goat
meat, were brought to the market in early Rome and continued
to be offered for sale there until the butchers' stalls were
crowded out by the money-changers' booths.

Fig. 23. Roman animal paintings: donkey and crocodile from
Herculaneum

Milch cows played only a minor part in the Roman agricultural economy. Milk was not very well likely in the city and
butter was prohibited as a barbarian food. Of the dairy products
only cheese was a popular food, though never as popular as in
Greece. In a practical sense raising livestock meant production
for meat, and producing good meat was the Roman breeders'
pride. On the great estates breeding was scientific. There were
good stalls and good fodder, and above all good breeding bulls.
For each seventy cows they kept two bulls, a yearling and a two-
year-old. After the second year all bulls were castrated. The
castration technique came from Asia, where initially it had been
practised on human beings. Romans abominated human castrates,
yet used castration widely among animals, since it made them
easier to fatten. Capons were considered to be an especial
delicacy.

Every Roman and Greek country estate had its beehives. Bees
were indispensable, for in antiquity honey was the only sweeten-

ing common in the west. Ever since the campaigns of Alexander the Great the people of the west had known that sugar cane grew in India. Though there was a lively commerce between India and Rome, the Romans made no attempt to introduce cane sugar except for medicinal purposes. Because honey was cheaper and better—raw sugar had not yet been refined—the bees retained their privileged position until the late Middle Ages.

The Sacrificial Swine

The use of animals in sacrificial ritual was much more characteristic of Rome than of Greece. Even in the greatest of their festivals the Greeks were usually content to lay flowers or fruits on the altar. As a rule sheep, less frequently cattle, were sacrificed to the gods only when, as at Delphi, divinations were sought, or some other special dispensation; but in Rome the temples were regular slaughterhouses. Yet here again there were class differences reflecting the inherent conflict between bread and meat. The plebeians had their own divinities—Ceres, Liber and Flora—protectors of the grain and the vines, who were brought fruits sacred to them. Ceres alone was occasionally offered a pregnant ewe as a symbol of fruitfulness. The large sacrificial animals were consecrated to the patrician gods, above all to Jupiter and Juno, who were worthy of snow-white cattle.

It is doubtful, however, whether Romans had always been sacrificially minded. In his *Natural History*, Pliny reports that in the old religious system of Numa Pompilius' days none but vegetable offerings were prescribed, supposedly for the same practical reasons that draught cattle could not be slaughtered. Yet it would seem that animal offerings were the order of the day at least as far back as religious belief among the Romans is historically recorded. The customary sacrificial animal was the pig. The offering up of a pig was part of any orderly covenant, and even in state pacts the ritualistic slaughter of a pig was considered the proper thing in sealing the agreement's validity. The representatives of Rome and of the other contracting party went into the temple of Jupiter and there attended while the priest killed the animal with the sacred sickle, meanwhile intoning this ceremonial formula: "If the Roman people injure this pact, may Jupiter smite them, as I smite this pig with the stone."

The Roman state religion was legalistic. All important rites were closely regulated. At the beginning of the Second Punic War the senate ordered a "sacred spring," that is, the mass sacri-

Fig. 24. Garlanding the sacrificial bulls in Greece (British Museum)

fice of animals born that spring. The *pontifex maximus* issued minutely detailed instructions for the execution of this order. If one of the animals dedicated to the gods died before the sacrifice, the order said, the flesh could be eaten without risk of impiety. If by mischance the offering were made on an unfavourable day, it would still count. And so on. The Old Testament book of Leviticus itself is not as finicky as the codes of the Roman priests.

Prophecy from the intestines of four-footed animals was also regulated with painful exactness. Roman prophecy was a kind of anatomical examination, unlike the spontaneous divination of the Greeks. Every fold and abnormal change in the soft parts, the liver especially, had its special meaning. It was much like the palmistry of modern times.

The flesh of the sacrificial animal belonged to the person who had brought the offering. Priests had no claim on it except in state ceremonies. This arrangement fostered the growth of the slaughter cult, since giving up a pig liver was a small price to pay for knowledge of the gods' will. In any case, not all animals

Fig. 25. Consulting the oracle. Roman augur
inspecting the sacrifice

could be used in these rites. Strict rules were laid down in this regard. On the big landed estates animals intended for sacrifice were reared separately from the rest. On the whole, Roman animal sacrifice, though it may seem strange to us because of its archaic appurtenances, was neither cruel nor wasteful.

HEROES OF THE ARENA

The animal in man had found fairly harmless release in the arena, in the Roman institution called the circus. The Roman circus was a place where chariot races were held, less frequently races on horseback, and occasionally animal hunts and gladiatorial contests. In the circus the Roman carried on the Greek tradition, coarsening and expanding it. The benches of the Circus Maximus could seat 385,000 people—the biggest stadium ever built. Twenty-four races were run daily throughout the whole morning and afternoon. As many as ten horses were hitched to a chariot, a vehicle that became of lighter and lighter construction as time went on and finally developed into a low, two-wheeled conveyance with a sort of knee guard for the driver. Under the republic, chariot racing had been an amateur sport for the upper class, but under the empire it became a professional affair, and a very risky one, for accidents were extremely common. It was highly paid, however. Juvenal says that one chariot driver earned as much as a hundred lawyers would.

Roman sports spectacles were run by capitalists on a big-business basis. The backers consisted of several groups who owned the stables and employed hundreds of people. Each group was supported by an army of bettors and fans who loved the sport of chariot-racing for its own sake. The various groups were known as the "Reds," the "Whites," the "Blues," and the "Greens," according to the colours worn by their drivers. The tradition of racing colours, of course, has survived to this day. The different groups sometimes merged, then were again at loggerheads and fought each other violently. The emperors were not displeased. From the dictatorial point of view it was better to have Romans breaking each other's heads over racing than over political issues. Yet in the eastern end of the empire the chariot-racing passion showed that it could be dangerous.

The Blues and Greens who ruled the hippodrome in Constantinople were more tightly organized than in Rome. They formed real *demoi*, that is, folk associations, with their own militia and a powerful voice in political and religious struggles. The Blues were on the side of orthodoxy, the Greens included many rebels.

When Emperor Justinian tried to eliminate both groups, they composed their differences and united in a common front. On a January Sunday in 532 the crowd in the hippodrome called for a new emperor with the cry of "*Nika*—conquer!" and "up the merciful Greens and Blues!" The Nika revolt assumed such dangerous proportions that Justinian, then at the start of his great career, was on the verge of fleeing the city. Only the proud words of the Empress Theodora dissuaded her illustrious husband from flight. The Empress might not have been blue-blooded but, having herself grown up as the daughter of a hippodrome bear-keeper, she knew the heroes of the arena. Urged by Theodora, Justinian took up the challenge. He first negotiated with the Blues, then turned on the Greens. The uprising was crushed, with the slaughter of thirty thousand spectators in the hippodrome by imperial troops.

Bloody contests designed solely for the pleasure of the spectators were held, as a rule, in amphitheatres. The largest and most complex structure of this kind was the Roman Colosseum, which had a seating capacity of 87,000. The Romans called it the Amphitheatrum Flavium, after the Flavian emperors who built it. The Emperor Titus, named by his biographer Suetonius "the ornament of the human race," dedicated the Colosseum with an enormous spectacle in which five thousand animals were slain. The Colosseum featured such ingenious novelties as underground stables and machinery which turned the arena into a lake for water battles or into a simulated wood where wild animals were hunted.

However, the art of killing men and animals for the amusement of the crowd went back much further. Its greatest patrons were the Asiatic rulers. The custom of keeping menageries came from the Tigris and the Euphrates, also the practice of throwing political prisoners, schismatics and common criminals to wild animals. Contests between human beings and animals combined the execution of justice with sadism.

In all probability the Romans first found out about lions and tigers in Oriental animal-training schools, rather than in the wild, and later imported them for various purposes of exhibition. The first contest between animals in the Colosseum took place in 186 B.C., shortly after the conquest of Syria. The Roman empire was so extensive that the capital was able to furnish a greater variety of exotic spectacles than any other city in ancient history. Asia, Africa and the barbarian lands of Europe met in the arena of the Colosseum. Elephants and rhinoceroses, bears and bulls, lions, tigers and panthers were matched against each other or against gladiators or were egged on to attack helpless prisoners. Nero, himself an excellent charioteer, conceived the idea of using exotic animals in chariot races and once had four camels harnessed to a chariot. Heliogabalus, the Syrian, maddest of the Roman emperors, went one better than Nero by staging chariot races using elephants, lions and tigers. He also tried to train red deer for this purpose.

WAR ELEPHANTS

One of the most revolting animal hunts ever contrived by the Romans was a fight between elephants and dogs. The young Lucullus who, with his brother, was supervisor of the circuses,

Fig. 26. Assyrian armoured war dog. Relief from Birs Nimrud

invented this fantastic *divertissement*. The Romans had first become acquainted with elephants two hundred years before in the war against King Pyrrhus of Epirus. Then the Roman soldiers had panicked at the sight of the grey giants, and at Heraclea and Asculum elephant charges had won the day for the Macedonian forces.

Roman watchdog. Mosaic from Pompeii

Pyrrhus's war elephants very probably came from Asia. Their military use was an old tradition in the east when Alexander went into India. Alexander had to fight against elephants again and again but himself was hesitant about adopting this enemy weapon. However, Alexander wanted all the trappings of an Oriental despot—tame lions were kept at his field headquarters—and so he did have elephants but used them mostly as beasts of burden. The favourite who carried the royal baggage he named Ajax. Occasionally the huge beasts were actually used during battle, as battering rams. Mobile archers took cover behind them, as do modern soldiers behind tanks.

Such manœuvres, here and elsewhere, had varied success. In the heat of battle the elephants, whom the Hindus regard as the very symbol and wisdom and knowledge, were unable to distinguish clearly between friend and foe and often trampled soldiers on their own side to death. The Romans soon discovered that war elephants were not such an effective weapon after all. In the First Punic War the Carthaginians brought over a hundred mighty African pachyderms to Sicily, but in the battle at Palermo they failed ignominiously. Metellus led the whole elephant troop back to Rome as part of his spoils of war and sent them to the circus, where they perished one by one.

Nor did Hannibal have very much luck with his famous war elephants. He appeared in Europe with fifty of them but by the time he got to the Rhone only thirty-seven were left. After the crossing of the Alps they had been reduced to eight and of these seven later died. One elephant out of the original fifty survived the rigours of the campaign. In spite of this discouraging experience the Romans were not to be outdone by their adversaries and themselves formed an elephant squadron, but their enthusiasm was shortlived. The Romans used elephants only occasionally, during their wars in the near east and North Africa. In these same regions elephants had a later day of glory among the Arabs but in Rome they were again downgraded and made to serve as circus animals.

IX

The Feudal Animal

THE folk migrations towards the end of the fourth century A.D., which saw millions of human beings from the Asiatic steppes to the Atlantic Ocean overflow political and ethnic boundaries, are to this day among the mysteries of world history. Mass migrations had occurred in other epochs, but displacements of such scope are unknown in either earlier or later chronicles.

The prevailing view among modern historians is that the internal collapse of the Roman empire was the main cause of these migrations. According to this interpretation, the general movement was centripetal, an invasion of spoils-hungry barbarians who turned towards Mediterranean lands because there was so much there to take away, but, despite all detours and side excursions, these fourth-century wanderings had a clear east-to-west direction. The wave was so extensive that it cannot be regarded as a simple gathering together of water drops into one forward-rushing stream. It would seem more likely that the pressure came from within, that the migration, at least in its initial stage, was in the nature of a centrifugal movement, an excursion rather than an incursion, an eruption rather than an irruption.

The original cause of the migration seems to have been a sharpening of the climate in central Asia which forced the nomadic tribes to seek other pasturage. They could not venture eastward, for there they would have run up against a military power which, in spite of the internal decay of the Chinese empire after the fall of the Han dynasty, was still stronger than themselves. Thus they set out in the direction of least resistance, which was the west.

RIDERS OUT OF THE EAST

The Huns, who were among the first to set out towards the west, were an equestrian folk. Ammian, a Greek from Antioch, reported the terrifying ugliness of the Huns and their horses. The Huns, he said, had crooked bodies. They lived on roots, they sat their steeds as if nailed to them, they kept raw meat under the

Fig. 27. Chinese war chariot of the Han dynasty, beginning of the Christian era

saddle to warm it a little while they were riding, for they never bothered to cook it. They had no religion, any more than animals, and were not even superstitious. The only attribute they had in common with higher forms of life was an uncontrollable passion for gold.

Although Ammian's portrait seems true enough to life, actually it was only a caricature. The Huns did not live like wild beasts at all. Indeed, they produced some very interesting and profound ideas about the nature of the universe. The history of their comet-like ascendancy shows that they were neither physically nor intellectually inferior to the barbarian peoples of Europe. They had an excellent military organization, orderly ways, diplomatic and strategic talent, and became accustomed to the good life as quickly as any other people.

It was mainly thanks to their horses that the Huns were able to found a great empire so quickly. These horses were bony, rough-haired animals with a small head, a long, down-sloping back and short, strong legs. They needed little water, and in desert country were able to cover over sixty miles a day. From the mares' milk the Huns made *kumiss*, a lightly fermented and much-prized drink which was their principal food during the summertime. Like most nomads, the Huns were not great meat-eaters. Their own flocks, too precious for ordinary use, served as a means of exchange and a reserve supply of skins and wool.

In spite of their poverty the Huns were better equipped for long migrations than the Visigoths and other European tribes who fled before them. For those who had become half-sedentary migration was an improvised manœuvre, entailing too much baggage and too little transport, as always in such cases. The cattle that these western emigrants took along with them proved to be a dead weight. What they really needed was horses. In these folk migrations the horse, hitherto an ornamental possession, an upper-class luxury article, became a common necessity. Anyone who had a horse could make a quick escape or be first on the spot when there was something to conquer and plunder.

It may be said without exaggeration that the horse brought about the collapse of the western Roman empire. To be sure, there was no lack of so-called internal causes, but the immediate cause was the military superiority of mounted enemy hosts which the Romans were unable to check. Cavalry had always been a neglected branch of the Roman army. As a rule there was one mounted man to every fifteen or twenty foot soldiers. The long

Stallion from the Erechtheum on the Acropolis in Athens

Horseman from the west frieze of the Parthenon, fifth century B.C.

Knight on armoured horse statue on the grave of Mastino II Scaliger
in Verona, fourteenth century

Silkworm cultivation in Japan, from a coloured woodcut by the Japanese master Utamaro

series of great Roman military leaders includes only one real
cavalry general, Marcus Antonius. In this regard it is also significant that whereas in some countries, e.g., Germany, the
knights of the military nobility bore the title of *Ritter*—the literal
meaning of which is "rider," the Latin equivalent, *eques*, was a
secondary title, given to the wealthy of Rome merely to signify
that they were substantial enough to own a horse. Romans
known by the title *eques* were private citizens without political
connection. With them the horse was more a symbol of affluence
than of real power. In any event, this low estimate of the horse
among the Romans now took its toll. The mounted troops of the
barbarians cut the Roman legions to pieces.

Cavalrymen became the conquerors, and for a thousand years
retained mastery over Europe, at least in so far as they did not
have to yield before another equestrian people who had forced
their way into the western world from North Africa. The Arabs
had no great herds of livestock, but many sheep, camels, donkeys
and horses. Their horses were their greatest pride, slim, tall and
proportionately developed creatures of nervous temperament
and great nimbleness. The best Arabian horses came from Nejd.
Throughout the entire near east they were considered to be the
noblest creations of nature. They were, in fact, the product of
careful breeding.

The horse played an important role in the beginnings of
Islamic history and legend. Mohammed himself was no Bedouin,
rather a town-dweller, but from his early youth was familiar
with animals. As a child he accompanied his uncle on journeys
to Syria, later he led commercial caravans through the desert
while in the service of a rich and elderly widow who owned a
transport business in Mecca and later became the Prophet's wife.
No doubt Mohammed made his business journeys on camel- or
donkeyback, but as he became a famous conquerer in the eyes of
Islam he was given a fiery steed to carry him on his spiritual
missions. On the wonder horse Alborak, so the faithful relate,
Mohammed, accompanied by the archangel Gabriel, made his

sacred midnight journey from Mecca to Jerusalem, whence he ascended into heaven.

On the rocky site from which Alborak took off into the firmament, the second caliph, Omar al-Khattab, erected a magnificent mosque. This mosque, which bears Omar's name, was built on the very spot where Solomon's temple had once stood. Omar himself, however, made his triumphal entry into Jerusalem in plain Bedouin fashion, on a camel. With him, slung across the camel's back, he carried a sack of dates and one of grain, and a leathern water bag.

Fig. 28. Horses of the Steppes (Scythian vase from Certomlyk)

The Arabs' military successes approached the miraculous. They subdued the greatest kingdoms with small armies made up of mounted men. The Persians tried to hold them back with a considerable elephant corps but after three days of struggle the elephant battle at Kadis ya was decided in favour of the Arabian lancers. Later three hundred Arabs and seven thousand Berbers took Spain. Not till they reached Poitiers, in the heart of France, did the Arab cavalry run up against a stone wall.

For yet a third time, some five hundred years later, a mounted army came out of the east and penetrated deep into Europe. The army of Genghis Khan was much larger and better organized than the Arabian shock troops. The great Mongol prince had established a post-house system throughout Asia which he used to maintain hegemony over conquered regions. Marco Polo's report that this superior organization included 300,000 horses and 10,000 post-houses may have been somewhat overdrawn. Nevertheless there is no doubt that it was the most significant communications system on land since the fall of the Roman empire.

THE KNIGHT'S CHARGER

In the west, too, the horse became the foundation of political power. The feudal system of the Middle Ages rested on the legal power of disposal over the saddle horse. At the beginning of the Carolingian period the chevalier, the knight, was by no means a man who had performed heroic deeds or who could show aristocratic descent. He was anyone at all who owned a horse and a complete suit of armour. Once he had these he was able to acquire land as well, by promising himself to military service under some liege-lord. The piece of land that he received for his services was in theory only loaned to him but in practice the property became his own to hand down, providing that he, the vassal knight, could equip a son as he had been equipped. Thus, a noble class with special privileges came into being. The knight was still considered a noble even if he worked his own land or even if he went out and took his chances as a robber-knight, or as a *Gluecksritter*. The *Gluecksritter*, or "luck-rider," was a professional jouster who followed the tourneys as cowboys do the rodeos. So long as he had horse and armour, he was regarded as a gentleman, a man of quality.

The heavy, costly armour of the Middle Ages, a heritage from Roman times, prevented cavalry from becoming as important in the west as it was in the east. The hosts of Genghis Khan who swept in from Asia consisted of common people on horseback while in Europe riders were a caste, a powerful, but small, minority. Armour also determined the type of horse used in the medieval west. The gaunt, light Mongol horse, and the tall, slender Arab steed seemed useless to western peoples. In Europe the heavy types were deemed the best.

After the Charlemagne period large, massive horses were bred. It took a long time to get the desired results, for the wild horse that had roamed Europe after the Ice Age was small and insignificant in build, and domestication had not contributed much to his improvement. Working with a somewhat stronger strain from eastern Alpine country—the old Roman province of Noricum—the breeders began to produce a new type, the "Noric" horse. He was a clumsy animal, made for carrying loads and heavy pulling. His back tended to sag, and he had mighty haunches, powerful enough to hold up a knight in full armour and perform heavy tasks in the fields. A good horse had to be able to carry four hundred pounds.

Inevitably these abilities were developed at the expense of speed. If whipped hard enough, the ponderous medieval nag could be made to gallop in a rather bull-like fashion, but no amount of whipping could make him keep up with the nimble horses of Asia and North Africa. This was the main reason why the eastern peoples forced their way so easily into Europe and why invariably they were able to escape unscathed even when they encountered stronger forces. During the Crusades, the horses bred in European studs failed completely. The animals that the Crusaders took with them into the warmer climate of Asia Minor perished in droves. "It is hard to know whether one should laugh or cry," William of Tyre writes in his *History of the Crusades*, "when one sees how we load our baggage on wethers, goats, or pigs for lack of larger animals. Many a knight may be seen riding on an ox, serving in place of a war horse."

The horses used in the knightly tournaments were also heavy and clumsy. Highly bred racehorses were unknown in the Middle Ages. Equestrian sport consisted of war games. Originally the medieval tourney was a regular military manœuvre within a gala setting, in which sometimes as many as two thousand knights took part. It was not a mock battle, as in modern manœuvres, between two groups from the same army, but a serious international contest.

As time went on, mass contests ceased to be the custom. They were very costly, for one thing, besides being less attractive to court society than a joust between two men coming at each other full tilt on horseback. By the middle of the eleventh century a French knight from Touraine, Geoffroi de Preuilly, had worked out a set of strict rules for tournaments, which came to be held

Fig. 29. French caricature of a troubadour
(twelfth century)

sacred throughout all feudal Europe. By and large these bloody equestrian festivals were knightly in tone. However, the favour of the ladies in whose honour the contests were often held was not the only attraction for participants. Tourneys were very profitable business for the winners. They received their vanquished opponent's horse and armour. Besides this, the loser, having, as it were, been "captured," had to buy himself off with a ransom.

As a result, a tough athletic professionalism developed among the knights, much like that of antiquity. Skilled jousters went from court to court to exhibit their prowess. In vain the popes, and some princes as well, tried to check the passion for jousting. Tournaments were still in vogue when muskets and cannon were being used on the battlefield. The bourgeoisie tried to emulate the nobility by staging jousts of their own, whereupon the knightly class, to protect its prestige, formed tourney associations. It was not until 1559, when King Henry II of France lost his life from a lance blow received while jousting in a tournament, that a move was made to substitute carousel riding, an exercise in which cavalry teams performed intricate manœuvres and tilting at the ring for this dangerous sport.

FALCONRY

The famous sport of the chase was actually much less an aristocratic diversion and more an economic necessity than one would ever gather from the court poetry of the Middle Ages. The raising of beef cattle far from filled the demand for meat, and so men went into the forests to get game for the pot. There was so much large game that one good hunting trip could provide enough meat for several weeks. The animal most commonly hunted was the wild boar, but bears were also plentiful in all parts of Europe and the hunters had no need to scruple about taking red deer and roe deer. Wild fowl, too, could be had in great numbers. Yet the hunters slew with such prodigality that in a few hundred years a good part of the game reserve had been wiped out.

People in medieval Europe ate a great deal of meat. War shortages and crop failures often cut down the diet of the poor, yet in peaceful times it was relatively good. Since there were few large cities, there was all the more meat left over for the rural population. However, the standard of living was not the same everywhere. France, previously reckoned the richest agricultural land in Europe, was so badly exhausted by the Hundred Years' War that the peasants had neither meat nor white bread.

Yet during this same period the regulations for servants in a large German establishment—it was the year 1433—stated that day labourers, statute labourers and household servants were to have the following provisions: meat twice daily, with half a jug of wine; on fast days fish or other dishes warranting them adequate sustenance; on Sundays, after mass, bread and meat in sufficient quantity to last the whole day; and on feast days a good portion of roast, with enough bread and meat besides for two persons, to take home for supper.

The cuisine of the rich in the Middle Ages was not as international or refined as that of Lucullus but at least it was superior to the modern menu in point of variety. A French wedding banquet in the thirteenth century offered boar, bear, venison, wild geese, peacocks, various roasts, purée of mutton and fattened oxen. Nor was it uncommon for swans, storks and cranes to be served on the aristocratic board.

Amid this gluttony, only one bird was sure of his life, the falcon, and this because he, too, was a hunter. Anyone doing the falcon injury laid himself open to drastic punishment. The art of falconry came from India and had also been practised in Persia at an early date. The Greek historian, Ctesias, personal physician to the Persian king, Artaxerxes Mnemon, about the year 400 B.C., was the first to bring news of the sport to the west, but falconry did not take the popular fancy either in Greece or in Rome. It was not until the period of the great folk migration that the technique came into Europe, where it was perfected by the Visigoths and the Franks. After the eighth century, falconry became the rage at princely courts and continued to be so for a thousand years. Louis XVI still carried a falcon on his left wrist for reasons of etiquette.

Yet it would be a mistake to think of falconry as nothing but an aristocratic pastime. It was one of the greatest methods, perhaps the cleverest of them all, ever devised by man for the killing of game. Falcons were used not only in bird-hawking but in hunting for four-legged animals as well. The Arabs hunted gazelles with the help of falcons, and the Tartars likewise trained eagles to attack wolves and antelopes.

Falconry in the Middle Ages was unquestionably a difficult and highly developed art, with a technical literature, to which such illustrious personages as the Hohenstaufen emperor, Frederick II, contributed. Frederick II's *De arte venandi cum avibus* or *The Art of Hunting with Birds* is the most famous book in the literature of falconry. A complicated apparatus, as well as a great deal of patience and a gift for observation, was needed for the training of hunting-hawks. At first a strategy of exhaustion was used. As soon as they were captured the birds were hooded, but not allowed to go to sleep for forty-eight hours. Then they were "armed," that is provided with leather bands for their legs, also rings and little bells. After a few weeks they were taken into the field, tethered to a long line and lured with doves. The falconers worked out exact rules to cover all these procedures.

Whenever the birds had performed to the satisfaction of their owners, they were "paid court." The *courtoisie* of the falconer consisted in his giving the falcon the victim's liver and heart. In other ways, too, these predators led a good life at the princely courts, as befitted such noble feudal birds. The particularly good hawks had an international reputation. Princes presented them to each other as gifts when they wanted to obtain some political advantage. At official ceremonies the knights and their ladies sat with falcons perched on their wrists as a badge of nobility. Bird-hawking with the peregrine was a noble privilege. Burghers had to use merlins or sparrow-hawks when they went out hunting snipe.

THE DOG BECOMES PRESENTABLE AT COURT

By taking part in the chase the dog, the hunter's most important helper, came to be greatly honoured. The dog is man's oldest companion. In antiquity, however, and indeed until well into the Middle Ages, the dog was a proletarian among the domestic animals. He was the beggar's companion and in Rome he was exploited in fine style as a worker, while in the arena he had to fight along with the wild beasts against the gladiators. Until predatory birds were trained to hunt, the dog was the only animal that man had taught to track down and fall upon other animals.

The dog played a part in the pasturing of livestock, as well as in the chase. Until modern times the sheep dog's main function was not to watch the sheep—that was the shepherd's task—but to protect the sheep from wild animals. He was their de-

Fig. 30. The unicorn from the classical *Historia Animalium* by Konrad Gesner (1551)

fender against all outside enemies. The great wolfhound was occasionally used for military purposes. Yet none of these qualities helped to improve the dog's social position. On the great landed estates he was kept among the servants, not in the manor house.

It was not until the late Middle Ages that he became presentable at court. After the fourteenth century he often appeared in the pictures of high-born folk. Usually he was given a pose consonant with his master's reputation. If the great man happened to be a rascal, like Charles the Bad, King of Navarre, the dog was shown chewing a bone. If he was a noble ruler, like Philip the Good, Duke of Burgundy, the dog was portrayed lying still and submissive at his master's feet. Princely preference ran to slim white greyhounds. Ladies' lapdogs did not come into fashion until the height of the Italian Renaissance.

Although feudal lords contributed more to the diminution than to the increase of the animal world, they still loved animals of all kinds. This can be seen from their coats-of-arms. Knightly heraldry drew on a whole menagerie of animals. Besides the lions and eagles of ancient tradition, there were bears, wolves, lambs, deer, falcons, oxen, bees, fish, lizards and fabulous animals too.

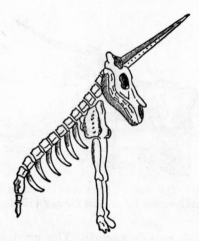

Fig. 31. Skeleton of the legendary unicorn (after B. Valentini, Musaeum Museorum, Frankfurt-on-Main, 1704)

The most important and longest lived of this last genus is the unicorn, which decorates the British royal arms to this day. For a long time the unicorn was thought of as a real animal, rare and exotic, to be sure, but one whose existence had been vouched for by such authorities as Aristotle and Pliny. This belief was so strong that in the oldest German translations of the Bible, the Hebraic word for wild ox, *reem*, was rendered as *monokeros* (Greek), *unicornis* (Latin) or *Einhorn* (German), all of which mean "unicorn" in English. This may have come about because the wild ox was confused with the rhinoceros, *Nashorn* in German, which is very similar to the German for "unicorn." In medieval heraldry the unicorn first came to look like a wether, but soon took on the appearance of a horse, one with a die-straight, pointed horn sticking up out of the middle of his forehead. The unicorn was the symbol for virginity and unlimited strength, and his horn could perform many wonders.

Fig. 32. Inn sign of the Fox Inn, Huntingdon,
England

On the whole, however, medieval man was not too superstitious about animals, less so than men in earlier times and in certain later periods. People in the Middle Ages really knew animals, for the good reason that they lived with them. They were well enough acquainted with their abilities and weaknesses to make use of them in a rational, if not very productive, way. The most remarkable thing is that scientific knowledge was so little furthered by medieval man's closeness to nature. As zoological literature the medieval bestiaries are far behind the Graeco-Roman models. As in antiquity, in the Middle Ages animals were used to disguise political and social satires. Animal poetry reached a zenith in the *Roman de Renart,* a French collection of fables from the twelfth or thirteenth century describing the war between Reynard the Fox and the greedy but brave wolf, Isegrym. The somewhat later *Reinaert de Vox,* written by a Flemish author, uses the same theme. The fantasy involves the same old types established by *Aesop's Fables*. Hardly any new characters were invented. People knew the animal kingdom of the ancient world, and their own seemed to have nothing new to add.

PART THREE

THE AGE OF DISCOVERY

X

The New World

FISHERMEN were the first to dare the perilous journey across the western ocean. Gunnbjörn, a Norwegian who plied the north Atlantic at the beginning of the tenth century, told his countrymen that he had sighted islands to the west of Iceland unknown before to any seaman. Two generations later Eric the Red set out to find Gunnbjörn's islands. Eric returned from a three years' voyage with the news that he had discovered land, which he named Groenland, or Greenland. This name was intended to make people less adventurous than himself emigrate.

An important colony grew out of this beginning. Eric and his son, Leif, founded a real state in Greenland, with two towns, sixteen churches, and fifteen thousand settlers. Leif Ericsson is also said to have sailed to America, perhaps to Rhode Island. Nothing came of this discovery, however, though the Greenland settlement lasted for five hundred years. A regular shipping service sprang up between Greenland and Europe. The Greenlanders sent furs and imported foodstuffs across the sea, since they were unable to live from hunting and fishing and the land was too barren for farming or raising livestock. Towards the end of the fifteenth century the colony, for all practical purposes, had either been abandoned or had died out.

It was therefore southlanders who reaped the fame of discovering the New World. Although the discovery of great continents had not actually been foreseen, the finding of the Americas was by no means a mere accident but the logical result of two hundred years of study and gradual advance. "Ever since the middle of the fourteenth century," writes Enriques de Gandia, a modern Hispano-American historian, "the most obscure navigator might at any moment have discovered America."

Still, it was a difficult business. Long voyages into the unknown took not only courage but a great deal of money as well. On this account the New World was opened up by stages. The first discoveries were a disappointment both to the romantically minded and the gold-hungry. By the beginning of the fourteenth century Genoese—Spanish or Portuguese in another version—navigators had reached the Canaries, the Azores and Madeira, but these Atlantic islands seemed to have so little to offer that for a long time no one tried to settle there. The fauna was much the same as that in the Mediterranean region, only scantier, and the people—the few there were—so poverty-stricken and primitive that it hardly paid to bother with them.

The only living things that fascinated these early seafarers were the birds. There were birds large and small, bright and dun, birds that sang, that chattered, that shrieked, and others that circled about the ships in silent majesty. Feathered creatures there were in endless splendour and they became ever more wonderful the farther west the ships sailed. The New World was first of all a veritable paradise of birds. The great discoverers were deeply impressed by this abundance and variety of bird life. Next to the saints, most of their discoveries were named after birds, the Canaries being one obvious example. The Portuguese for the Azores is *açores*, which means "hawks." Brazil, to be sure, was named after brazil wood, or *pau brasil*, a heavy wood rich in red dyestuff, but its nickname all through the years has been "Parrot-land." In the Gulf of St. Lawrence, off Newfoundland and Labrador, the French named several *Îles des Oiseaux* ("Bird Islands") and *Îles des Margaux* ("Magpie Islands"), after the now extinct great auks that once nested in this region.

THE LITTLE RABBITS OF PORTO SANTO

The first reports outdid each other in describing newly discovered territories as a true paradise. Actually, however, only a few places provided enough food to support even a small company for any length of time. Had there been time enough, vegetable food could have been grown in sufficient quantity; but agriculture in the first stage of settling foreign lands is always an uncertain matter. It was meat that was needed, and where meat was lacking, livestock had to be raised.

A plan for the colonization of domestic animals had been worked out two generations before the discovery of America by a young Portuguese prince. Prince Henry the Navigator himself never made a long sea voyage, but he provided the stimulus for many great explorations. At Sagres, on the extreme southwestern tip of Europe, he established the world's first geographic institute, a sort of laboratory of exploration employing astronomers and cartographers. At the same time, however, he took a serious interest in producing seed grain and in breeding livestock useful in feeding new colonies. Most people believed that the Isles of the Blessed lay to the west, that manna fell from heaven there, that all the game one might need was within easy reach. The prince, however, was not one of these fantasts. He had very clear ideas about how new lands should be settled. Useful plants and livestock—the latter above all—should in his opinion be taken to newly opened regions before the colonists came on the scene.

To learn how this should be done, practical experience was required. The first experiment was a tragi-comic failure. Dom Henrique's agent, the hidalgo Bartholomeu Petrestrelo, colonized the uninhabited island of Porto Santo, near Madeira, with rabbits. These rabbits multiplied so fast that within two years, so the story goes, they had eaten the island bare and made it unfit for human settlement.

These Porto Santo rabbits even played a part in the history of genetics. Having become sole masters of the island, for there were no larger animals to menace them, in their isolation they became so different in size, colouring and behaviour from their European relatives that they looked like an entirely new species. It was even believed that they could no longer be crossed with the European rabbit. This change came to be regarded as one of the most striking proofs for the origination of species through spatial separation, a phenomenon on which the zoologist Moritz Wagner based his "migration theory" of evolution in 1868.

The Porto Santo rabbits of 1419 were among the first European immigrants. The settlement of Madeira in 1425, the next step on the way west, was undertaken with greater foresight. Cattle, as well as different kinds of seed grain, were brought to Madeira from Portugal and flourished on the Madeiran pasture land. Even on the barren *Ilhas Desertas* nearby, sheep, goats and Indian-fowl were successfully reared.

The most interesting experiment of all was carried out in the next decade on the Azores Islands, which apparently had little animal life outside the thousands upon thousands of hawks. Henry the Navigator had cows, sheep, goats and chickens turned loose on the islands before any attempt was made to settle them, and for some years these animals lived and multiplied in abso-lute freedom. Henry's secondary object was a create an animal depot for the victualling of ships voyaging to Guinea, but his primary aim was from the very start to ensure a dependable food supply for the people who ventured far from their native Portu-gal or Africa to settle on the *Ilhas Perdidas* or Lost Isles, as they were called. These domestic animals took hold well on the green pastures in mid-Atlantic and did not revert to the wild at all quickly. In 1493, when Moorish peasants began to colonize the Azores, sheep-rearing was their first means of support.

COLUMBUS'S EIGHT PIGS

Columbus was undoubtedly familiar with the Portuguese method of colonization when he set out on his voyages to the west. He had lived in Portugal for a long time and had tried there to get backing for his project from the Portuguese king before turning to the Spanish crown.

The crews' rations of Columbus's three caravels were typical of the period. Each man received one pound of hard tack and a pint of wine daily. Enough meat and fish were stored to provide two pounds of one or the other each day for every three men. Cheese, onions and other vegetables eked out the diet. Columbus's first voyage was purely exploratory and consequently neither plants nor animals were taken along, for Prince Henry had taught the navigators that colonization should proceed in three stages: first, the land had to be found; then useful plants and animals had to be taken there; and only after a food supply had been assured should the actual settlement begin.

Columbus followed this prescription. His first trip out was entirely a voyage of discovery, which ran its course in much the same manner as the shorter Portuguese voyages. It was the custom on these trips to catch fish to eke out the ships' victuals but the caravels found that fish were scarce in these waters. The captains had to make shift as best they could with what they had and this led to grumbling among the crews. However, during the night of 9 October 1492, thirty days after leaving the Canary Islands, a rushing sound was detected in the air. A flight of birds had given notice that land was in the offing. *"Toda la noche oyeron pasar pájaros,"* Columbus wrote in his log—"all night we heard birds flying over." These are the first words ever written about the animal life of the New World.

As yet the New World was only an indeterminate something. As the caravels came closer and closer to land, nobody had the least idea what the new country would be like, whether it was Cipango, the great island in east Asia, or some uninhabited mid-ocean island. Three days later the caravels landed at a small island of curious aspect. It was not a desert place nor yet a paradise. Trees and animals were all quite different from the European, as were the people, who plainly lived in great poverty. The parrots aroused most interest among the newcomers. These birds were larger and more brightly coloured than any known in Europe, and Columbus secured some specimens to take back home to Spain. By chance he also found some glittering stones, which he took to be gold. People would have to believe now that he had pressed forward across the ocean as far as the Orient and its fabled riches.

On his second voyage Columbus set out as Great Admiral in command of a powerful squadron of ships. This time he took with him means to ensure a food supply for prospective settlers in the New World which offered no dependable supply of its own. Most of these supplies were taken on board at the fertile island of Gomera in the Canaries west of Teneriffe. They consisted of orange, lemon, melon and other seeds, also calves, goats, sheep, chickens and eight selected pigs. "From the increase of these eight pigs," says Bartolomé las Casas, missionary historian of the discovery of America, "have come the pigs found everywhere today in the lands of the Indies, all which ever were there and ever will be, which have been and still are endless."

SPANISH CENTAURS

On this same second voyage, when Columbus was returning to the New World as viceroy with a complete viceregal household, he took with him a small troop of mounted soldiers. If all went well Columbus's intention was to use them as background rather than as warriors, but already the time of peace with the Indians was past. One of Columbus's lieutenants had to defend the fort of Santo Tomas with 360 foot soldiers and sixteen men on horseback.

The natives of Haiti do not seem to have been particularly impressed by horses and the art of riding. Since the ships with the monster sails had appeared off their coasts they had seen so many incredible things that nothing astonished them any more. The polished armour, the hellish weapons that made thunder and lightning and not least the strangers' beards made a deeper impression than the horses. Nor does any later report tell that the Indians of the Antilles were alarmed by the conquistadors' horses. To them the great, tall animals on which the white men sat seemed no stranger than the oxen, sheep or goats, which they had also never laid eyes on before.

When Hernando Cortés invaded Mexico, however, something unexpected happened. The fifteen cavalrymen in Cortés's command evoked real panic among the Aztecs, for they thought that horse and rider were one, a kind of centaur. This is even remem-

Fig. 33. Conquest of the Aztecs by the horsemen
of Cortés

bered as one of the most remarkable animal episodes in military history. Prescott's classic history of the Cortés expedition was not the first to record this analogy with the bearded centaurs of Greek mythology. Long before Prescott the incident had been mentioned by the greatest woman poet of Latin America, the Mexican nun, Juana Inés de la Cruz, in her mystery drama, *El Divino Narciso* ("The Divine Narcissus"), written in 1688. "*¿Que centauros monstruosos contra mi gente militan?*"—"What monstrous centaurs are these who take the field against my people?" —exclaims the nymph, America, when the Spaniards come.

The Incas reacted like the Aztecs when Pizarro's riders went into action in Peru, and their terror knew no bounds when one of the cavalrymen fell from his horse. The Incas fancied that the great creature, whatever it might be, had broken in two. So thunderstruck were they that they completely lost their heads, thus enabling the Spaniards, who up to this point had been in dire straits, to flee to their ships.

However, neither in Mexico nor in Peru did the natives long continue to be afraid of horses. Montezuma had the head cut off the first horse killed by his Aztecs and exhibited it in the cities of his domain to wean his soldiery from their dread of the Spanish centaurs. Presently the Indians were boldly attacking the Spanish cavalry and in one assault seven horses were killed. This was a heavy loss, for it took several months to get new mounts to America. However, the Spaniards had consistent success with large dogs trained for fighting. They, too, were a novelty to the Indians. In Central and South America dogs were very small and used by the natives only for food. The bloodhound was a present from Europe.

PUMA AND LLAMA

The Aztecs, however, were familiar enough with the wild animals of Mexico and had mastered them to such a degree that their emperor, Montezuma, in the manner of ancient Egypt was able to keep a whole menagerie in the capital. The animals were lodged in a temple and in all probability were used in connection with religious ceremonies, although there was never a genuine animal cult in Mexico as in Egypt. The following is the report of an eye-witness who accompanied Cortés on his first visit to Montezuma's palace:

"In this palace there was a splendid bird house, containing every kind of bird found on this continent, and besides this another large building, which was a temple and which contained animals called the brave tiger and two kinds of lions. In this accursed place there were wild vipers and poisonous snakes with something on their tails that sounded like castanets; these are the most dangerous of all and are kept in boxes filled with feathers, where they bring up their young, and where they are fed with the flesh of dogs and human beings. These beasts and the frightful reptiles are held there to keep their hellish gods company, and when these animals roar and hiss the palace seems like hell itself."

Fig. 34. Pre-Columbian drinking vessel of the Incas
(Museo Nacional, Lima)

Columbus, too, in his famous letter to the Catholic kings sent from Jamaica in 1503, told about lions and a man-sized cat. Probably these animals were pumas. On the whole wild animals did not give the conquistadors much trouble. Reports refer to them more as a curiosity than anything else. Indeed, large animals were rare in sub-tropical America. Columbus ran into peccaries, wild members of the pig family with large, misshapen heads. An Irish wolfhound, he wrote, would not dare attack one. The only domestic animals were dogs and turkeys.

In Peru, however, there were two additional domesticated animals, the llama and his smaller brother, the alpaca. Both were bred chiefly for their wool. The Inca empire was a police state with an agrarian system of government favouring a small upper class. Arable land was carefully parcelled out and farmed under state supervision. The common folk had no power of disposal over livestock. The herds were a state monopoly. Officials collected the shearing, and not even the skins of wild animals could be used without the approval of the authorities. Milk as a food was unknown in Peru, as everywhere else in America. Animals were seldom slaughtered, and meat-eating was a privilege enjoyed almost exclusively by the ruling house, the priesthood and the official nobility.

Llamas, then as today, were used as pack-animals but could carry only very small loads. There were no draught animals at all in the Americas comparable with the European horse or ox. So much more amazing, then, were the prodigious architectural works of pre-Columbian times—the colossal walls of stone in the Peruvian highland and the great pyramids and temples of Mexico. These were built by manpower alone, without aid of any kind from draught animals.

The Land of the Parrots

The farther south the conquistadors went, the richer the animal life became. The region opened up by the Portuguese especially gave the impression of being a vast zoological garden. Whereas in Spanish accounts of the period the search for gold and silver is the dominant theme and animal life is mentioned only incidentally, the Portuguese made keen observations on the living things in the lands that had fallen to their share. From the very first their descriptions of Brazil are studded with references to animals.

The creatures of the air aroused the greatest wonder. Brazil seemed like a bird paradise to them. The parrots whose numbers and brilliance had so greatly fascinated newcomers to the Antilles paled before the magnificence of arara, anapuru, araruna, and ajurucarao. The chroniclers could not find adjectives enough to voice their rapture. The Indians, too, idolized the birds. They ate them only when driven by hunger, preferring to keep them as pets.

In accounts from the age of the discovery little mention is made of the butterflies which later became the cliché of the Brazilian landscape. There were other animals besides birds that were deemed marvellous, though, animals which in most cases had no counterparts in the Old World. Here everything was garishly coloured. It was a new world, indeed. It seemed remarkable that in a land where trees and fruits grew so large the animals should be relatively so small. Even the largest of them, the tapir, was hardly as big as a cow. The jaguar, leopard of the Brazilian forest, was far smaller than the Asiatic tiger. The giants of the Indo-Ethiopian fauna, the elephants and rhinoceroses, had no South American relatives. The jacares of the Amazon were smaller than the crocodiles of the Nile.

Human beings suffered less from the large animals than from the small. Europeans complained about the vampires, which at night bit their toes and sucked blood from the wound. Biting insects swarmed. Yet life was not too difficult or dangerous. The Indians were good hunters and willing to eat any kind of food: dogs, cats, monkeys, rodents, marsupials and armadillos were regularly included in their diet. They were especially fond of armadillo meat. The only large animal missing from the Indian menu was the ant-eater, a creature feared even by the jaguar. As for the highly prized armadillo meat, there were twenty different species of the animal. The armadillos, or tatus, were as big as young pigs. Although equipped with sharp claws and steely hard armour, they were not aggressive and could easily be tamed. Their flesh was as tender as chicken, but really the Indians kept tame armadillos more for fun than for food.

The finest of all roast meat was man himself. There was a ban on eating members of one's own tribe, but throughout all South America tribal law permitted that captured enemies could be treated like beef cattle. The slaughtering and the ensuing banquet proceeded according to a rigid ceremonial formula. The occasion was both a cultic act and a victory celebration. However, it would be a perversion of fact to interpret cannibalism as purely religious or psychological—an expiatory act, a uniting of souls in brotherhood or the like. Nor can the custom of eating human flesh be called a mere act of revenge. The enemy's body was in fact a particularly valuable piece of material booty. All connoisseurs in this department of gastronomy praise the flavour of human meat, with the qualification that fat victims taste much better than lean. The Indians therefore fattened their captives before the kill, as civilized peoples fatten cattle.

One of the most popular tales from the early history of Brazil concerns "Caramuru," whose Portuguese name was Diogo Alvaro Correia. With six of his countrymen Caramuru was taken prisoner by cannibals and was the only one to escape being eaten, because he was so skinny. The ones picked for slaughter were treated well during the fattening period and allowed to couple with their butchers' daughters as they wished, for if sons came as a result of this cohabitation, in due time they, too, could be killed and devoured, since the Indians believed that sons came from the father. Girls, coming from the mother, would be permitted to live. The Indians simply feared that the son might revenge the father.

Cannibalism in the Brazilian forest entailed more than occasional bouts. It was, indeed, a carefully organized part of the economy. Old women collected the victims' lard in buckets and a portion of the meat was smoked and hung, as fish or animal flesh is preserved.

While some Europeans were warring on cannibalism, others were selling the natives bigger and better iron knives to facilitate their human butchery. Not until the imported herds of grazing animals had increased sufficiently to provide a surplus for Indian consumption did the savages—those who had not been exterminated—come to accept the moral law of civilized man, which decrees that whereas it is perfectly proper to kill humans, it is wrong to eat them.

回 XI 回

The Conquest of the North

In zoo-geography, since the time of A. R. Wallace, the American continents have been divided into three zones: a northern zone, running down from Arctic regions more or less to the Great Lakes; a neoboreal zone, which includes the United States and part of Mexico; and a neotropic zone, which includes Central and South America. This partition originally applied to the distribution of song birds, but also lent itself, so far as such lines of demarcation have any value, to the distribution of mammals.

Most important in this scheme is the separation of the northern zone from the other two. Canada and Greenland belong, zoo-geographically, to the Old, rather than to the New, World, and make up a region called the holarctic zone. Despite all climatic differences this holarctic zone has more in common with southern Europe and North Africa than it has with the Mississippi Valley. The criterion is the last Ice Age glaciation, which in North America extended approximately to the 45th parallel. South of this line is "Neogaea," where the fauna in pre-Columbian times had its own characteristic stamp, a stamp which in part has been retained to this day. It provided South America with many of its present mammals. Some North American mammals are closely related to the Eurasian fauna. Almost all their ancestors made their way into this northern zone either from east to west, or from west to east via the Bering Strait. On this account the region is called "Arctogaea."

This is not meant to imply, however, that the animal kingdom in Arctogaea comprises exactly the same forms as that of the Old

World. Man is the only Primate and he emigrated to America at a very late date. The horses which originally came from America, as we have earlier noted, had become extinct over the western continents by the time of the age of discovery. There were few pigs or hoofed animal types. The fauna of the western holarctic zone on the whole had fewer animals with edible flesh than the eastern part, though this did not lessen their appeal to hunters and trappers out for skins and pelts.

Fig. 35. Stranded whale (after Olaus Magnus, 1532)

It was not merely by chance that the western continents were opened up from two divergent directions, these corresponding roughly with the zoological division into Old World and New World types of fauna. The conquest of the north from the very start presupposed a different kind of man from the conquest of the south. The first explorers in the north, such as the Italian Cabotos—better known as John and Sebastian Cabot—and the Portuguese Corte Real, were seeking a northwest passage which would open up the way to the treasures of the far east, but when no passage was found and it was discovered that there were no easily gained valuables to bring home, the southern Europeans soon lost all appetite for this inhospitable region. To succeed in the far north great patience and toughness were needed. It called for self-subsistent settler types and "lone wolves" who would not feel lost amid a landscape so vast and forbidding, who liked the great silences and who could track wild animals.

Although there are dramatic episodes and gripping personalities in the history of the north, on the whole the process of settlement was much more anonymous than in the south. The most difficult deeds were carried out by people who are now completely forgotten or at best barely mentioned in local histories. These people were in no sense a softer breed than the conquistadors of the south in their shining armour, but they were less egotistical and autocratic in character. For this reason control over both human beings and animals eventually fell into the hands of large trading companies who ruled from afar and from afar decided which animals were worth the price of a musket ball and which were not.

The Herring Shortage and the Hanseatic League

The fishermen had come to the shores of the far north before the trappers. Though not strictly proved, it is quite possible that, several decades before the voyages of the Cabots, i.e., about the year 1497, Breton vessels had made regular trips to Newfoundland. In one account from the year 1514 the monks of Beauport report that for sixty years they have been in receipt of a tax in kind from the cod and whiting fishermen who fished off the coasts of Brittany, Newfoundland and Iceland.

At the beginning the Newfoundland fisheries may have been connected with the Iceland-Greenland fisheries. However, the first authenticated Breton voyages to North America did not take place until after news of the Cabot brothers' discoveries had spread throughout Europe. The Cabots had found an island which they named "Terra de Baccalaos," or "Cod Land." This island was later called "Terre-Neuve" or "New Land" by the French, and "Newfoundland" by the English. The Cabots firmly claimed they had reached the land of the Great Khan, which interested the chanceries of Europe, but the Breton fishermen and those of Bristol as well—some of whom had helped to outfit the Cabots—were more excited by the news that enormously rich fisheries lay on the other side of the ocean.

At about this period the European deep sea fisheries were experiencing a serious crisis. Fishing in Europe had certainly never come to have as much significance as in Asia—in India and Ceylon fish hooks were the most ancient form of money. Nevertheless, in Europe as well as Asia fish was a more important food than meat for millions of people. The great majority of the coastal population lived from the fisheries. The fish trade was one of the few branches of the European economy already organized on an international basis in the Middle Ages. The main catch was herring. Up to the thirteenth century Sweden had supplied half Europe with herring for the Lenten season. Then the cities of the Hanseatic League seized control of the herring trade. At the same time the Dutch were not minded to let such lucrative business slip out of their hands. By the fifteenth century they had become foremost in the herring trade, the English having granted them the right to seine in their waters. The rise of Amsterdam was made possible by the herring industry.

Meanwhile the Hanseatic League had been enjoying a virtual monopoly in the Baltic Sea. In about 1500, however, the herring stayed away, disappeared completely. To this day no one knows whether it was marine currents, the depredations of larger fish or a plague that brought about this catastrophe. In any event it was a terrible blow to the Hanse. Many historians believe that this biological event, rather than later political conflicts, started the downfall of that great commercial organization.

The immediate result was a great scarcity of fish for the people. Prices shot up and fish had to be obtained from other grounds to supply the Lenten market. The demand was so great that it paid to send fishing fleets out to distant waters. This situation apparently helped the overseas fisheries off Newfoundland to get under way. In any case, it is more than doubtful whether the Breton fishermen were interested in exploration. A generation later, when one of their countrymen, Jacques Cartier, was commissioned by Francis I to find the northwest passage to China, and concurrently search for islands near Newfoundland where gold had been reported, the shipping masters and merchants of St. Malo tried to sabotage the expedition so that Cartier would not deplete the crews of the fishing fleet. A royal command was needed to secure priority for the gold-seekers over the cod fishermen.

Fig. 36. A great problem: providing England with
fish (Angler, 1496)

Jacques Cartier found neither the sea route to Asia nor the anticipated gold, but this voyage proved to be informative for fishing and natural science. On one of the very first islands he found so many great auks that he was able to revictual at will. Not far from this island there were not only cod in vast quantity, but salmon, herring and wolf fish as well. Cartier's first hunting trophy was a polar bear, "big as a cow and white as a swan."

BEAVER WAR

Cartier's report also contained the first detailed description of
the land fauna of the American holarctic region, where the
Portuguese had already been amazed by the great wapiti elks
that strode about like kings under firs as high as towers. On their
second voyage the French explorers under Cartier penetrated
deep into Canada. This time they stayed long enough to observe
the smaller animals as well. Most surprising of all was the fact
that there were so few surprises. The people were different, of
course, but the flora, fauna and landscape were so much like the
European that Cartier, who had once seen Brazil, was moved to
write: "The land is of the same kind and nature as France."

This report did not prove to be an unqualified incentive for
the adventurous. The kind of man willing to go to America was
looking for a new world, not a replica of the old. However, Canada did offer one feature that fired the imagination—the great
hunting and trapping grounds. Cartier first became convinced
of the possibilities of wealth in Canadian furs when he reached
the big Indian settlement of Hochelaga, which meant "Beaver
Dam." Hochelaga was a village surrounded by a circular palisade
and consisted of huts made of wood, bark and skins. The French
named the place "Montreal." In the wintertime the Indians
clothed themselves exclusively in the skins of beaver, marten, fox
and deer. In summer they went about naked. Furs were so plentiful that they were not highly valued. The Indians were willing to
barter a whole bundle of valuable pelts for an axe or a knife.

The Indians of the north were extraordinarily good hunters.
They used refined methods which they had apparently learned
from the animals themselves. The Canadian moose was easy prey
not only for man but for smaller predators as well. Badgers and
foxes were said to hunt together, the foxes usually in threes. They
trailed their victim, driving him to where the murderous carcajou,
or badger, lurked in ambush. The Indians followed the example
of the animals, with the difference that they used arrows and

wooden lances tipped with stone, as befitted members of the species *Homo sapiens*. Often they took dogs along with them, trained not to attack prematurely. As for howling at the moose to scare them off their runs, this business the Indians took care of themselves.

Fig. 37. Indians stag-hunting. In order to approach the animals un-noticed they have clad themselves in deerskins (illustration, about 1570)

To catch beaver, however, all the Indians needed was a pair of hands. In the wintertime they stationed themselves along the banks of streams where the beavers had built their mound-like homes. The entrances to these mounds were always under water. Having carefully surveyed the terrain, the Indians were ready to reach into the water and haul out the beavers returning from their nocturnal labours. For white men this was a tedious procedure which they left to the Indians, themselves preferring to buy furs with brandy or weapons.

Having had no experience along these lines, the French made

some experiments. Champlain, Canada's great governor at the beginning of the seventeenth century who himself had come to the country as a fur trader, tried to maintain peaceful and friendly relations with the Indians. He brought over young colonists who were expected to go into the deep woods and attach themselves closely to the hunters on their forays. Before long, however, these *"coureurs de bois"* were taking matters into their own hands. Some of them became completely Indianized, others went into smuggling; and so the colony languished.

Under Louis XIV the opposite system of strict centralization was introduced. The Indians had to collect their furs at certain elevated storehouse points. Frenchmen were ordered to keep out of the woods. The Indians proved agreeable to this arrangement and for many summers brought a hundred thousand pelts or more into the markets, for which they received a goodly quantity of alcohol. The *coureurs de bois* had become so despotic, however, that they did not intend to be satisfied with working as commissioners under state supervision. Two of them, Pierre Redisson and the Sieur de Grosseilliers, turned to the English who had long been waiting for a chance to get into the North American fur trade. An English company was formed under the protection of Prince Rupert, and a ship was sent to Hudson Bay in northeastern Canada, whence it returned home with a valuable cargo of skins.

The experiment having turned out so well, in 1670 the company was granted an unlimited monopoly by King Charles II on furs taken in all lands watered by rivers emptying into Hudson Bay. This was the beginning of the Hudson's Bay Company, officially known as "The Governor and Company of Adventurers of England Trading into Hudson's Bay." It was to be the most important and longest lived trapping enterprise in the world, one that even to this day handles a considerable part of the world fur trade.

For both commercial and political reasons the French were unwilling to recognize the English monopoly. On the urging of the two aforementioned *coureurs de bois,* who meanwhile had gone back to the French side, a rival company was formed. The resulting trade war over beaver fur soon developed into a full-fledged colonial war with small arms and ships' cannon. The conflict spread when the French pressed southward, and finally culminated in a great war in which France lost all her North American possessions.

The chief sufferers in this hundred years' war over the beaver were the animals themselves. Fearing they might lose their royal patents, and intent upon making good losses brought on by war, the rival companies behaved worse than Indians on the trapping grounds. They killed every animal they could lay hands on, completely disregarding the most primitive rules of hunting. Males and females were slaughtered indiscriminately and the animals were not let alone even during the mating season. This ruthless killing not only produced a glut in the European markets but nearly ruined the supply of animals, which it took many decades to restore. A number of species was all but exterminated.

BOYAR PELTS

When the English began to drive the French-American beavers out of their mounds, they had already had a hundred years' experience in the fur trade gained in the Old World. Since 1553 the Muscovite Company of London had had a fur-trading monopoly in the new tsaristic empire. The English provided Ivan the Terrible with modern firearms and other cultural products of the western world and took furs in exchange. The Muscovite Company rapidly grew into a powerful enterprise. It was for this company that Henry Hudson, the Don Quixote of the polar seas, made his first two voyages to the north. He was unable to carry out his fantastic plan to reach Asia by the shortest route via the north pole. However, he did get as far as the great bay in northern Canada that today bears his name. His explorations had far-reaching effects.

The merchants began to show an interest in northern Asia after the Russians had penetrated this hitherto utterly unknown region. In the history books the opening up of Siberia used to be treated as a mere expansion into neighbouring territories. Actually the settlement of Siberia was one of the greatest accomplishments of the age of exploration. Although Siberia had appeared in some fashion or other on the older maps, in fact little was known about the region in the sixteenth century, except that Tartar peoples lived there and that Siberian weather was frightfully cold.

Fig. 38. Polar expedition of the Dutchman Barents (about 1596)

The first advance into this unknown region was made by the Cossack chieftain Yermak. In 1580 Yermak, with a small troop of armed adventurers, crossed the Ural Mountains. His backers were the Poyarskis, a rich merchant family, and it was they who were made rich by Siberian exploration. Reports from the east aroused as much interest in Russia as did the discovery of America in the western world. Thousands upon thousands of peasants wanted to settle at once in the new territory. They had to be restrained by force, whereupon the serf system came into being. As usual this initial enthusiasm ended in disillusionment. Not much could be grown on the steppes and ice fields of Siberia. The only profitable occupation was fur-trapping. The Siberian fauna was essentially like that of northern Europe but much, much richer, the land being almost entirely devoid of human beings. Polar bears did not venture very far into the hinterland, but of other fur-bearing animals there were red fox, white fox, blue fox, silver fox and, most valuable of the martens, the sable. Sable fur was the pride of the boyars, a piece of merchandise worth owning.

Like the men who opened up North America, the Cossacks left hunting to the natives and at first did not even try to barter with them, instead making them give up their furs as tribute. After the Russians had established a fairly good foothold, they organized a chain of depots covering all Siberia—at Tobolsk, Omsk, Yeniseisk, Irkutsk, Yakutsk, Okhotsk. All these places became great fur-trading centres. When the Russians advanced as far as Kamchatka, they found a new and unexpected source of furs. The Bering Sea was alive with sea cows and fur seals. These animals were hunted so intensively that before long one Bering Sea species, Steller's sea cow, a huge animal sometimes reaching thirty feet in length, was completely wiped out.

From the extreme northeast tip of Asia it was only a short jump to the North American continent, and for more than a century the Russians were in possession of Alaska. The Russian drive to the east was a powerful thrust. Though it did not give rise to so much shedding of blood, in boldness and duration it was not inferior to the Anglo-French exploration and settlement of North America. As men followed the trail of fur-bearing creatures, a new world was opened up within the old.

Rebirth of Superstition

THE net results of the discovery of America were disappointing. The gold and silver shipped by the Spaniards to Europe brought on an international inflation. Thoughtful people began to ask themselves whether there might not be more useful things than precious metals in the New World.

Attempts to train the Indians as slaves came to naught, nor were there any four-legged draught animals to put to work. On the contrary, the colonists had to take riding horses and draught oxen with them. Except for fish from northern waters, scarcely anything edible was exported. No one dared transport large numbers of untamed animals. Meat spoiled on the voyage through the tropical zone. Therefore, even where feed animals multiplied and became plentiful, as on the Argentine pampas, the owners had to be content with slaughtering them for hides, leaving the meat to the dogs and vultures.

In other epochs the remarkable animals of South America might have stimulated gourmets to try them but in this respect the people of the Renaissance were not very inquisitive. The only animal the New World gave to the European table was the Mexican turkey, and Europeans did not, in fact, consider this fowl to be a novelty. As the English name "turkey" suggests, the bird was thought to have originated in the near east.

The yield of vegetables was somewhat more abundant. Introduced into the Old World soon after the discovery of America, maize became acclimatized in southern Europe. With it, unfortunately, came a frightful malady, pellagra. This disease was called "Columbus's sickness," whereupon syphilis, the gift Columbus actually had bestowed on Europe, was called the *"morbus gallicus,"* or "French disease." The potato, which with maize is the most important plant of American origin, came to Spain in about 1534, but was very slow to gain acceptance in Europe. At the beginning of the seventeenth century princes were still sending each other potatoes as a curiosity. In some places potato culture was forbidden on the grounds that tubers caused leprosy.

Without maize and potatoes animal husbandry in Europe would never have become extensive enough to fill the continent's demand for meat. Therefore it may be said that America richly repaid Columbus's purchase of eight swine. If pig-breeding in America is a European gift, pig-breeding in Europe depends in good measure on feed of American origin.

Yet in the early days this development could not be foreseen. During the first century after its discovery, the most valuable food product coming from America was sugar. Europeans themselves first introduced sugar cane into the New World. Negro slaves laboured so industriously in the cane fields of Central America and Brazil that colonial sugar quickly became a significant commodity in international trade. It not only competed with the cane from east India and Syria naturalized in Europe since the Middle Ages, but at the same time had a powerful effect on bee culture. Honey became too expensive to use for sweetening when the Portuguese were dumping molasses at cut prices on the Antwerp market. Soon honey became a special knd of food. This spelt catastrophe for many bee-keepers. The shift from honey to cane products was also a significant event from the standpoint of cultural history. It was the first time in recorded history that a vegetable product had dislodged an animal product.

SEA SERPENTS AND MERMEN

Even if the tangible wealth of the New World turned out to be not quite so dazzling as at first expected, the consequences of its discovery ought not to be measured solely in terms of material results. The opening up of distant lands and seas had a powerful effect on man's imagination. Long before the phrase had been coined, America was the land of unlimited possibilities. The more information about the New World accumulated, the more apparent it became that very little was really known about the creatures of this earth. Perhaps all that travellers related about the wonders of the New World was only a tiny part of what was actually there.

Deliberately or otherwise, sailors played on the public's gullibility in telling tales about the unknown. They eked out what they had really seen with monstrous products of the imagination. Thus a whole kingdom of fabulous animals came into being, animals which were quite lacking in the symbolism of the infernal creatures of the Middle Ages. They were represented to astonished contemporaries as real, live beings. However, a close look at the products of the zoological imagination during the age of discovery reveals old acquaintances. It is not so easy to invent new animals; only great thinkers and artists are able to do it— and the men who went to the New World were not artistic geniuses. It is characteristic that not one of the many accounts written and published by them has ever become a standard work in world literature.

The written descriptions, drawings and "eye-witness reports" concerning these imaginary beasts were far from original. As a rule they took the form of exaggerated caricatures of known animals. Sometimes they involved mixed forms or abnormalities. Not even the unique animal sculpture of the Central American Indians lent wings to the European imagination. In the last analysis nothing came forth but slyly boastful exaggerations and childish absurdities. To prove what strange adventures they had experienced, travellers told of people with wolves' heads or without any heads at all or with faces on their chests. Such "human races" are illustrated in Sebastian Muenster's *Cosmography* (1550), a book which also contains the first map of the *Nuew Welt* that was in any degree accurate. In a book of this sort, how could the reader tell the difference between truth and fiction?

The French Potter Palissy was one of the first to explain correctly the nature of fossils

Albertus Magnus, Bishop of Regensburg (1193-1280)

"The Peaceable Kingdom," painting by Edward Hicks (1780-1849)

The marvellous creatures of the New World were described as numerous indeed. The inhabitants of Labrador had tails. In the sea there were sharks three times as big as caravels, so big they could take a whole ship at one bite. The bats of the western world seem to have made a particularly strong impression on the mariners. Many believed they were giant insects, others thought them to be a kind of living leaf which could fly through the air like the offspring of the miraculous tree of the Orkneys, whose leaves changed into birds or crawled along like caterpillars.

Fig. 39. Fabulous snake from the *Buch der Weisheit der alten Weisen* (1483)

One of the most favoured among these abominable beasts was the sea serpent, known in earlier times but most famous during the age of discovery. Olaus Magnus, a learned zoologist and the greatest authority of his day on the animals of the north, in 1555 wrote a description of the sea serpent. Fifty years later this same description was embellishing a treatise supposedly the last word in authoritativeness, that is, the natural history of Konrad Gesner, the Swiss. In the illustrations of this book the sea serpent is shown as a monster some six hundred feet or more in length, long enough in fore part alone to wrap round a large sailing vessel. In his description, however, the sea serpent is reported as being only about ninety feet long, hardly bigger than the largest fish or marine mammals. Nevertheless, so far as real snakes go, the sea

Fig. 40. The sea serpent is immortal. The Daedalus
Sea Serpent, which was "sighted" 1848

serpent had a magnificent advantage over its relatives. Real sea snakes, which belong among the poisonous adders or Hydrophinae and of which there are some fifty species in the tropical waters between East Africa and the Pacific, seldom grow much over two yards long.

Seamen of later times also claim to have seen these giant serpents again and again, though to date none has ever been caught. Today their disrepute has become proverbial. Yet the sea serpent question has a more serious side. Up to very recent times specialists have given earnest attention to the problem of whether sea serpents actually exist or may have existed some centuries ago. At the end of the nineteenth century Dutch and English scientists engaged in a heated argument on this subject and when a sea-serpent monster allegedly appeared in one of the Scottish lochs during the present century, a beast reported as looking astonishingly like reconstructions of prehistoric mosasaurians, the polemics were renewed, but without arriving at any unequivocal yes or no.

Another species of imaginary animal, of smaller incidence than the sea serpent but no less unsettling to the mariners of the age of discovery, was the *homen marinho* or merman. Mermen fall more or less into the realm of romantic-symbolic fable, together with the sirens of the Greek sagas and the nixies of the Middle Ages, but in sixteenth-century writings they are included among the marvels of the New World. It would seem that Europeans first heard of these monsters from the Indians, though the Indians themselves believed mermen were shipwrecked people from the other side of the ocean. Mermen were thought to be extremely dangerous perverse beasts, more malignant than the most rapacious sharks.

Two reputedly sober and dependable observers, the Jesuit Father Fernão Cardim and the sugar manufacturer Gabriel Soares de Sousa, give a detailed description of the mermen. Mermen, it seems, practised their nefarious calling only in the summertime, and then usually in the vicinity of fresh water. They looked like men, were quite tall, and had deeply sunken eyes, and the females of the race resembled women with long hair. The mermen grappled to their victims, Negroes and Indians exclusively, then strangled them, after which they crushed them to pulp. Having murdered, they let out curious sighs, then fled. Often, too, they carried off their victims for cannibalistic purposes, but ate only the eyes, nose, finger and toe tips, and the sexual parts. It is exactly this habit, says another observer, Frei Vicente do Salvador, that differentiates the mermen from the sharks, who prefer the legs and arms. The same goes, too, for real human cannibals. These *homens marinhos—igpupiara* or *upiara* in Tupi, words which also mean "shark"—are the Jack-the-Rippers of the Brazilian coast. Apparently shipwrecked seamen who murdered the Indians gave rise to this horrible species of marine monster.

The Wonder Beasts of the Humanists

In cultivated Renaissance circles such tales from the Wild West were treated with scepticism and contempt. In other respects, however, these educated people were superstitious, with the difference that they had a touchstone which, they supposed, enabled them to tell the true from the false. Anything found in Plato was indubitably true and anything written by Pliny was very probably true or, at the very least, possible. Meanwhile Aristotle's authority had gradually waned. In any case, anything not mentioned at all by the ancients could be confidently repudiated as a fabrication. It is quite possible that the discovery of America would not have been so quickly believed had it not been foreshadowed in Plato.

On the whole the Renaissance was not a rationalistic age. Men like Leonardo da Vinci and Pomponazzi, the philosopher, were exceptions to the rule. On the other hand the men of the Renaissance were not really mystics who got lost in the supernatural. Rather they were surrealists, who projected the antique tradition and the products of their own imagination into reality and by so doing increased their range of vision without ever quite leaving the plane of the real. The fabulous animals of antiquity now took on a reality they had never had in the Middle Ages. All forms of them were admitted into zoology, where they were counted just as real in every attribute as animals that had actually been seen.

The basilisk, the Egyptian phoenix, the gryphon, the salamander, again came into their own during the Renaissance. The three sirens mentioned in Columbus's log fall into this surrealist category, rather than into the class of primitive superstition exemplified by the *homens marinhos*. Columbus assures us that he himself had seen them leaping about in the sea. He was not particularly impressed by them, he says. They were not as "harmonious" as in their pictures. In Benvenuto Cellini's autobiography we are told how his father showed him, then a boy of five, a little lizard-like animal sitting unconsumed in the glow of a wood fire.

The father explained that the "lizard you see there in the fire is a salamander, a creature that no one from whom we have had credible reports has ever seen." Benvenuto's father was only an artisan, but the greatest physician of the period, Paracelsus, likewise believed that the salamander was the elemental spirit of fire.

The Paduan doctor, Julius Caesar Scaliger, one of the most famous philologists of the sixteenth century, swore to the existence of the basilisk, a frightful snake, whose gaze alone was enough to kill human beings. It was characteristic of a vast change in outlook when, in later years, the name "basilisk" was given to a

Fig. 41. Young dragon (after Petrus Bellonius, 1553)

small and harmless lizard that is found climbing about the trees in Mexico. The wonder bird, the phoenix, which on the testimony of Herodotus flew every five hundred years from Arabia to the temple of the sun at Heliopolis to sit beside its father's remains, had a firm place in Renaissance ornithology. The phoenix was pictured as a splendid heron with feathers of glittering gold. Not until the middle of the seventeenth century did the English physicist, Sir Thomas Browne, dispute the existence of this fabulous bird in his *Vulgar Errors*. Another savant replied with grim irony that the only reason the phoenix did not show himself was fear of human beings, the tyrants of creation. Some rich glutton, he pointed out, would certainly have killed and devoured the poor bird if he had ever got hold of him.

Belief in the wonder beasts of antiquity left a mark on practical medicine as well as on deductive thinking. Medieval medicine was primarily a matter of administering herb mixtures. Modern medicine began to experiment, at first to excess, with mineral substances. Between these two epochs was the heyday of medicines made from animal substances. The horn of the unicorn, for example, was a panacea. Actually, of course, there was no such animal but clever swindlers knew how to get round this difficulty. They offered the gullible a material that had all the qualities attributed to the unicorn's horn by the authors of antiquity. Usually whalebone, ivory or rhinoceros horn served as a substitute. In this traffic the danger lay in flooding the market, thus lowering the price of the product. As for the buyers, naturally people who knew what they were doing very carefully tested the offered product before making a purchase. Only when convinced by the application of all rules of the medical art that the horn had come from a unicorn did they venture to grind it into a fine powder or break it into small pieces for therapeutic use.

The horn of the unicorn was particularly prized at court, for it had a saving property which was in strong demand—protection against poisons. During the Renaissance, murder by poison was a salient means of settling disputes over the succession to the throne and such conflicts. A universal antidote, therefore, commanded a high price. An especially fine specimen of horn fetched three hundred thalers in Dresden. A piece of horn was considered to be a princely gift. When Catherine de' Medici married the French dauphin, her uncle, Pope Clement VII, who performed the marriage ceremony, gave the bridegroom's father, Francis I, king of France, a piece of unicorn horn. This remedy kept its reputation in England up to the second half of the seventeenth century. Indeed, it was not discredited until the Royal Society had proved that an allegedly poison-proof royal goblet in fact gave no protection at all.

Only one other medicine was supposed to have anything like the same curative properties as the unicorn horn. This was the bezoar, a substance from the *materia medica* of Arab medicine introduced into Europe via Spain. The wise Avicenna of Córdoba, one of the most famous doctors of the twelfth century, is supposed to have been the discoverer of this excellent medicament. Avicenna recommended a bezoar, a stony concretion from the head of a large red deer, supposedly formed by the tears shed by the animal after eating snakes, as the most dependable protection against poisons. Modern biologists like to consider this theory as indicative of the beginnings of a serum therapy. In any case, an obvious course of action suggested itself to Avicenna's contemporaries. Since genuine bezoars were not easily come by, they took a chance with substitutes such as gallstones from antelopes, apes and wildcats. In view of the fact that even these were rather rare, all sorts of adulterations appeared, which the authorities took stern measures to suppress. Genuine, guaranteed bezoars were literally worth their weight in gold. In Córdoba a stricken man of wealth gave a castle for one.

The bezoar retained medical favour for some six hundred years. In Paris it was an indispensable feature of the court apothecaries' *materia medica* until the great surgeon, Ambroise Paré, by means of an experiment on a condemned cook convinced Catherine de' Medici's son, Charles IX, that the supposedly marvellous stone did not protect against poisons at all. Yet the bezoar remained in the pharmacopoeia of London apothecaries until the middle of the eighteenth century.

Fish Portraits

The avidity with which the humanists embraced superstitions of all descriptions may now and then have resulted in an accidental discovery, but on the whole this predilection hindered the advance of the natural sciences. Whereas men of the Renaissance blazed a trail in the mathematically grounded branches of science such as astronomy and mechanics, achievements were modest in both zoology and botany. Here scientific productivity tended towards the broad, not the deep. It was mostly a collecting activity and entailed no basically new ideas. Even this stock-taking process was far from thorough, since the savants were not especially interested in the New World. Zoological knowledge lagged far behind geographical knowledge.

Nevertheless Renaissance biology was superior to that of the Middle Ages in two respects; in the art of precise description; and in the tendency to specialize. Animal drawing, a genre to which Leonardo da Vinci and Albrecht Dürer contributed notably, reached a high level of perfection. Textual descriptions, where not clouded by antique anecdote, were far better than anything that had appeared before. The results of explorations in the near east, e.g., the Egyptian drawings made by Pierre Belon, were added to existing information on European fauna and on the animals in the menageries kept by princes and municipalities. Like almost all the sixteenth-century naturalists, Belon was a polyhistor. He was equally interested in the pyramids, and the embalming of mummies, in crocodiles and hippopotamuses. Yet he was one of the first naturalists to specialize. He published an account called the *Natural History of Strange Marine Fish, with Their Portraits Engraved in Wood; Including a True Picture and Description of the Dolphin and Several Other Strange Animals of This Kind.* The title has an air of showmanship, but in point of fact the work contained much new material. With his *History of the Fishes,* which came out somewhat later, in 1555, Belon laid the cornerstone of modern ichthyology.

Although the rich possibilities of American material were hardly taken into consideration, this widespread scientific interest in fishes was a sign of the times. In the Middle Ages people tended to look up into the air: among all animals it was birds that interested them most. But in the age of discovery men's eyes were turned towards the sea, and marine animal life was the zoologist's favourite theme. Belon's work on fish was honoured by being incorporated into Gesner's great compilation, the *Historia animalitum,* which for two hundred years was Europe's most comprehensive source on animals. About this same time some naturalists turned to the study of lower marine life. A dispute arose as to whether corals were real animals. Wotton was one of the first to give an affirmative reply to this question, both in respect to corals and other plant-like marine organisms such as sponges and medusae. The old name for organisms of this general type—"zoophytes," literally "animal plants"—reminds us how difficult it was to clear up the problem.

In the second half of the sixteenth century this interest in marine organisms led to a discovery, or rediscovery, which at the time created no great stir but which was later accorded a place of honour among the great achievements of natural science. The famous manufacturer of faïence and enamelled ware, Bernard Palissy, undertook an investigation of rocks filled with shells. Hitherto, whenever anyone had stumbled onto such a phenomenon it had been thought of as a mere curiosity rather than as an accidental revelation of scientific pertinence. According to accepted medieval theory, nature had a preference for certain forms, regardless of the material content. Nature was characterized by a *vis plastica*, a "plastic force." This idea lies behind the expression *"lusus naturae"* i.e., "sports (or freaks) of nature," which persists to this day.

According to this idea nature, seemingly, often carried sportiveness to exaggerated lengths. Jean de Joinville, chronicler of the last crusade, tells how, at Sidon, a stone was found containing the perfect impression of a fish. The stone was brought to Louis IX. "The fish was of stone," the chronicler reports, "but its form lacked nothing, neither eyes nor bones, nor yet colour, or indeed anything that might have prevented its being recognized as a living fish. The king gave me a stone, and in it I found a tench, brown in colour, and of such sort as a tench should be." This was certainly very odd, but neither the pious king nor his wise counsellor troubled their heads further over the matter.

Palissy, however, was not satisfied with the usual explanation. In his opinion it was not a question of freaks of nature in point of colour and form but of the petrifications of real animals carried, long ago, by water to the places where found. In other words, fossils were organic, rather than mineral, in origin.

Palissy was certainly not the first to voice this conjecture. Among students of nature in antiquity this thesis had prevailed for many long centuries. As early as the turn of the sixth century B.C., the Ionic philosopher, Xenophanes, enemy of all superstition, had seen fossil fish on the Mediterranean islands and correctly

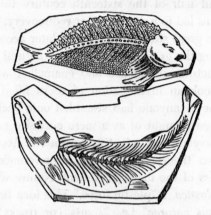

Fig. 42. Fossil fish (Aldrovandi, Musaeum metallicum, 1648)

identified them as such. Herodotus reported that shells could be found in the mountains near Memphis, that is at a site far from the coast. From this he inferred that at one time Egypt must have been covered by the sea and that the shells came from that period.

Similar observations and theories are found in the writings of Aristotle; of his pupil, Theophrastus of Lesbos, author of the first book on geology; and of Strato of Lampsacus, a learned man of about the third century B.C. The same general outlook also prevailed among the educated during the Augustan period of Rome. These ideas found poetic expression in the works of Horace and Ovid. The Greek geographer, Strabo, likewise went deeply into the fossil question and came up with much the same answers as those arrived at by his predecessors. Then came Pliny who, in this instance as in other contexts, substituted nursery tales for the results of Greek investigation and thought. Stones exhibiting an animal form, so Pliny thought, were originated by lightning, or had fallen from the sky during a lunar eclipse.

For a century and half Pliny's ridiculous explanations held sway. Only a few brave and independent minds—such as Albertus Magnus, Bishop of Regensburg in the thirteenth century, and Albert of Saxony, Bishop of Halberstadt a century later—dared acknowledge the ancient Greek interpretation. Leonardo da Vinci followed their example. The last name in this distinguished list before Palissy was the great Veronese physician, Girolamo Fracastoro, investigator and namer of syphilis. In 1517 a large number of fossils was discovered during the construction of the cathedral of Verona. Believers and sceptics entered into an argument over them. Where did these extraordinary forms come from? Fracastoro answered the question as Herodotus had answered it two thousand years before: at one time the sea must have covered Verona and the fossils were the remains of marine animals.

However, Bernard Palissy, the pottery-maker from Périgord, land of truffles and rocky caves, could hardly have known about all this, for he had had only an artisan's education. Yet for his class he was a well-read man, though he understood neither Latin nor Greek, a deficiency which alone sufficed to cut him off from what others had discovered before him. Nor was Palissy, unlike his countryman and contemporary, Montaigne, obsessed by a thirst for universal knowledge. What really interested him was anything connected with the painted pottery that he manufactured. He made up his mind to master all knowledge in this field. As a young apprentice he had wandered through France, Flanders, the Netherlands and the Rhineland, and from these countries had gained many ideas on the techniques of glass and faïence manufacture. Beyond techniques, he was interested in knowing the origin of everything used in his work. Thus the artisan became a geologist, a physicist, a chemist and a zoologist.

Palissy's artistic goal—and he was first and foremost an artist

—was the production of enamelled ware decorated with pictures of fishes, shells, snakes, lizards and frogs. Oval-shaped dishes by Palissy—he modestly called them *"rustiques figurines,"* or "rustic terra cotta"—became an individual line that held public favour for centuries. (The Palissy tradition still lives on in the modern Picasso treatment of clay.) These decorative considerations also encouraged Palissy to delve deeply.

In Paris, where he had been commissioned by the regent, Catherine de' Medici, to make an animal grotto in the Tuileries gardens, Palissy gave public lecture courses which attracted so many students that they were soon offering serious competition to the university. Court society crowded to hear his talks, given between 1575 and 1584, for he had more novelties to show and tell about than the ossified professors of the Sorbonne. Palissy's main attraction was a rich display of fossils, the contents of which he explained in his lectures. He compared the forms of petrified organisms with those then extant, showed how shells and marine animals had come to Champagne and the Ardennes and how the organic substance of marine deposits had gradually become transformed into stony material. The quintessence of his observations was this: stone can come from animals, but nothing which, under close scrutiny, appears at all animal-like can come from stone.

This was a revolutionary idea for the times and of course elicited an unfavourable reaction. Palissy was attacked from a quarter where scientific rebuttal could do him no good. Earlier he had turned Protestant, and once already, while living in the south of France, had been thrown into prison and threatened with the death penalty, only escaping because of his royal connection as purveyor to the court. In the meantime the religious conflict had sharpened and Huguenots had been outlawed in Paris. A fresh denunciation brought Palissy into the Bastille. He did not survive to see the day of peace among the religious factions. He died in prison in his eighties. His theories were completely forgotten. Documents of the life of the past again became showpieces in curiosity cabinets.

⧉ XIII ⧉

Merchant Tailors

THE Renaissance was a period of sumptuous elegance, the like of which has never been seen before or since. True, the ruling classes of the Middle Ages, at least after the Crusades, had dressed more richly than the aristocrats of antiquity. Whereas in sheer extent and in the richness of their furnishings the palaces of the ancient Oriental rulers threw everything thereafter into the shade, as did the cuisine of wealthy Romans in point of refinement and extravagance, both Romans and eastern potentates were extremely modest in their dress. In the east clothing was somewhat more pretentious and colourful than in Rome, but in comparison with the sumptuary expenditures of later epochs the material and tailoring were quite modest. In Greece and Rome clothes were almost puritanical. Men wore the simplest of white woollen robes. The women's robes were made of thinner wool and linen, artistically draped, but there was no fine tailoring in the modern sense. The fashion seldom changed, and this tended to limit the consumption of clothing. Gold-embroidered material appeared in the hellenistic period but was far less sumptuous than similar material much worn at princely courts during the semi-barbarous times of the early Middle Ages.

Nor was silk unknown in classical antiquity. A detailed description of a "large worm with horns that is different from others" is found in Aristotle. He reported that the creature underwent various changes and eventually produced a cocoon which the women unwound and spun. "It is said that this spun yarn," Aris-

163

totle relates, "was first made on the island of Cos by Pamphylia, daughter of Plato."

It is very likely that Chinese silk was known in Greece but the material would have been so expensive as to be out of the reach even of the well-to-do. In Rome, too, silk was considered to be an unheard-of luxury. Even the Croesuses who would squander a fortune on a banquet were not inclined to pay fantastic prices for a textile, no matter how beautiful it might be. The first recorded purchaser of silk was Julius Caesar. On one occasion he is said to have permitted himself the luxury of decorating a theatre with the material.

The Romans of imperial times were the first to use silk for clothing. The consumption of the costly stuff was immediately limited, however. Tiberius, and Titus after him, forbade the wearing of silken clothes by men and Aurelian considered the practice to be indecent even for women. Silks did not conceal the body properly, rather brought out its curves and protuberances, and among Romans the sense of frugality and of propriety went hand in hand. There was a great scandal when, in the third century the young emperor Heliogabalus, a half-mad homosexual from Syria, flouted the ban on silk imposed by sumptuary law and showed himself publicly in a robe made of thin red silk. Yet a hundred years later commoners were wearing silken clothing. This material, however, was probably a pseudo-silk from Cos, from the cocoons of the *Sphynxotus*, a moth of the near east, with caterpillars feeding on cypress and oak trees, and not the Chinese silk of the *Bombyx mori* which feeds on the mulberry.

THE SILK ROAD

The origin of silk long remained a mystery to peoples of the west. Until the Middle Ages it was generally believed that silk was a plant rather than an animal product, something of the order of cotton. Indeed, people had only the vaguest idea what cotton was, although it had been in use in the Orient ever since the memory of man. Not until the sixth century, during the reign of the emperor Justinian, did light begin to penetrate the mystery. Two Persian monks of the Nestorian sect, so the story goes, brought mulberry seeds and silkworm eggs back from China to Constantinople in a hollow stick. Justinian himself is said to have sent out these smugglers to secure the precious stuff after he had failed in his attempt to gain control of the Asiatic silk trade with the help of an Abyssinian prince.

In any case, Justinian set up a silk manufactory in his place and made the processing and sale of silk a state monopoly. No doubt Empress Theodora was active in this enterprise, for silk culture was everywhere a woman's, and particularly a princess's, privilege. According to Chinese tradition the Empress Si-Ling, wife of the great Huang-Ti, "constructor of boats and maps," discovered silk about 2640 B.C. An old Chinese tract tells how:

"The great prince Huang-Ti was desirous that Si-Ling-Chi, his legitimate wife, should contribute to his people's happiness. He commissioned her to examine silkworms and test the threads for utility. Si-Ling-Chi collected a quantity of these insects, and herself fed them on a place built for just that purpose, and not only found out how to rear them, but also the way to unroll the silk and use it in making clothes."

Posterity conferred divine honours on the empress out of gratitude for her great service. She was named the "goddess of the silkworms" and on her feast day silkworms were fed in a public ceremony. Thereafter the empresses of China were the patrons of Chinese sericulture. When the growing season was over, the noble ladies of the land brought the empress the cocoons. The silkworm breeders were rewarded with a sheep and a pig cooked in the imperial kitchen.

The rulers of China tried their best to keep sericulture a secret process. The export of silkworms or eggs was a crime calling for the most severe punishment and for a long period the control measures proved effective. It was not until the third century B.C. that silk culture came to Japan. According to one version a Chinese princess betrayed the secret but the Japanese chroniclers say that the Koreans were the ones who spread the art. Before this time an important trade in silk had developed between the east and the west. A Syrian Greek of the second century B.C. tells of the "Silk Road" that ran from China to Mediterranean lands by way of Turkestan and Persia.

Fig. 43. Winding silk, from a Chinese picture of the eighteenth century

At the same time silk was being imported from India. Whether Indian sericulture was of Chinese or native origin is not known. However, the Indian silkworm was not quite like the *Bombyx* of China. The Hindus were less concerned about keeping their silk culture secret than were the Chinese. No Great Wall protected and shut off India. In any event, it was from India, apparently, that silkworms were first brought by ships to the west though

Game of polo at the Mogul's court, Indian miniature of the eighteenth
century (Berliner Staatl. Sammlung)

"Bullfight" by Goya

Capriole of the Spanish Riding School in Vienna

the artistic tradition came from Persia and Byzantium. By the eighth century the Arabs had mastered the techniques of spinning and weaving silk, and soon surpassed the Byzantines. It was actually the Arabs who transmitted sericulture to the countries of the west. The Asian "Silk Road," through the Arabs, was extended across North Africa and from there silk production and processing spread to Sicily and Spain, especially to the latter.

Queen Elizabeth's Stockings

Europe was very slow to accept silk. True, people marvelled at its beauty, and the old Roman prejudice against its feminizing and weakening effects faded when princes of the Church began to wear silken robes. Sericulture was none the less fraught with great difficulties. Sometimes the mulberry plantings would fail, and sometimes the silkworms could not adjust themselves to the climate. For one reason or another silks continued to be very expensive; but after the late Middle Ages there were great silk-trading centres in Upper Italy, France and Spain, which serves to show how widespread the silk market had become. The first commodity exchanges were organized for the purpose of trading in silkworms. At the Lonja de la Seta (Silk Exchange) in Valencia, which goes back to 1483, there is an inscription which says: "Who cheats here will never reach eternal blessedness."

In Spain sericulture was considered so profitable that Cortés, in 1522, approved special functionaries to take charge of the planting of mulberry trees and silkworms in Mexico. The attempt failed. A century later the English were also unsuccessful when they tried to introduce silk culture into Virginia. By the sixteenth century, however, the demand for silk textiles had become so great that the European silkworm breeders could not supply the large manufacturers of Tours and Lyons with enough raw material. This forced them to turn to Oriental silk. Francis I of France sought to remedy this situation by founding a silk-raising industry in the Rhone Valley, using a little coffer load of *Bombyx* eggs taken as military booty from Milan. Under Henry IV twenty thousand additional mulberry trees were planted and the silk industry otherwise expanded. In the environs of Paris things did not go so well. Investors who had lost money became so enraged that they cut down the mulberry trees and killed the silkworms as if they were beetle pests. Results were better in the south, however, and France was on the way to becoming the leading silk producer of Europe.

England, where unsuccessful attempts had been made to raise silkworms, now tried to outstrip France at least in the manufacture of silk textiles. During the reign of Queen Elizabeth silk became the great fashion on the other side of the Channel. Queen Bess, who liked beautiful clothes almost as much as power, had her "silk lady," Mrs. Montague, make her stockings of the finest silk. Prior to political conflict with Spain which made trade with that country impossible, the English aristocracy had been wearing long silk stockings imported from that market. This war with Spain encouraged the rise of an English silk industry, and England welcomed Flemish weavers seeking refuge from the Spanish régime in the Low Countries.

While this industry was going through its birth pangs a reverend doctor from Cambridge by the name of William Lee presented an amazing invention at court, a machine which, with but little application of motive power, could knit stockings. With the ingenious Mr. Lee it was allegedly a case of love's necessity being the mother of invention. His adored one, it seems, was always busy with her knitting needles when by rights she should have been listening to him. Queen Elizabeth was impressed by Mr. Lee's technical daring but was somewhat dashed to learn that the machine could not make silk stockings, nothing but coarse woollen ones. Lee tried to remedy this deficiency and in 1598 sent the queen the first pair of silk stockings ever made by machine. His product earned him the highest praise, but neither patent nor monetary reward. The queen admittedly feared that the machine would throw thousands of textile workers out of a job.

Lee offered his invention to the French court, but in the confusion following the assassination of Henry IV nothing was done and so the French textile industry was not mechanized after all.

For two centuries the art of processing silk remained essentially the same as that taught long ago by the Empress Si-Ling. One reason for this lack of progress was the fact that great lords and ladies thought of silk as a mark of rank and wanted it to remain so. If the costs of silk manufacture had been lowered to make the product more widely available it would have lost a good deal of its attraction.

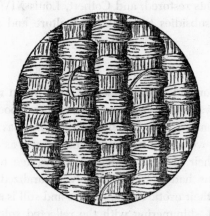

Fig. 44. The first magnified picture of a piece of silk,
taken and drawn by Robert Hooke (1665)

Until very recent times the Mikado of Japan reserved silk from the fagara silkworm for imperial use. The fagara caterpillar lives on the ill-smelling ailanthus tree or "tree of life" as it is sometimes called. None except members of the imperial family could wear clothing made from this kind of silk, although it was in no way superior to *Bombyx* silk. The export of imperial silk was prohibited on pain of death but this did not prevent its being smuggled into Europe, where it gave rise to a flourishing industry in Alsace.

The luxury-loving Francis I, King of France, and later the

spendthrift Henry IV, who heaped the costliest of silken gowns on his *mignonnes*, decreed that the lesser nobility and the bourgeoisie should not be allowed to wear silk, but this ban turned out to be completely unworkable. Then young King Louis XIII came along and began his reign like a Puritan. This time it looked as if the last hour had struck for the French silk industry. The silk mills in Lyons were shut down; six thousand workers were forced to live on alms. The mulberry plantings ran wild and no one bothered any more about silkworms. However, this crisis did not last very long. Under Cardinal Richelieu the silk industry had its old rights restored, and Colbert, Louis XIV's secretary of state, offered subsidies to coddle sericulture and silk manufacturing.

SHEEP OF THE UNBELIEVERS

The battle for and against silk was to be often repeated until artificial silk was made for the masses from wood. In all controversies on matters of dress silk was thought of as the seductive rival of honest wool. The moralists pictured silk as a siren luring people from their old and honourable marriage to wool. Even when silkworms had been thoroughly naturalized, as in Italy, there was still their exotic aura. Silk was and still is a marvel from an alien world, shimmering with the reflected splendour of the east.

Sheep, too, very probably came from Asia but this migration occurred in prehistory. Throughout the Old World sheep are thought of as indigenous fellow nationals, even where they are not. Actually very few breeds of sheep are identical with those existing in the same countries a thousand years ago, for sheep are the greatest travellers among the mammals. Either of their own accord or, more often, under the guidance of shepherds and breeders looking for a chance to make money sheep have wandered all over the earth in historical times.

The greatest globe-trotter of them all is the merino. This breed of sheep came into Europe, like so many other things in the

agricultural sphere, from the Arabs, and was apparently introduced into Spain from Africa in the twelfth century. The sheep
soon developed into splendid specimens with heavy fleece and
beautifully curved, closely set Ammon horns. Despite their thick
woolly coat, however, the merinos were sensitive to extremes of
temperature and, even more important, good pasturage was not
available on the Spanish upland plateau during the wintertime.
So twice each year the merinos had to be driven many hundreds
of miles across country in search of fodder. Sheep of both religions wintered together amicably enough in Andalusia and then
spent the summer months in Castile.

When the conflict between Spaniards and Moors became more
serious, these movements were no longer possible. The Moslem
sheep were in a relatively better position, for whereas in an
emergency they could feed on southern pasturage in the summer,
the winter pasturage in northern Spanish territory was too scant
to feed Christian sheep. This circumstance was not the least
among the many provocations which fired Spanish determination
to drive the infidels from the peninsula.

Even after this expulsion had been nearly accomplished, the
merinos still had no peace. Besides making their long annual
migrations, now, often enough, they had to flee from the Spanish
gendarmes, for the question as to where they should be allowed
to eat their fill continued to be contested by jurists for several
centuries. The very name "merino" suggests the idea of peace and
civil order. Quite often occupational and even personal names
are taken from animals, but in this case the reverse is true.
Merinos are named after the Spanish word *merino*, meaning a
sort of royal superintendent or inspector of sheep walks, a title
related to that of mayor. When the four-legged merinos arrived
in Europe, two-legged ones were awaiting them, that is officials
called *"merinos mayores"* and—those with only local authority—
"merinos minores." These officials were appointed by the kings
of Castile. Their method of partitioning the pasture lands gave
rise to so many abuses that the Crown installed new officials with

the high-sounding title of "*consule.*" Meanwhile the name "*me-rino*" became identified with the sheep.

A change in official title did little to remedy the vagaries of the law. Local authorities continued to contest the right of outside flocks to pasture on their lands. The owners of the flocks responded by banding together into an association, which in Aragon was called the "*Casa de Ganaderos*" or "House of the Sheep Breeders," and in Castile the "*Mesta,*" an organization that became one of the most powerful guilds of the mid-medieval period. The *Mesta* fought for and finally won the right to pasture their merinos wherever they chose. They also secured for their shepherds the privilege of cutting down and burning up trees to clear more land for spring pasturage, a practice that contributed a good deal to the deforestation of Spain. Nevertheless local quarrels over pasturage went on and on as the cities gradually became stronger, and were thus enabled to oppose the *Mesta's* claims.

REVOLUTION IN WOOL

The merinos were a source of controversy on an international as well as a national scale. Their only worthy competitors in the European wool market were the long-fleeced sheep of Shropshire, Herefordshire and the Cotswolds. Spanish wool was exported to England even while Spanish breeders were importing English sheep to improve the quality of their flocks by cross-breeding. Notwithstanding this fraternization between Spanish merinos and English sheep, competition for foreign markets developed into a conflict of interest between Spain and England even before the struggle for supremacy on the sea had become acute.

Towards the end of the sixteenth century, when the Spaniards observed that colonial conquest was making them poorer rather than the reverse, they began to sing the praises of the good old days. Shepherds, they told themselves, live like little princes. The pastoral situation was never quite so rosy as it was pictured by Cervantes's contemporaries, yet it was still pretty good. Reports from the late Middle Ages indicate that even the hired hands of the great sheep breeders were well paid. Besides a minimum cash wage they received a fifth of the lambs born during the year and a seventh of the cheese produced from the sheep under their care. They were allowed to pasture their own sheep along with their masters', and they were respected socially.

A pastoral culture usually connotes little land and less inclination for the pursuit of agriculture. This was as true in England as in Spain. English historians use the expression "agrarian revolution" in describing the transition from the cultivation of grain to sheep-rearing. This transition proved to be a social and economic catastrophe for England. The small farmer was eliminated by the owners of the large estates, the flatlands were depopulated, and the food supply was dislocated to such a degree that heavy imports became necessary. Peaceful though they are in themselves, sheep are revolutionary in their effect on mankind, more subversive than any other animal. When attempts were made in the sixteenth century to reverse the great pastoral revolution and restore the land to cultivation it was too late. The enraged opponents of the new economic régime unburdened themselves in a great number of pamphlets, in which sheep are spoken of as the wickedest of beasts. "Sheep have eaten up our grassland and our bottomlands, our corn, our woods, whole villages and cities," one pamphleteer wrote. Another complained that "God gave the world to people to dwell in, not to the sheep and the wild animals."

The initial consequences of the change to a pastoral economy, though unquestionably severe, were soon compensated by the development of a large textile industry. By turning to the manufacture of woollen and worsted cloth England got the upper hand over the Spaniards, who imagined they were doing well when they sold their raw wool abroad. As for the English, they held on to their wool. The export of wool from England was forbidden up to the nineteenth century, to assure England a monopoly in the manufacture of high-grade textiles. Long before their spinning jennies and looms had given them an economic advantage over other countries, the English had secured a commanding position in the world cloth market. "The sheep's foot turns sand into gold," they said, and did business accordingly. When they had become too rich to bother with sheep-breeding themselves, they founded a new pastoral industry far across the ocean in the Antipodes, an enterprise supporting a standard of living as good as that of the best-paid American workers.

XIV

The Beautiful Animal

IN SPITE of all the wonderful things encountered in the New World, the age of discovery was in no sense an American century. The eyes of Europe were turned towards the east rather than the west. The circumnavigation of Africa, the discovery of the sea route to India, had more immediate and consequential results than the crossing of the Atlantic. Vasco da Gama seemed more important than Columbus, even in the Iberian countries. Victory over the Turkish fleet at Lepanto in Greek waters was more enthusiastically celebrated in Spain than all the famed deeds of conquistadors. In Portugal there was much more interest in the new African and Oriental possessions than in Brazil.

As late as the beginning of the seventeenth century, Cervantes, in his vast novel, *Persiles y Sigismunda,* described Lisbon as the greatest and most flourishing city in Europe on the grounds that: "Here come the treasures of the Orient, and from here men go out into the whole world." To sum up, wealth came from the east, rather than from the west. This was true mainly of the spice trade, but it held for everything connected with the animal world as well.

If a man wanted to exhibit his riches, he made a show of the exotic animals of Africa and Asia. The fauna of the New World did not come up to popular expectation: it was not even amusing. The animals from the Americas did not accord with the Renaissance ideal of beauty, an ideal favouring large, noble forms rather than the picturesque. The princes of the Renaissance were not particularly interested in the spiny, scaly little creatures brought

by the sailors from South America. Not one of the great painters
of the day introduced any New World animal into his pictures,
not even into so much as a corner. The only living things caught
overseas which found favour in Renaissance eyes were a few of
the brightly coloured birds.

THE MEDICIS' MENAGERIE

It was characteristic, too, that the menageries should not have
been affected by the discovery of the Americas. Lions, tigers,
leopards, elephants, rhinoceroses, ostriches and the like continued

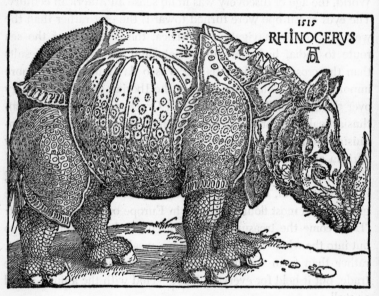

Fig. 45. Dürer's rhinoceros (1515)

to be the main attractions. In some Italian cities there was a zebra
or a giraffe as a particular rarity, but that was all. The giraffe,
incidentally, was not absolutely a novelty. Three hundred years
before this period the first giraffe had been brought to Europe
by the Hohenstaufen emperor, Frederick II. The most beautiful
specimens in the Renaissance zoos were gifts from Oriental

princes but at the same time there was a regular trade in exotic animals. Fanciers were willing to pay fantastic prices for the unusual.

One of the most magnificent zoos of the Renaissance was in Rome. Pope Leo X, a Medici, was as much interested in having a fine menagerie as he was in patronizing the arts. It was an old family tradition. At the reception held in Florence in honour of Pope Pius II, the wise Cosimo de' Medici had put on a show worthy of Nero. Lions, bulls, dogs and a giraffe were penned together in the square in front of the Signoria, with the idea of

Fig. 46. Picture of a triumphal procession of the Renaissance period (Francesco Colonna, Poliphili Hypnerotomachia)

promoting a battle royal. But things did not turn out as planned. The lions were more pacific than the Italians and showed no desire to harm the other animals. Under Lorenzo the Magnificent, however, the lions exhibited more temperament. The finest of the lot was torn to pieces by his fellows. Meanwhile a giraffe, sent to the uncrowned ruler of Florence by a Mameluke sultan, was spared.

In any event, Lorenzo's son in Rome revived the regal custom of keeping a menagerie for sheer glory. Princes vied in adding to the papal zoo but here, too, American novelties were lacking.

When King Manoel of Portugal was moved to pay the pope his respects, showing off the treasures of his realm the while, rather than send animals from his South American colony he shipped an enormous elephant, two selected leopards and a tame panther which rode on the back of a Persian horse. He had also intended to deliver a rhinoceros but the vessel carrying it to Italy foundered.

Even without this showpiece the ceremonial procession through the streets of Rome was one of the strangest spectacles ever witnessed in the Eternal City. Leo X, surrounded by all his cardinals, received the representative of the Portuguese empire at the castle of St. Angelo. Reverently the elephant dipped his trunk into a container filled with perfumed water and three times sprayed the pope and the crowd while cannon salvoes roared and all the church bells rang.

Burlesque as this scene may appear, it indicated a new attitude towards animals. Even in public celebrations intended only to divert the crowd, the fashion of showing animals in the wild was on the wane. The tendency was to subdue wild instincts by training, to conquer the animal through the exercise of a higher intelligence. Such was the goal man now set himself and found delight in reaching. It was a typical Renaissance ideal. Animals might be strong, but man, because of his superior intellect, was stronger. The more man substituted sheer will and intelligence for weapons and force in attaining the goal, in a way that all could see, the greater his conquest.

The High School

The horse was the animal on which human beings could most impressively demonstrate their masterfulness. The horse of the Middle Ages had been an instrument of war. Even in the tournaments he had kept something of this initial character. Horses were decked out, but little value was placed on perfecting the animal's physical form for its own sake. In jousting, the horse had been covered from head to tail, with his legs barely visible. The beauty of equine movement had gone entirely unnoticed. By the end of the fifteenth century, however, stud farms owned by Italian princes were breeding spirited horses at Milan and even more notably at Mantua. These animals could both hunt with the hounds and race, a sport which now showed signs of revival. Freeing the horse from his jousting armour was an advance but not really an innovation. It was well known that when a horse is spurred, he runs faster. Making him gallop was not an art.

The modern technique of manège began in Naples in about the middle of the sixteenth century. Methodical training revealed equine abilities never witnessed before. It was found that a horse could be made to stand stock-still on one spot, his every muscular movement subjected to man's will. He could be taught to lift his foot just as high as the rider wished or made to rear on his hind legs as if about to take a powerful jump then instead sink back submissively on to all fours. He could be made to move in circles round one position or turn his head as desired. Altogether, he could be stripped of the last vestiges of wildness lingering in his nature after a thousand years of domestication. Yet with all his submissiveness the horse should never appear slavish, like a dog. He still had to look like a master animal, to whom the rider belonged as surely as he to the rider.

Mastery over the horse was thought to be incomplete unless expressed in beautiful forms. The new equestrian art was thought out in terms of the aesthetic down to the last detail. The rider was expected to let the audience see the signals used in directing the animal. The horse was supposed to obey the least nod, but the nod had to be visible to the audience, otherwise the exhibition would be nothing but a prearranged game, a mechanically memorized circus dressage. The high art of riding was action, continuous improvisation, not merely something learned by rote. The horse's virtuosity had to be such that it was impossible to tell whether he was acting of his own will or repeating something learned.

The founder of this new art was an Italian nobleman, Federico Grisone. The text in which he laid down his tested principles and technical exercises created a furore, and his success as a practical riding master was even more sensational. The riding academy he established in Naples drew pupils from all over Europe. Gentlemen of rank rushed to Naples to learn manège. Some may have seen in the riding academy an opportunity to train horses for war, but the High School's main influence lay in the sphere of sport. As the High School became the mode, tournament horsemanship lost its last adherents. It became a sort of joke, a burlesque in which the champions of the joust dressed up as Roman gods or as national heroes. A certain German knight went one better than this by fighting with the lance while masked as Venus.

Grisone's successor as the greatest riding master of the day was another Italian, Pignatelli, who earned lasting fame with his invention of a new bit. From Pignatelli stemmed a whole school of famous equestrian performers and riding masters who went out to the courts of Paris, London, Madrid and Vienna to initiate kings and princes into the mysteries of the High School. With the passage of time horsemanship became a veritable science. Every great riding master worked out his own method of teaching animal and rider.

In Italy a form of theatre developed from the new art. The *fola,* or riding to musical accompaniment, became a feature of both court and popular festivals. In this performance the horses had to bring their feet down in exact time with the music—or at least the musicians had to adjust their timing so skilfully that the horses seemed to the public to have a musical sense. To this day the equine ballet is still part of any good circus repertoire and the High School tradition has held its own as a social sport at court and in the army. In France manège was the rage right up to the Revolution and in Vienna the tradition is still carried on at the famous Spanish Riding School. Of all sports in which animals are involved, manège is by any reckoning the best to watch and the least injurious to the beasts themselves.

BULLFIGHTING

Another and much more violent sport came into fashion at about the same time as manège. Spanish bullfighting can look back on a venerable past. Many authorities include in the history of the sport the hunting scenes depicted in cave paintings. Even if bullfighting does go back so far—and overlooking the fact that bulls were diligently stuck to death in the Roman circus—the peoples of the Iberian peninsula must be credited with priority in this sphere. The Visigoths were fighting bulls in the early Middle Ages. At the coronation of King Alfonso VII of Castile in the twelfth century a bullfight was on the programme of entertainment. It is not until the beginning of the sixteenth century, however, that reports of bullfights begin to increase.

Even then bullfighting continued to be in the main a knightly sport, if not entirely a privilege of the aristocracy. The greatest lords of the realm engaged in it. When a son, later to become King Philip II of Spain, was born to Emperor Charles V, the father expressed his joy by killing a bull in a public bullfight staged in the Valladolid market place. Cesare Borgia, the most politically powerful figure in Rome—the Borgias were of Spanish origin and had a bull on their coat-of-arms—amused himself by having half a dozen wild bulls driven into a castle courtyard where he speared them to death one after the other.

Among the aristocracy bulls were fought from horseback and killed with a lance. This method did not make the contest any safer. In modern bullfighting the picadors, or lancers, are as liable to get hurt as the rest. Of course, the horses used by the great gentlemen of the past were undoubtedly more agile than the old nags used in the modern bull ring. None the less, accidents were so frequent that the rulers of Spain were moved to take countermeasures. After seeing several men lose their lives, Queen Isabella ordered the bulls' horns to be padded. In the time of Philip II, Doctor Cristóbal Perez Herrera invented a special method of blunting the horns but neither of these innovations was enthusi-

astically received. Only the Portuguese were satisfied to have the
contest end without spilling either the bull's or the bullfighter's
blood. The Portuguese fitted a leather cap over the bull's horns,
and the bulls, instead of being killed, were thrown to the ground
after being wearied out by long lances and harpoons. In Spain
the people wanted to see blood; otherwise it was not a real bullfight.

Fig. 47. Bull-baiting with dogs. Spanish woodcut of the eighteenth
century

In Spain bullfighting was and still is more in the nature of a
hunt than of a sporting contest. Not only do several men attack
the beast with a variety of weapons, but the scales are weighted
against the bull. No matter how well he fights, the animal has no
prospect of escaping the ring with his life. Even if he should hurl
one *torero* up into the air, another will come out, or a third, if
necessary, to stick a sword into him. The moment the bull sets
foot in the arena he is doomed to die, by some means. There is
no way out for him. Even if he defeats his adversaries, he is not

granted an honourable exit as would be the case in other truly sporting contests. He may not, as a reward, retire to fat Andalusian pastures but must bleed to death on the sand.

Indeed, the bulls seem almost to sense this. The most painful thing about bullfighting is that the animals are obviously far less eager to fight than their human opponents. A regular system of provocation has been worked out to enrage the bulls. Before the fight they are kept in the dark. Yet this is not enough. When they are let out of their pens into the bright light plainly their only wish is to flee the ring. This they may not do; the gates are tightly closed. Often the red cloths used to make the bulls stop their wild coursing about the ring do not get the desired result. Even after the picadors have ridden onto the scene and maltreated the bulls with their lances, the animals do not immediately turn on the horses and impale them.

Not until the *bandilleros* have rammed their iron barbs into the bull's shoulders and blood is streaming down his hide does his temper begin to mount, and very often even then he must be further stimulated with rockets. A regular fireworks display has to be set off on his back to make him wild enough to satisfy the spectators. After all these preparations the *torero*, hero of the piece, strides onto the stage. Often by this time he is facing an animal which is weary and all but harried to death. Sometimes the beast is so far gone that he must again be incited with the red cloth to get him to charge, instead of lying down in the sand and resting from his wounds.

The rigid ceremonial procedure governing bullfighting in the great Spanish rings is of relatively late date. It developed towards the end of the eighteenth century. Before that time bullfights were more of a free-for-all, as they still are when staged in village market places. However, the *lidia* or fight with the bulls had been partly a business for professionals since the first half of the seventeenth century. At first the bullfighting profession did not command much respect. The *matadores*—literally, the "butchers"—had a lower social status than the *bestiarii* of ancient Rome, but as time went on bullfighters became heroes in the public estimation. Their biographies comprise whole collections of thick volumes. And the names of the most famous bullfighters are deeply implanted in the Spanish consciousness.

GENEALOGY OF THE BULLS

Like the *toreros* and the auxiliary staff in charge of the bullfight preliminaries, the bulls themselves, so to speak, have become professionals. They are as carefully bred for their calling as racehorses for theirs, with the difference that whereas a racehorse

Fig. 48. Bullfight in Peru, from El Toro (Instituto de Arte Peruano)

makes many public appearances, they make but one. Like all animal sports, bullfighting has brought about striking improvements through careful breeding. Spanish bulls have actually achieved an international reputation as combative animals. In ancient times Spain was renowned for its horses, and in the Middle Ages for its sheep, but cattle are hardly even mentioned.

Spanish bulls are not a uniform, autochthonous race. An older strain is descended from the north European aurochs which became extinct at about the same time as their semi-domesticated scions were celebrating initial triumphs in the Plaza Mayor of Madrid. The last aurochs were killed in the Polish forest of Jaktorowka in about 1630. The younger strain of fighting bulls is of African origin and supposedly descended from the Egyptian bull, several types of whose offspring are found in North Africa. One of these, the so-called Andalusian bull, is darker than the north Spanish cousin of the aurochs and has very powerful horns and a concave back. The Moors brought this line into southern Spain.

A third strain has been bred by crossing the northern and the African races, a strain called the *Bos taurus ibericus* by Spanish zoologists. This type of bull was produced on the stud farms of Castile and has provided many splendid specimens for the ring. To this day, however, experts on the *lidia*-zoology carefully distinguish between mixed races, according to whether the northern or southern strain is dominant.

Any idea that breeding for the ring has had a generally favourable effect on the quantity and quality of Spanish cattle must be relegated to the realm of legend. Bullfighting has certainly given the business of breeding livestock in Spain a certain direction, whether for better or for worse. More than a mere chance dictated that draught oxen should be supplanted in Spain by horses and mules as early as the seventeenth century, earlier than in most other European countries. This shift occurred at exactly the time when bullfighting was becoming a popular sport necessitating the sacrifice of many animals. For many years there were bullfights daily in Madrid and Seville, with morning and afternoon contests as in the arena during the days of imperial Rome. During one period eighteen bulls were killed daily in Madrid, and sometimes as many as twenty-five. Not until the beginning of the nineteenth century was this number limited to sixteen. Modern bullfights, with six or seven bulls appearing on Sunday afternoons during two rather short seasons, seem rather niggardly by comparison.

Each year great numbers of these noble creatures were driven to graze on the upland pasturage. Not being castrated they were, of course, exempt from the plough or the hay wagon. This custom may well have been a prime contributing cause to the decline characteristic of Spain in rearing beef cattle. Today Spain is one of the poorest of European countries in beef cattle. The quality of cattle bred for slaughter also suffered from competition with fighting bulls. The rich owners of large estates in the best position to breed cattle for the market have considered it more honourable, if less profitable, to breed bulls for the ring.

This seems to be a peculiar sort of quixotry but considered historically it is nothing unusual. Man has never raised animals exclusively to provide himself with food and clothing; his need for diversion has always been a factor in the rearing and breeding of them. One might even say that breeding bulls for the ring is at least less egotistical than keeping animals in a preserve to be hunted, an activity giving pleasure only to a few. Bulls bred for the ring serve the people's pleasure. To this day bullfighting is the supreme delight of millions.

It is twisting folk psychology to try to explain the Spaniard's joy in bullfighting in terms of sadism and bloodthirstiness. Greedy impresarios have had no success with the Spanish public when they have tried to revive straight animal fights such as bulls against lions or leopards and the like. Nor has the revolting sport of cockfighting ever gained much of a following in Spain. Bullfighting affords the *aficionado*—and most Spaniards are well-versed in the art—an aesthetic pleasure in contrast, for example, to horse racing, which in most countries has sunk to the level of a pure betting activity. It must also be admitted that bullfighting, its horrors notwithstanding, is a more stirring spectacle than the boxing and football matches which provide recreation elsewhere.

The custom of pitting man against the strongest, and next to

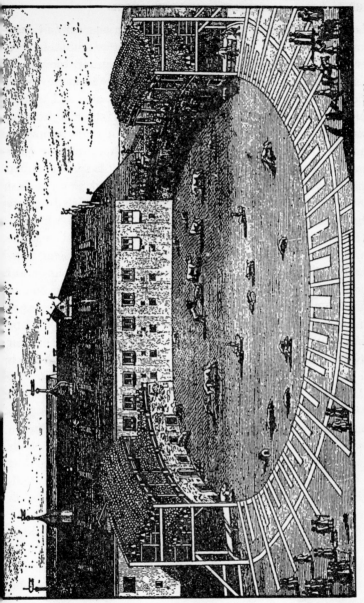

Fig. 49. An animal fight in the "Jägerhof" at Dresden (copper engraving, 1746)

the horse the noblest, animal is a genuine carry-over from Renaissance times. It is an amoral and unfair institution, but these negative qualities are concealed by the pageantry and the play of beautiful forms. A bullfight is not an honest, Homeric contest such as the Greeks loved but rather the expression of imperious self-confidence and self-assertiveness, of an absolute belief in man's superiority to all other creatures. Any antique strain there may be in bullfighting is Roman. It is not Greek, even less Persian. Although the Spaniard's enthusiasm for the sport has never spilled over into his religion—the Church, though she must bear with this Spanish custom, has kept it strictly at arm's length—at the same time it brings to mind the Mithraic cult which the Roman soldiers took along with them to the remotest provinces of the west. Mithra, the divine bullfighter of the Persians, killed the bull not as other mythological heroes killed dragons or such monsters to free mankind from their menace but rather because the *élan vital* is shown most perfectly in battle and because new life springs from the body of the dead bull.

Bullfighting is not symbolic of a Darwinian struggle for survival. It does not represent a struggle for self-preservation fought in fear and dire necessity. It is a contest freely entered into. The idea behind the ritual is that man, most bellicose of all living things, needs to fight, for battle is his element, and if no opponent offers it is natural for him to go out and find one.

PART FOUR

THE AGE OF IDEAS

XV

Battle for the Soul

WHEN the great Renaissance period was over, men began to wonder why human beings oppressed and killed each other. They
refused to rest content with the old reproaches and consolations
springing from the idea that people behave in this fashion because of a lack of piety, because man is cursed with original sin,
because a devil possesses him. They wanted at least a new formula, though there might be no final solution to the mystery of
man's nature.

As always, when man becomes dissatisfied with himself, animals had to pay by being made to mirror man's depravity. Francis
Bacon and, later, Thomas Hobbes both came by different ways
to the conclusion that by nature man is a ravening beast. *"Homo
homini lupus"*—"man is a wolf among his fellows"—a judgement
Plautus had uttered two thousand years before, was hailed as a
truth that would hold through all eternity. Aristotle over-esti-
mated man when he called him a *"zoon politikon,"* a socially inclined being. The social tie which bound him to his own kind was
no greater than that which bound the wolf to the hunting pack.

The French were even more sceptical than the English. The
Seigneur de Montaigne, a man who led a far more comfortable
and carefree life than most philosophers, was of the opinion that
"we give ourselves superior rank over other creatures out of
foolish pride and stubbornness, rather than because of solid
justification." This pronouncement was not a casual observation
intended merely to provoke argument, as has been erroneously
maintained. It was a conclusion arrived at by Montaigne after a

painstaking investigation of all the then available information on the animal world within his reach. Montaigne said that animals had more technical capability than human beings but also a more highly developed moral sensibility. Some animals fight with each other, certainly, and in this they are like man, but on the whole they are more peaceable. They have a feeling for justice and friendship, they come to each other's aid. Unquestionably they have a language of their own, and a high intelligence, one in many respects superior to man's.

A great deal found in Montaigne's apology for the animal world has a strange ring to our ears, as when he assumes that tunnies have a mathematical understanding because they swim in definite geometric patterns, or when he supposes that elephants, after having cleansed themselves, engage in a sort of religious exercise, standing at certain hours lost and still in their devotions with their eyes turned towards the east. In spite of these oddities, most of which Montaigne got from the ancients rather than from personal observation, his essay on animals was a great feat for its time. Montaigne boldly shifted man into the animal kingdom and, having put him there, did not even give him first place unconditionally. According to Montaigne man is superior to the animals not in native intelligence but in imaginative power, yet even this attribute is not exclusively human. The horse and dog also have a high degree of imaginative power which, as in man, continues to work while they sleep, for animals, too, have dreams.

SPEECH AND THOUGHT

If Montaigne was the founder of modern animal psychology, it was thanks more to his courage than to the originality of his thinking. Indeed, a generation before him an Italian cleric, Hieronymus Rosarius, had entertained similar ideas, but Rosarius, a papal nuncio to Hungary and Poland, had felt it wiser to keep his notes on animal psychology to himself, for the times had begun to grow dark and cloudy and independent thinking was dangerous. Rosarius's account was therefore not printed until a century later. Rosarius also believed that animals are endowed with intelligence and often make better use of it than do human beings. Although Rosarius's principal aim, like Montaigne's, was to curb the arrogance of mankind, his book was logically sounder and continued to elicit a strong response up to the eighteenth century.

When Rosarius's book appeared, greater men than he were in the midst of a dispute over the question of whether animals had "souls." The disputants were Descartes and Gassendi, foremost French philosophers of the age. They disagreed violently on how much animal and human psychology could be correlated. In this *Discours de la Méthode* Descartes had taken a radically negative attitude. Even the highest animals, and the wisest, he said, had nothing at all in common with man.

Descartes based his main argument on the faculty of speech. Some animals, he admitted, could chatter words imitatively but no animal had ever attained a symbolic language worthy of being regarded as a vehicle of thought. "And this does not merely prove that animals have less intelligence than human beings," he wrote, "rather that they have none at all; for obviously little intelligence is required for speech. And even though it is possible to observe that animals of one and the same species, even like people, are unequal, one being easier to train than the other, still it is not credible that a monkey or a parrot, though the most perfect of his kind, should thereby be considered equivalent to the most stupid child, or even to an idiot child, if his (the animal's) soul in its very nature is quite different from our own."

Descartes agreed that some animals have capabilities that are missing or at least not so highly developed in human beings; but this kind of superiority, he said, is a purely mechanical thing, no different from the ability of a clock consisting only of wheels and weights to keep track of time more accurately than man can keep track of it with his intelligence. Capabilities of this kind, he maintained, belong to individual organs, whereas intelligence is a "universal instrument" and it is precisely this universal instrument that animals do not possess.

In his *Méditations*, which he published some years later, Descartes barely touched on the question of animal *v.* man. Gassendi, however, to whom the new work had been given for critical appraisal, made the most of his opportunity to attack Descartes's earlier thesis. As if he had foreseen the famous experiment which the Russian physiologist, Pavlov, was to carry out two and a half centuries later with the dog and the sausage, Gassendi showed that physical functions and reactions in animals are as closely bound up with the emotions as they are in human beings. "A piece of meat casts its image on the eye of the dog," Gassendi wrote, "and after this image has advanced to the brain it attaches itself to the soul and becomes united with it by means of invisible hooks, whereupon the soul itself and the whole body, to which it is bound by secret and impalpable chains, turns to the piece of meat." So far as speech is concerned, it is not to be expected that animals should talk human language, Gassendi pointed out, since they have their own to use in communicating with each other. Even if their intelligence is inferior to man's, there is no justification for assuming that they have none at all. Man is the most distinguished and perfect of the animals but this does not exempt him from being included among the animals.

Descartes flew into a rage when he heard of this argument. He accused his adversary of "shamelessly" (*"impertinemment"*) putting words into his mouth that he had never used at all. Actually Gassendi, without quoting literally from Descartes, had followed the sense of his argument closely. The fact is that, as far as the issue at stake went, Descartes's rebuttal was rather a shabby one. How could anyone know, he challenged, whether a dog distinguished and judged objects and events as human beings do? Certainly an awareness of the cause and effect relationship could be detected in animal behaviour, but that proved nothing. Just as mysterious was the reason why Descartes himself wrote books under the assumption that others would read them, since he had no solid proof that his readers were psychically organized like himself. If such were the case, he could know it only by analogy, not from the consciousness of the thinking ego.

PERCEPTION AND APPERCEPTION

The intransigence of the Cartesian viewpoint chilled even his most ardent followers. Descartes's most important pupil, Spinoza, while not entirely disavowing his master departed notably from the Cartesian outlook in framing his ideas on animal psychology. Spinoza conceded that animals "do not have the same nature as our own, and their emotions are different in nature from human emotions." At the same time he judged animals to have feeling, one of the most fundamental psychological characteristics, and elsewhere in his *Ethics* he remarked that "all individuals, though of different grades, have a soul."

According to this theory there are no grounds for assuming that a dog craving for a piece of meat has feelings and emotions completely different from those of a ravenously hungry human being. If this parallel is admitted, other conclusions must by analogy be admitted too. Suppose a dog takes a certain path to get to a bone. He is acting like a human being going into a butcher's shop to buy food. If a dog begs in order to get a piece of meat, the similarity between him and the customer who pays a price for what he gets is even greater.

In spite of such approximations, another question remains unexplained. Does the animal have a trace of man's ability to think abstractly? Can a dog know what a "bone" is? Or is it the appearance of a real bone, its particular form, colour and smell, that incites the dog to take possession of it—this bone and none other. Even if the event is repeated a hundred times, the bone must always be a particular bone and not "bone" as an abstraction. Altogether, the ability to generalize, to form abstractions, to have conceptual ideas which exist without any concrete object, is an ability peculiar to human beings alone. Thus Aristotle had taught, though he recognized the unity of nature and assumed, in physical nature, fine and imperceptible transitions between the various individual natural kingdoms. The medieval scholastics had made a dogma out of this. Animals, they maintained, have feelings and, conversely, in many situations human beings behave as instinctively as animals. Yet only human beings have an intelligence that makes it possible for them to think in terms of abstract ideas and to draw logical inferences.

It was a dangerous thing to cast doubt on this dogma. Another quality, the immortality of the soul, was bound up with man's unique intellectual position. Since the days of antiquity few thinkers had dared to quibble about the doctrine of the immortality of the soul. One who did, however, was the Italian philosopher, Pompanazzi, a contemporary of Pope Leo X and Luther. The last doubts had been silenced by the *autos-da-fé* of the counter-Reformation. Even such a materialistically minded philosopher as Gassendi held fast to the idea of the immortality of the incorporeal soul. Yet if animals were assumed to have even as much as a spark of rational intelligence, to that degree they had to be recognized as having an immortal soul, thus surrendering one of mankind's most cherished prerogatives.

The first to pull down this barrier between human beings and animals was Leibniz. This Leibniz did with such diplomatic skill that his revolutionary thinking caused no offence. Cleverly and neatly he wrapped the immortality of the animal soul in the silver paper of his monad theory. Everything corporeal, Leibniz said, consists of very small units, each unit having a little soul. Even organic matter is soulfully equipped, and by the same token animals to even greater degree. However, animal souls are not so complete as human ones. The animal psyche is able to have perceptions of the outside world and it has memory, a faculty denied animals by most of the older psychologists. But the animal lacks the gift of apperception, that is, the kind of understanding which is capable of ordering in terms of causes and relationships, the intellectual ability to rise above the data content of the individual consciousness.

Leibnizian apperception is basically not very much different from the spontaneous and innate capacity to abstract which Descartes had ascribed to his "universal instrument," the human intellect. But notes make the music. With Descartes rational intelligence is the exclusive possession of a master class, *Homo sapiens*. With Leibniz human intelligence differs from animal intelligence only in degree. Leibniz taught that in nature there is a complete hierarchy of states of consciousness. At the bottom of this hierarchy is the quiescent "soul" of dead matter, doomed as it were to eternal sleep. Then comes the passive, defenceless being of the plants, and above the plants the dreaming souls of the lower animals. Further up the scale is the more wakeful consciousness of the higher organisms, and at the top the most perfect and active kind of self-consciousness, that of man. The human being stands at the tip of the pyramid, yet at the same time he is part of the great structure of the universe and in principle is no different from other creatures.

THE WORLD UNDER THE MICROSCOPE

The Leibnizian monad theory greatly stimulated inquiry in the natural sciences. It was now possible to interest oneself in the details of animal psychology without immediately being considered a heretic. Factual data in this field were still very scant, and though seeking out facts and taking notes on detailed observations was not everything, it certainly represented a step forward. In any case, from now on students were no longer content to collate what Plutarch, Seneca and Pliny had said about this or that subject. Instead they began to look round for themselves in the budding zoological and medical literature.

The immediate gains, certainly, were not very great. The study of the optic nerve and other organs intimately involved with psychic functions yielded new information without, however, producing any decisive argument for or against Cartesian theory. Indirectly, though, physiological inquiry had a powerful influence on philosophical ideas concerning the animal mind. Malpighi's work on the respiration of the dog, the turtle and the frog, Swammerdam's subtle experiments on molluscs, flies, bees and worms, and discoveries in the field of embryology and tissue theory had brought about a reorientation in biology. Under the microscope the differences between man and animal seemed to vanish completely.

Fig. 50. The first illustration of microscopic fossils
(Aldrovandi Musaeum Metallicum, 1648)

Through the lenses made by the optician Leeuwenhoeck a most remarkable phenomenon could be observed. When Leeuwenhoeck's assistant, van Ham, examined a drop of semen under the microscope, he observed, swimming about in the liquid, little filamented objects with an astonishing resemblance to the recently discovered infusorians. Leeuwenhoeck decided that the objects were alive and named them "spermatozoa," that is, "seed animals," a term which has persisted. After such findings who could hold to the idea that an unbridgeable chasm separated man from the animals? For all its multiplicity, nature was one. So it was in the physical world and so it must be in the psychological world as well.

Yet, was it not possible on the whole to draw a sharp line of demarcation between the physical and the psychological? That the heart pulsed and thus kept the bloodstream in motion was a commonly acknowledged physiological fact, likewise the movement of muscular tissue. That the retina received images of the outside world could also be counted a physiological process. But in the brain everything must be quite different, some said. Yet the greyish-white mass which both human beings and animals carried about inside their skulls would be nothing but superfluous ballast if matter could not think, as the orthodox claimed. Actually, thinking might be nothing but a physical process, and the soul a myth.

In any case, it no longer seemed feasible to preserve the old order of precedence in respect of mind and body. The theory that the mind, or soul, was something higher than the body ran hard up against the facts of modern anatomy and physiology. As insight into the detail of physical structure and function increased, the more marvellous seemed the wonderful mechanism that sustains life in both man and animal. The aesthetic of antiquity, which had been reaffirmed by the Renaissance, was after all only a surface appreciation of beauty, a joy in beautiful external forms. The true aesthetic consisted of recognizing inner relationships, in understanding the clockwork of nature. All the soul's badges of rank paled into insignificance beside this great physical mechanism, a complicated apparatus, to be sure, but one which functioned according to immutable and knowable laws. The soul, by comparison, was uninteresting and therefore irrelevant. Indeed, it was too simple to be beautiful.

Nature's Clockwork

The aesthetic element, though often obscured by dogmatic wrangling, was the mainspring of the materialism of the eighteenth century, the age of reason. When Descartes called animals "machines," the expression had a pejorative tone. But in eighteenth-century philosophy the term "machine" became a title of honour. Indeed, there was no greater accolade. The perfect mechanism was an aesthetic ideal embodying the beauty of logic, the highest form of lawfulness and nature's creative spirit.

The prophet of this new gospel was a French physician, Julien Offray de La Mettrie. La Mettrie, needless to say, soon found out that in one respect, at least, spiritual theory was superior to his materialistic one. In all ages the champions of the soul have been in league with the police department, and whenever they have felt the privacy of the soul threatened, have not hesitated to call on their confederates for help. After La Mettrie, in his *His-*

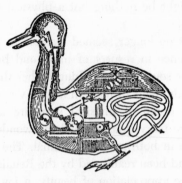

Fig. 51. Jacques de Vaucanson's mechanical duck, which picked up grain, digested and expelled it

toire naturelle de l'âme, had cast doubt upon the existence of the soul, he was relieved from his post of regimental surgeon and had to flee his country to escape being thrown into the Bastille. He could not even find asylum in Holland, although for two centuries that country had been a refuge of spiritual freedom. However, Frederick the Great invited him to Prussia and gave him a pension to live on.

In his main work, *L'homme machine,* published in 1748, La Mettrie openly took exception to Cartesian ideas. He exactly reversed the Cartesian argument. If animals were machines, then man, too, must be a machine. Human speech was an important distinguishing characteristic between man and the animals, yet it should be remembered that man had not always had this faculty. Speech is an invention. Some especially gifted members of the human race had at some time or other devised the phonetic symbols we use in communicating with each other. Then the rest of mankind had had to learn how to talk; and it was possible that animals could also learn how to talk, not in the sense of mimicking, but so as to make themselves understood by words like human beings. La Mettrie recommended experiments with the large anthropoid apes. Not all apes, of course, would prove teachable but some of them, he thought, might succeed if given the same kind of training as deaf mutes.

Although La Mettrie's hypothesis was wrong, for apes have proved to be highly unteachable so far as language goes, at least a new idea had been mooted. From La Mettrie's point of view the species of the animal kingdom, including man, had come into being as the result of evolution and had not been unchangeably created, each in its place. The main principle in the developmental process, according to La Mettrie, is education. This belief in the omnipotence of education, which was so characteristic of the literature of the age of reason, in a certain sense anticipated the Darwinian-Spencerian idea of progressive evolution. Before they had learned how to talk, human beings were inferior to animals in many respects, but through learning man became the highest of all creatures. By being taught, apes, too, could be raised to a level approaching that, say, of primitive man. If the idea was pursued to its logical conclusion, the possibility took shape of a complete transformation of the animal kingdom.

This form of evolutionary thinking, incidentally, was not peculiar to the materialists. It was foreshadowed by Leibniz and even more clearly expressed by his followers. A year after the publication of La Mettrie's *L'homme machine*, a work by a German professor appeared in which all the animals were seen as endowed with a developable soul. The animal soul, the professor claimed, is improving by degrees and some day will be equal to man's.

Even the great eighteenth-century German philosopher, Immanuel Kant, came close to embracing such views, though he expressed himself more cautiously on the body-soul relationship. In his *Anthropologie*, which came out in 1798, he voiced the thought that in the course of the great natural evolution "an orang-utan or chimpanzee will develop the organs which serve him in walking, feeling objects and speaking, into the structure characteristic of man, whose innermost being is an organ for the use of understanding, an organ which has gradually developed through social culture."

It was easy enough to put forward such ideas on a purely speculative basis, and in this context a receptive audience was always assured, but La Mettrie tried to explain his views on the physical characteristics of animals strictly in the light of the physiological, physical and chemical knowledge of his day. He was one of the first to use animals in experiments designed to secure material proof that man and animals react in the same fashion. Even death, he found, is similar in both. The body does not die all at once, as would have to be assumed if the soul left the body at a definite moment in time. Actually individual organs may continue to live on, even when separated from the body.

However, as La Mettrie himself had to admit, the lower the animal on the evolutionary scale, the more tenacious is life in the separated parts. Hydra can be cut into pieces and after eight days each piece will have again become a whole. The flesh of cold-blooded animals, such as turtles, lizards and snakes, quivers longer after death than that of warm-blooded animals. A frog's heart, he noted, continues to beat for an hour after having been removed from the body. Yet all these are differences in degree. Compared with the animals man is like one of those ingenious instruments used in observatories for measuring time as compared with an ordinary clock.

La Mettrie's book evoked amazement—and opposition—all over Europe, but whereas the ones who marvelled and approved kept quiet the opposition showered the *L'homme machine* with lampoons. When the author died a miserable and premature death from eating a Périgord pie, that is, a partridge pie flavoured with truffles, his enemies said that La Mettrie had got well-deserved punishment for his many heresies. None the less, his book continued to be influential. Although La Mettrie had given no final answer to the basic question as to whether the animal's psychic characteristics were different from man's in kind or only in degree, for all practical purposes the gap between the two had been bridged. Among the natural scientists, at least, after La Mettrie no one ventured to give man an absolutely unique position in the natural scheme. Even among the philosophers animals came to be so highly regarded that Schopenhauer, in his last will and testament, left a legacy of three hundred gulden for the care of his dog, and Nietzsche publicly embraced a horse standing in a Turin square.

Equality of Rights

NEVER since the great days of Greece had so many fertile ideas been promulgated as in the relatively brief period between the first half of the seventeenth and the second half of the eighteenth century—or more explicitly, between Descartes's *Discourse on Method* (1637) and Kant's *Critique of Pure Reason* (1781). During this century and a half, which comprised Newton's physics, Rembrandt's painting and Bach's music, the spirit of the western world freed itself from the shackles that had bound it for fifteen hundred years.

Among the prejudices which went by the board at this time was man's arrogant attitude towards the animals. Curiously enough, too, man recognized animals as having rights as valid as his own at exactly the time when he was lifting himself mentally further above them than he had ever been. The new attitude was not a Franciscan feeling of brotherhood with the birds. It did not arise from humility before the Creator who had made both man and the animals nor was it based on a sentimental love for species other than our own. Rather it was a purely intellectual recognition of the fact that we are as much a part of nature as the animals, that they are closely related to human beings, some differences notwithstanding, and that they, as much as ourselves, must be accorded the right to live so far as this concession does not conflict with human self-interest. Even Spinoza's completely anthropocentric moral theory gave animals this right to live, and in a form that went far beyond anything offered by other moralists. "Men have the same claim on animals that they have on us," Spinoza wrote. "Yes, because the claim of each is measured according to his abilities or his power, men have a far greater claim on animals than animals on men."

This idea, in contradistinction to Spinoza's animal psychology, is clear and unequivocal. Man has only the right of the stronger in respect of animals. In principle animals are man's moral equals and they even have a positive claim on him. Whether this right in respect of man is a right to be helped by him or whether it is only the right to attack and eat him when compelled by hunger is something dependent on circumstance. In any case, animals are not subject to man simply because he is the crown of creation. Between man and animal there is a sort of international law not so different from the colonial law of the period. Because man is actually superior to the animals he has the right to use them as he wishes; the fact that animals have feelings does not contravene this right, since even among human beings, as defined in Spinoza's *Theological-Political Treatise,* the "right to rule is limited only by power." But no intelligent ruler would let himself be carried away by violence on this account, though by the same token he would resist giving way to pity. Reason itself determines how man shall behave towards his fellows and towards the animal world as well.

THE FIRST MODERN ANIMAL PAINTER

This cool, rationalistic logic now came to govern relationships between man and the animals in lands north of the Alps and the Pyrenees. Even before being philosophically formulated by Spinoza, it had found artistic expression in Dutch animal painting. Spinoza's fellow countryman, Paulus Potter, a man seven years older than the philosopher, created a new way of seeing animals. In a certain sense Potter was the first real animal painter since the great anonymous artists of the prehistoric cave-painting period.

During antiquity splendid animal sculptures had been produced in Egypt, Assyria, Greece and even in Rome, but in painting animals had been used only as background figures in depicting the deeds of god or hero or as purely decorative subjects. In medieval art animals had been used more prominently but, even in sculpture, had served almost exclusively as symbols or background. Hardly any purely secular animal portraits existed. At the most some great lord had occasionally had himself painted with a favourite dog or falcon.

During the Renaissance painters began to make studies of animals as studio subjects. Pisanello's animal drawings are among the treasures of the early Italian Renaissance. Dürer's water colour of a hare is a masterpiece as true to life as if the animal had sat for him for hours at a time. Yet animal painting even at its highest peak was not given full recognition either by the public or the painters themselves. Drawings of this character, unless used to illustrate books, were regarded as a sort of preparatory exercise. There were no animal portraits for their own sake as there were portraits of people, historical or religious paintings and the like. The theme was considered to be too trivial. Whenever an animal was shown dominating a landscape or better placed than a human figure, he had to be given an allegorical name so that no one should get the idea that the painter was trying to upset the divine order of precedence.

Animals first became emancipated in seventeenth-century Dutch painting. The Flemish painters, Rubens and Snyders, meanwhile continued to dramatize animal life. Wild hunting scenes, often with Diana as literary pretext, were the main theme; or the victim of the chase might be seen gracefully arranged in a still life. To sum up, man had conquered and now the animals might rest in peace.

Animal painting of a peaceful kind first arose in the low country about the Zuyder Zee. Although thematically this type of painting appears to be ripe and old, it was, in fact, the work of a very young man. Paulus Potter was a prodigy, one of those geniuses who stepped, a finished master, onto the stage and vanished at an age when others would have barely completed their apprenticeship. Some of his best-known works were painted when he was only twenty years of age. By twenty-nine Potter was dead. The paintings that he is supposed to have turned out during his brief lifetime are so amazingly numerous that one suspects many pictures signed with his name were actually done by skilled imitators. Even if this is the case, it serves to show how influential he was.

The novelty in Potter's art is not the finely detailed brushwork over large surfaces, nor yet what has been called its photographic likeness—actually colour photography has never achieved such precise effects—but primarily the spiritual interpretation. He discovered something that apparently no one had ever noticed before: the fact that animals, if people only let them alone, are by nature peaceful creatures. Potter showed them standing in the grassy pasture untended by herdsmen, untroubled by their environment. They need no Garden of Eden to live in peace, nothing but green grass and some water. In his pictures cattle become the symbol of a peaceful animal kingdom. A few sheep or goats often keep the cattle company, and they, too, ask only to be left alone.

Potter depicted the peaceableness of the animal soul without any dramatic trimmings. The cow in the famous painting at the Hermitage in Leningrad is shown relieving herself, a performance which earned the picture a not very gallant title in the catalogues of the tsaristic period. Contentment is the basic theme even in Potter's few allegorical compositions. Orpheus is shown taming the animals by the sweetness of his music. But all that, Potter made clear, happened in the ancient past. Now it is the animals which are tame and only man is wild.

LA FONTAINE'S SOURCES

The most truly great animal painter of the period was an artist who painted with quill and ink rather than with brush and paint. In his homeland Jean de La Fontaine has the reputation of being the most Gallic of all French writers. The fact that his *Fables* evoked a powerful response in other lands indicates that he offered something which struck a universal chord or at least something easily assimilated outside France.

La Fontaine's international fame is undoubtedly based on the material content of his writings, even though in this connection he created little that can really be called his own. La Fontaine was no inventor of fables. Like the older fabulists, he drew heavily on Aesop. Indeed, he made no attempt to conceal his principal source and thought of his work as a re-creation of Aesop, whose biography he put at the beginning of his first collection of fables. Next to Aesop the Macedonian-Roman fabulist Phaedrus was La Fontaine's principal source for plots, though most of Phaedrus's stories derived from an older school of Greek fable. La Fontaine knew the collection of Hindu fables called the *Pan chatantra*, or the animal fables of Bidpai, which at that time had just been translated into French from the Persian. He was also well acquainted with the fable poetry of the Middle Ages. Since La Fontaine's animal poems were composed in the course of a quarter of a century—his first collection of *Fables choisies* was published in 1668 and the twelfth and last volume in 1693, shortly before the poet's death at seventy—he had time and occasion enough to search for little-known material of attractive quality.

La Fontaine was not in fact the rediscoverer of the fable, for animal poetry had long been in vogue. The public's pleasure in hearing animals talk like people had never died out, and in France the fabulist tradition was livelier than anywhere else. Since the Renaissance countless editions of Aesop's fables had been put into circulation. Some of the leading French writers, including Marot and Rabelais as well as a host of lesser lights, had written fables in verse and prose. In addition there was the rich Italian literature of fable coming into France from the south.

All the more surprising, then, that the modern fable should be as closely identified with his name as the ancient fable with Aesop's. But La Fontaine's fame is not undeserved. He gave the fable a form accessible to those without a classical education. His

fables could be understood and enjoyed by children as pleasant,
interesting short stories. At the same time these stories brought an
understanding smile to the lips of adults. La Fontaine's is a wise
poetic art in the best sense, amusing and informative and quite
lacking in any intrusive pedantry or Philistine moralizing. In
spite of their very firm lineal thought structure, the fables are

Fig. 52. Illustration of La Fontaine's fable—"The
Stork and the Fox"

playful in effect, pleasantly wavering between popular wisdom
and profundity. Everyone finds them comfortable to read, since
there is nothing in them to provoke resentment. They are a little
ironical, but never offensive. Although they aim at generalization,
so carefully are they formulated that one can always say: "Well,
not everybody's like that, only some people. As for you and me,
we're exceptions, of course."

THE CREATURES OF PROMETHEUS

The animal kingdom which La Fontaine exhibits in his fables—
not all of them, by the way, concern animals—is a colourful and
wide world. Almost all the domestic animals are represented in

his zoological garden, together with an impressive number of animals from wood and field. Wolves and foxes dominate as in ancient and medieval fables. Snakes and adders, turtles, frogs, porcupines and weasels, rats and mice, bees, flies and ants populate the scene. They make war on each other, they befriend each other, they vex and delight human beings. On one occasion even a flea comes onto the stage. There are very many birds but few fishes. Among the exotics there are the usual circus animals— lions, tigers and elephants. There is a strikingly increased emphasis on monkeys. Since the sixteenth century monkeys had been pushing their way into the foreground both in scientific and poetical literature. In La Fontaine's fables they have the comic role of mimic. Even before Voltaire's day the monkey had become a stock figure with literary wits. In La Fontaine the cat is portrayed as an unpleasant, malicious creature. In one fable borrowed from Aesop, however, a cat is described as changing into a beautiful young woman, albeit one who gets everybody into trouble. The sexual motive which prevails in modern French "cat literature" is but tentatively developed in La Fontaine.

As in the fables of antiquity, La Fontaine's animals appear for the most part as anonymous representatives of their kind, endowed with the traditional character traits. Some species are represented by several different individuals. La Fontaine found it amusing to take over some of his predecessors' famous animals, skin, hair, name and all, for example the cats Rodilardus and Raminogrobis and the sheep Robin from Rabelais's *Pantagruel*.

La Fontaine has often been called a "naturalist." It is quite true that he is but only in point of style. His language is devoid of the artificiality and stiltedness of the preceding generation of *précieux* and he is a master at drawing a scene realistically in a few strokes. Yet in his animal descriptions he is not a naturalist in Potter's sense but rather an atelier painter. Indeed, he is much less closely bound to nature than many of the older fabulists or his gifted follower, the Russian Krilov. In his youth, of course, La Fontaine had an opportunity to observe animals close at hand.

His father was a water and forest master (*"Maître des eaux et forêts"*), and La Fontaine himself was to have pursued this calling, but all this was ancient history at the time when he began to write fables. Meanwhile he had become a Parisian, a city-dweller to the core. He lived in a world where he never had a chance to see nine-tenths of the animals whose adventures he recounted. In any ca   tuck close to the traditional characterizations e   old fables and added no essentially

t his zoology out of books, not from

be no strict line of demarcation be-
. Even though the fable is a masked
es that animals have moral qualities,
ling those of human beings. In his
lière, La Fontaine took part in the
whether animals had a soul, and
Descartes's theory. In the brilliant
bles, a book dedicated to the
d the Greek legend of Prome-
ed to form human beings," he
characteristics of all the animals; from
parts he assembled our kind; he gave form to
which we call the microcosm. And so these fables are
ainting in which each of us finds his likeness."

In these sentences we can detect that deep scepticism from which no sage can escape, the idea that man is a mirror of the animal world with all its traits, good and bad. Is it possible that man might improve if he saw himself mirrored as he really is? La Fontaine does not count on it. At the end of each of his stories La Fontaine states the moral, introducing his summary with the phrase *"sans cela tout fable est un œuvre imparfait,"* that is "without this all fables would be imperfect." Most of these summaries are sober in tone and seem intended more to console than to convert. La Fontaine was far from being a saint either in his writing or his personal life. Until an advanced age he was the protégé of young and pretty ladies with plenty of money. This circumstance compensated for the humiliating services that he had to perform for the court society of Louis XIV. In any event, La Fontaine, unlike Aesop or Phaedrus, had none of the resentment of the freed slave. Either he did not feel the crook in his back that should have been there from so much obeisance or he chose not to.

THE BEE STATE

La Fontaine was no revolutionary. If one is looking for the great fables of social satire one must go to England. In this genre two names stand out high above the rest, those of Bernard Mande-

Fig. 53. A drawing by Grandville: the queen bee
takes the salute

out of frugality and a love of peace, are not spending anything on armaments. The last survivors of the swarm withdraw to the hollow trunk of a tree, there to end their melancholy existence.

This fable of the bees attracted a great deal of attention—indeed caused a scandal, although England was not a prudish country in this period. A court pronounced Mandeville's poem a threat to the public morality. People continued to read it avidly, nevertheless.

It was shortly after the fable of the bees had been publicly outlawed that a dignified gentleman of seventy, dean of St. Patrick's in Dublin and Jonathan Swift by name, came to London with an even more dangerous manuscript stowed in his pocket. Swift had the work privately printed and brought it out in 1726 under his cousin's name, with the misleading title of *Travels into Several Remote Nations of the World, in four parts, by Lemuel Gulliver, first a surgeon and then a captain of several ships.* As *Gulliver's Travels* Swift's book has since become world-famous.

Jonathan Swift is not considered a *bona fide* fabulist. Yet the fourth and grimmest book in *Gulliver,* that is, the "Journey into the Land of the Houyhnhms," is entirely in the guise of a fable and is one of the bitterest ever written. While sailing in the south Pacific, Gulliver comes upon a land ruled by horses. The horses are intelligent, amiable, helpful animals, gifted in many of the arts. It is only in language that they are rather awkward; their vocabulary is not very rich. In the same land there is another kind of animal, repulsive inside and out. The horses call these animals "Yahoos." To his horror Gulliver realizes that the Yahoos are nothing more nor less than human beings.

This scene, in which a man discovers his own species in all its offensiveness, is one of the most ingenious and gruesome in world literature. Never has mankind's black side been characterized more plastically. Swift's final dictum would seem to be that man is not only an animal, but an animal belonging morally and even physically among the lower orders.

By exposing people to their own bitter mirth Swift's aim was to drive home a fearful truth. But something quite unexpected happened. The readers' laughter drowned out their resentment; whereas Mandeville's *Fable of the Bees,* after languishing for years in limbo, came into high honours in the field of political science where the author was hailed as a precursor of liberalism. Swift's *Gulliver's Travels* came to be known, because of its picturesque notions, as a rollicking book of fable, the kind one gives to children so that they may be amused by reading how a shipwrecked captain kissed a horse's hoof.

🔲 XVII 🔲

Organization of the Animal Kingdom

PHILOSOPHICAL views on animal nature had been clarified after heated struggle but in natural science itself growing confusion reigned. The factual material had increased tremendously. The zeal of zoological collectors in Europe, findings brought back by travellers overseas, the microscope—all had increased the number of known creatures by many thousands. Even the most foresighted specialists had no idea what to do about such an abundance. The technique of pictorial representation had been greatly refined, but textual descriptions were rich in words and poetic allegory and poor in the formulation of diagnostic differences among species.

The educated people of this period loved encyclopaedic works with a pretence of collating all knowledge past and present. These encyclopaedias did more to garble than to clarify the factual material. Marcgraf's excellent monograph on the fauna of Brazil, for example, was in later editions lumped together with descriptions of southern Asia, and having read the text the reader could hardly know for certain whether he was being told about Old or New World animals.

Aristotle's *Natural History* was still the prime source of zoological classification, though this work had been written at a time when only about five hundred species were known. The Aristotelian division of the animal kingdom into organisms with or without blood, supplemented by the division of higher organisms according to reproduction, still served a useful purpose, but it did not cover the great manifold of the animal kingdom in all detail, with each particularity correctly pigeon-holed. The science of botany was even more confused. Plant material, all cleanly pressed for safekeeping in herbariums, had reached mountainous proportions. Even the greatest experts hardly knew their way round their own collections.

FIXING THE SPECIES

It was generally recognized that something would have to be done. But where and how to begin? That was the big question. The first to try to find a practical solution was the Englishman John Ray, son of an Essex blacksmith. Having made a long student tour of the Continent, Ray recorded what he had seen, not, like so many others, in a motley, mixed-up fashion but with the penetration and sense of order of the born systematizer. First he took the botanical material and for it created some permanent classifications. Then he tried his hand with zoology.

Ray did not venture as far in the zoological field as he had in his *Historia plantarum*. He tended to cling to the ideas of the ancients, as when, for instance, he classified the whales with the fishes. Even so, he did pioneer to some degree. In a series of monographs on four-footed animals, snakes, birds, fishes and insects, he covered a good part of the animal kingdom, assigning, as he went along, a place to everything that crept or flew.

Ray's most important achievement was in sharply defining the concept of "species" and in placing this category as the smallest unit below the genus. This made it possible to distinguish several thousand animals and at the same time relate them to each other according to larger viewpoints. Ray cannot be blamed for the fact that his fixation of the species later gave rise to a pedantic biological theory. He, personally, inclined to accept the idea of a kinship among the species.

The "methodical synopsis" which Ray first used in his work on four-footed animals published in 1693 served for half a century thereafter as a model for all studies in comparative anatomy. Then a new luminary appeared in the north, Carl von Linné, better known as Linnaeus.

In contrast to Ray, Linnaeus was a prodigy. His father, a country pastor in the Swedish province of Småland, wanted to make a trained theologian of the boy, but Linnaeus was more interested in natural science and his teachers at the gymnasium found that his accomplishments in other subjects were far from satisfactory. As a result his father was on the point of putting his son to work in a cobbler's shop, but friends intervened and so the boy went on to the university after all. He completed the first phase of his education at Lund, a provincial university in southern Sweden, and the second at Uppsala, intellectual centre of the north. From time to time Linnaeus had to starve his way along. Eventually a generous archaeologist, Olaf Celsius, guaranteed the young student the wherewithal for food and shelter. Out of gratitude to his patron Carolus Linnaeus, as he proudly signed his name, wrote his first scientific work, a treatise on the plants mentioned in the Bible.

Linnaeus's unusually quick grasp, his phenomenal visual memory and his amazing sense of order did not go unnoticed. The Society for Literature and Science in Uppsala gave him a scholarship which enabled him to take a trip to Lapland. His future father-in-law, a prosperous physician, later made it possible for him to continue his studies in Holland at the incomparable Cliffort Garden, at Hartecamp. Thereafter, while still a student, he made short visits to England and France. It would be wrong to imply, however, that Linnaeus's definitive experiences were gained, as were Darwin's, from the direct observation of nature in the wild.

In spite of the rich experience gained during his wandering student years, Linnaeus was, and all his life remained, a man most at home in botanical gardens, herbariums and libraries. He was as familiar with the world that he had never known from personal observation as he was with the world around him. The

story is told of how he visited the Jardin des Plantes in Paris just
as the famous botanist, Bernard de Jussieu, was asking his students a tricky question about the geographical origin of a certain
plant. None of the students knew but the stranger called out:
"*Facies americana!*" De Jussieu recognized Linnaeus by his
answer. The two savants struck up a great friendship. Young
Linnaeus was introduced before the French Academy of Sciences
and was immediately elected a corresponding member. Upon returning to Sweden, Linnaeus founded an academy of sciences
there and became its first president.

By the time he was thirty Linnaeus, by common consent, was
the most learned botanist in Europe. He had already published
three major systematic works as well as a number of lesser ones.
Anybody who wanted to know the genus of such and such a
plant from Asia Minor or South America made inquiry in
Sweden. Linnaeus never failed to furnish an answer. But theoretical botany is a hard way to earn a living. The world-famous
Linnaeus practised medicine in Stockholm until highly placed
patrons created a chair for him at Uppsala, first in medicine, later
in botany and natural history. Only from then on could Linnaeus
live free from care and carry on research.

The plant kingdom was Linnaeus's great love but at this period
specialization had not narrowed the scientific mind. Linnaeus
conducted investigations in mineralogy and zoology as well as
botany. Although he was apparently not very much interested in
mathematics, he was intellectually responsive to the times, which
were among the greatest of mathematical epochs, and the best
minds of the day assumed that all nature could be resolved into
a system of numerical relationships. Number was believed to be
the key to the structure of the world. A few simple numerical
series—six, twelve, twenty-four or four, eight, twelve, or perhaps
five, ten, twenty, and so on—were purportedly the basic relationships according to which nature worked. The scientist must proceed in such a way that the observation of nature became a systematic science corresponding to reality.

LINNAEUS, CORRUPTER OF MORALS

Numbers are more of a help in finding one's way round among plants than among animals. There are, however, some amazing arithmetical and geometrical phenomena among animals, beginning with the symmetry of almost all creatures, but at this early stage no one had any real idea why this should be so. Malpighi's microscopic investigations of the hen's egg had brought embryology a great step forward but science had only the vaguest idea of the germinal development of other animals. In the plant world nearly all the once unfathomable mysteries seemed to have been solved. All the puzzling things suddenly fell into place once botanists began to study the sexual life of plants.

The classification of plants according to their sexual organs, pistil and stamen, was not actually Linnaeus's idea, though the system based on it bears his name. Nor was he in other respects a great discoverer or inventor. But out of the arrangements of others he made a system at once masterful and expedient. It was a daring thing to place such emphasis on the sexual. No one needed telling, of course, that sexuality was an important feature of animal life but most thought of plant life as something virginal and chaste, as "pure" nature in a moral as well as in a material sense. Now Linnaeus came along and claimed that to give a plant its proper place in the herbarium it was first necessary to pry into its sexual organs.

This imputation did not fail to elicit protest. Linneaus went through much the same experience that Freud had to endure two centuries later. Zealots held him up as a corrupter of morals. Although the Linnaean system of classification took hold rather quickly, few learned men of the day offered to defend its author against charges of immorality. In any event, a definite tendency soon began to appear in the work of Linnaeus's pupils, who had dedicated themselves to the study of the fertilization of plants and who for the first time clarified the part played by insects in pollination. Observations and experiments in this field led to generalization, as in the "epigenetic" theory of Kaspar Friedrich Wolff, who came out in opposition to the older theory that offspring were preformed in the parents.

Linnaeus himself did not try to transpose his botanical theory of sex into the animal world. He approached the problem of classifying animals on the basis of one great criterion, one which was not sexual. The critical characteristic of animal life, Linnaeus said, was the fact that the whole body was activated by one central organ. The heart and the blood were the most essential diagnostic criteria of the animal, and they must be classified accordingly.

The two Aristotelian categories—animals with blood and those without—now became animals with red blood and those with white blood. The red-blooded animals were further divided into warm-blooded and cold-blooded but this was common knowledge in Linnaeus's time. Then, however, modern anatomy and physiology had their say. Warm-blooded animals have hearts with two ventricles and two auricles, whereas cold-blooded hearts have only one ventricle and one auricle. White-blooded animals have a ventricle but no auricle. Each of these groups comprises two classes. Warm-blooded animals include the "mammals" or breast-sucking animals—the term "mammal" was coined by Linnaeus—and the birds. Cold-blooded animals include the amphibians and the fishes. White-blooded animals include the insects and the worms.

Striving for the greatest possible simplicity, Linnaeus tried to arrange the whole animal kingdom in terms of these six classes. This system was adequate so far as the vertebrates were concerned but fell down badly when applied to the invertebrates. A host of lower animals, microscopic and macroscopic, of diverse form and life habit, were known to exist. Yet in the Linnaean system they had to get along as best they could—all lumped together as "worms." Had such a division been proposed by anyone less famous than Linnaeus it would not have received much consideration, but the lawgiver of the botanical kingdom had such

René Descartes "no"

Has an animal a soul?

Gottfried Wilhelm Leibniz "yes"

Hawking. Engraving, seventeenth century

Animal picture by P. Potter, Holland, seventeenth century

Carl Linné, the great classifier of
the animal kingdom

Buffon, Linné's adversary, was a forerunner
of the evolutionists

"Old Brehm," father of the well-known naturalist

a great reputation that his codex for the animal kingdom was received with a great deal of respect, and for a time obeyed.

PRIMATES, THE ARISTOCRATIC CLASS

In any case, Linnaeus introduced some startling novelties into
his zoological system to make up for its glaring deficiencies. The
most daring and the most lasting was the idea of an upper
stratum, which Linnaeus gave the self-revealing name of "Primate." This aristocratic class among the mammals consisted of
four apparently very different races. Linnaeus defined the
Primates as comprising the bats, the lemurs, the apes, and man,
the very summit of creation. In respect of man himself, there
were four human races, he said, but only one species, a species
which, according to the Linnaean binomial nomenclature was
defined in terms of genus and species as "*Homo sapiens.*" Like so
many other plants and animals, this long-since familiar but for
zoologists relatively new member of the animal kingdom had the
word "Linnaei" added to his name in honour of his classifier, so
that the name now reads "*Homo sapiens* (L.)" in all the natural
science texts.

The concept of "Primate" was a stroke of genius. Yet laymen,
and many professionals as well, found it hard to imagine bats as
members of the animal aristocracy. What did these ghosts of the
night with their clumsy wings and tiny bodies have in common
with the apes, so large and so intelligent? Only such a thoroughly
grounded master of anatomy as Linnaeus would have dared to
attempt to justify such a classification.

It was even bolder of Linnaeus to place human beings in such
society. Certainly no one, except some hopeless diehards, questioned the idea of man's belonging to the animal kingdom, but
even the freest minds believed that man must be accorded a
special place, a class or order, of his own. To classify man not
merely with the monkeys and lemurs but with the bats was a
revolutionary act which even in the so-called age of reason might
easily have resulted in persecution on the grounds of heresy. Any

man of lesser stature than Linnaeus would never have been permitted to get away with it.

Even Linnaeus was not entirely spared from accusations of having let down mankind. The strongest complaints came from a scientist whose rank was scarcely inferior to that of Linnaeus. Buffon, the grand master of French zoology, accused Linnaeus of having devised a classificatory system that was a "humiliating truth for mankind." In science a humiliating truth is more valuable than mendacious flattery. But even enlightened minds agreed with Buffon. Striving for truth had its limits if the process tended to lower man's self-esteem. At least the truth had to be expressed so that it would not gratuitously injure people with different ideas. Moreover, was it really valid to force organisms into genera, classes and orders? This striving for classification, was it not an idle game played by pedants? Did it not, at the bottom, run squarely counter to nature herself? In living nature, Buffon explained, there are only individuals, not classes, genera and the like. Divisions that transcend the unity of the individual are artificial. On paper it may be possible to draw lines of demarcation but in reality these lines simply do not exist. One species or genus merges imperceptibly into another. Aristotle had shown this to be true and the truth cannot be shaken.

A Monster Disturbs the System

The great question of the origin and transformation of creatures sharpened the conflict between Linnaeus and Buffon. In his *Botanical Philosophy* Linnaeus had laid down this principle: "We count as species only as many forms as were created at the beginning." Even if the general thesis were accepted, the formulation seemed rather presumptuous, in view of the fact that Linnaeus himself was constantly correcting and adding to his zoological as well as his botanical classifications. Plants and animals wandered from one group to another with each new edition, which fact Linnaeus's opponents did not forget to throw in his face with studied irony.

A seeker after truth need not feel ashamed if he makes mistakes in detail providing he is willing to correct them as soon as he knows better. Thus on one occasion Linnaeus was tempted to abandon the principle of the immutability of the species. In 1742 a student by the name of Zieberg brought Linnaeus a plant from one of the little Baltic islands not far from Uppsala. People often brought Linnaeus plants he had never seen before and he duly identified them according to his classificatory rules. This particular plant took him aback. The genus *Linaria*, of the flaxes, to which the plant otherwise obviously belonged, had only one spur at the base of the corolla, whereas this specimen had five. This phenomenon so greatly astonished Linnaeus that he called the harmless plant *"Peloria"* or the "monster." The matter did not end there. If it was only a monster, its offspring would have but one spur, as called for by the rule, but presently fresh monsters with five spurs sprouted from the *Peloria* seeds.

Seldom had this quiet, well-balanced man been more deeply impressed. "The century in which such phenomena are discovered," he proudly informed his students, "will go down in memory as a happy one indeed." But what had caused the phenomenon? Had the aberrant *Linaria* always existed? Did it belong in the divine plan of creation and had it been overlooked up to now by chance? In any case, Linnaeus's system would be overthrown.

Linnaeus studied the problem for many years and finally came to believe he had found a solution. The monster was a hybrid, a mongrel. It must have arisen from the fertilization of a common flax plant by the pollen of another genus. To prove his point Linnaeus sketched out a very learned transmutation theory which was warmly welcomed by the specialists. New species, Linnaeus announced, could arise from the union of two different genera, with one providing the woody substance of the plant, the other the pith, that is the two basic elements necessary for propagation. After this explanation the theory of the immutability of the species, in the strict sense of the word, was abandoned, but the principle was saved. For henceforth the genera would be the enduring, unchangeable factors while the number of species could change.

Although the new classification of *Peloria* was not based on experimental evidence, Linnaeus's theory attracted a following. Transmutation became the fashion among botanists. Anything that did not fit into Linnaeus's scheme was counted a hybrid and from botany the mongrel theory passed over into zoology. There, too, it seemed, the species had been too rigidly delimited. Certainly there was no need to go to such extremes as did Réaumur, who in all seriousness maintained that rabbits could impregnate hens, thus producing furred fowl. But there were mixed forms, derived from crossing and able to hold on to their identity.

With this concession, Linnaeus had ostensibly moved closer to the position held by his great French opponent. Had not Buffon himself always pointed out that all classification, the whole business of parcelling out organisms into families, genera and species, made sense only when the organisms of the same group were adjudged to have a common source? If the horse and the ass belonged to the same family, that is, if they were blood relatives, then they must have had ancestors in common. If this connection were once recognized, Buffon explained, the inference would necessarily follow that "all animals derive from a single organism, which in the course of time has brought forth all other races of animals through improvement or degeneration."

Linnaeus did not rise to such heights of logical abstraction. That was pure speculation, not science. The idea that all animals might have descended from one primordial animal contradicted the very plan of creation, a plan that bared itself, step by step, to any observer of nature. Moreover, was Buffon's formulation actually deduced from his own general theory? Had he not, as a matter of fact, got himself tangled up in more contradictions than Linnaeus with all his vacillations and errors? At one point Buffon talked about a "primitive and general design—a plan that can be traced out in wide areas—according to which all seems to have been created" but two hundred pages further along what did he do but maintain that a man's arm bears not the slightest resemblance to an animal's fore leg, and as little to a bird's wing? How did he reconcile this refusal to see the obvious with his *"dessin primitif et général,"* with the idea of the unity of nature and a common origin for all organisms? No, Buffon's outline of a theory of descent could never convince such a careful observer of the real world as Linnaeus. The gulf between the two men was never bridged. The nearer they seemed to come together, the deeper it became.

BUFFON THE SCEPTIC

The ancient epistemological problems had again been set—the conflict between ideas and appearance, between logic and fact, between unity and multiplicity. The battle was waged in monologue rather than in public debate. Linnaeus and Buffon were too proud, and too deeply committed to their own points of view, to become involved in petty quarrels. Yet this did not prevent them from reading each other a curtain lecture from time to time. The whole world knew that the two greatest naturalists of the time were enemies to the core.

Their mutual aversion sprang from a fundamental difference in character and career. Although the king of Sweden had made Linnaeus a member of the nobility for his scientific achievements, at heart he remained a *petit-bourgeois*, a man who had fought his way up step by step. The chevalier, and later the count, Georges-Louis Leclerc de Buffon was the scion of a great house. His path had been smoothed for him from the start. His father, a high official of the landed class from Burgundy, had engaged a learned botanist to accompany his son as tutor when the young man made his first student journey to Italy. At the age of twenty-six Buffon had been given a post in the Academy of Sciences. Soon thereafter he became supervisor of the Royal Gardens. Although he was a very industrious man and lived on a modest scale—besides many small treatises Buffon wrote thirty-eight thick volumes, with the assistance, admittedly, of a staff—he still had the manner of a grand seigneur. When foreign princes came to see him, he received them as equals. The Scottish philosopher Hume, who visited him in Paris, said he seemed more like a marshal of France than a man of the pen.

As for Linnaeus, in spite of his many-sided knowledge his world-picture was limited. His ambition was to be a good artisan who copied nature as faithfully as possible, who put everything in its right place, giving each detail its correct name. More than that, he believed, no one could do. Buffon, on the other hand, saw the world like an artist. He gave the most prosaic things of his profession a glittering and rather pretentious form. It was Buffon who coined the phrase "style makes the man." Society women devoured his zoological books because they were written in such an elegant style.

The essential difference between these two great eighteenth-century naturalists was that in their ideological trend and temper they were not really contemporaries, though both were born in 1707. Linnaeus looked at the world with the inflexibility of the scholastic. Thus had the world been made, thus would it remain forever. Variations might arise either from immanent causes or because of human intervention working from without. But variations were not a main consideration. The main thing was the fact that species, or at least genera, have always been, and will always be, immutable. The world structure is rigidly static. This justifies thinking of classification as a final kind of knowledge.

For Buffon nature was of great fluidity. He was not really an out-and-out evolutionist, yet he admitted that dynamic forces are at work in the animal kingdom, forces which in the past have occasioned deep-reaching transformations and which are still operative to this day. Since mutability is characteristic of the world, all classification is only an illusion, an expedient useful for purposes of orientation but in no sense a mirror of reality.

The only thing that is real and true, in Buffon's opinion, is the individual. With this avowal Buffon, in effect, had embraced the new liberal outlook that was then spreading all over Europe from England and which, after the second half of the eigtheenth century, got the upper hand in the sciences as well as in the arts and in social attitudes. For Linnaeus nature was an immobile, medieval class-state. Buffon, like so many of his aristocratic kind, tended to undermine the idea of fixed social estates. Of course he would have nothing to do with the subversive *encyclopédistes* and d'Alembert was his arch-enemy. In his writings Buffon was very careful about what he said and even in private he expressed his inner convictions only to a few close friends. Basically he was a sceptic. Once he let fall the ironic remark that it would be a great temptation to try to find a common origin for horse and ass, and for man and monkey, too, were not the story of the Creation so expressly laid down in the Bible. Then he hastened to retract these heretical notions.

It would certainly have been much easier for Linnaeus, who had his first writings published in liberal Holland and who lived in tolerant Sweden, to repudiate tradition than it was for a French court savant. Even in Voltaire's day the Sorbonne was a frightful inquisitorial power and held natural scientists accountable to a strict censorship. When the first volumes of Buffon's *Histoire naturelle* appeared, 120 doctors were commissioned to examine them for orthodoxy. Happily for the author, only seven censors found anything objectionable.

Buffon was not an original thinker, any more than Linnaeus was, but he at least tried to dig deeper below the surface than his Swedish adversary. Buffon borrowed his philosophical equipment from Leibniz. To some extent he transposed the Leibnizian monad theory into a zoological context and in so doing clarified it, but without making it any more believable to the average person. For monads, the smallest psychophysical units, Buffon substituted molecules, which could unite and separate but which themselves are eternal and indestructible. Buffon thought that according to a variation of the theory of metempsychosis these molecules could shift from one organism to another and that in this manner new life springs forth from decomposition. Buffon was a strong adherent of the theory of spontaneous generation.

Spontaneous generation—this, too, is Leibnizian—presupposes predestination. The process conforms to a *moule intérieur*, an immanent mould. Only when all predispositions concur do plants and animals come into being. Molecules form the organs, in consequence of which the individual, so to speak, is a monad of a higher order. Animals as well as man have individuality, and every animal mirrors the whole universe and is a microcosm.

Views of this nature, which Buffon shared with such confirmed materialists as La Mettrie, Maupertuis and Diderot, in other periods had usually been limited to the realm of metaphysics; but in this age of reason men's minds were practically inclined, despite a wide interest in philosophical theses and hypotheses and the broad natural relationships. Buffon's theory of the unity of the manifold, of organs and organisms, soon found practical application. François Xavier Bichat—perhaps the outstanding genius among French biologists before Pasteur, a prodigy who, before he died at thirty, had turned anatomy and physiology into entirely new paths—was the one who resolved Buffon's *leitmotiv*. Organs have membrane and tissue in common, Bichat pointed out, and in them reside both vital energy and disease. This insight led the way to Virchow's cellular pathology, which reigned supreme half a century later. Buffon, though himself no innovator, marked the inception of a new period which was to sweep far beyond Linnaeus's systematic approach.

▣ XVIII ▣

The Fifth Continent

ALL systematization assumes that its objects are pretty thoroughly known. In about the middle of the eighteenth century, when Linnaeus began to make his great inventory of nature, it seemed that this knowledge had been achieved. Of course there were still plenty of white spaces on the maps but even in the New World explorers had pushed their way so deep into the interior that one could say with some assurance: "The globe and all that lives upon it look like this: certainly not much more can exist."

At just about the time that Linnaeus's lawgiving mind was slipping into the twilight of senility, however, news arrived of something new and marvellous. Captain James Cook, whom the Royal Society of England had sent to the south Pacific to observe a solar eclipse, had found a land so immense that it could not be passed off as just another island. Cook's painstaking notes showed it to be an entirely new continent, one quite different from the rest and so large that there need be no hesitation in ranking it as a fifth major division of the globe.

As a matter of history Cook was not the first to discover Australia. Dutchmen had repeatedly sighted or touched on the continent while on South Seas voyages and a hundred years earlier, in the time of Columbus, a Frenchman, Binot Paulmier de Gonneville, was said to have been driven on to a coast later identified as Australia, although some dissenters claimed it must have been the coast of Madagascar. Still earlier the Chinese seem to have visited Australia. Marco Polo, at any rate, reported at the beginning of the fourteenth century that the Chinese spoke of a great continent lying to the south of Asia. Long before the actual discovery of the continent, Australia had been sketched on the maps. The cartographers located this southern land mass in various spots in the ocean, to the southeast and the southwest. On one map of South America dating back to the end of the sixteenth century, the cartographer drew in a continent which he placed south of Patagonia and called "*Chafdia seu Australis Terra.*" Rising endlessly in a northwesterly direction, this region bounded the Pacific Ocean.

Yet all these surmises and accidental visits no more contributed to the knowledge and exploration of Australia than had the Viking voyages to the settlement of North America. Not until Cook's voyage to the South Seas in 1769–71 was the fifth continent really introduced into western man's world-picture.

The Discovery of the Kangaroo

One fact had hitherto penetrated the ears of the zoologists: that on this southern continent lived a creature as big as a man with a deer's head and a long tail. The animal went about on its hind legs like a bird and jumped like a frog. The Dutchman Pelsaert had reported this curious animal in 1640, a report substantiated at about the same time by East India Company captains. All this had sounded as far-fetched as the legend of the giants that Tasman had seen on the South Sea islands; but after a conscientious and scientifically trained man like James Cook had corroborated these earlier accounts, even the most cautious zoologists had to admit that the animal kingdom was more diverse than Linnaeus or Buffon had suspected.

The animals of this fifth continent, unlike those of North America, were in no way similar to those of the Old World. The unique character of the Australian fauna, moreover, could not be explained away by difference of climate or diet. Here one stood before something new and completely strange.

The kangaroo continued to be regarded as the most extraordinary animal of the southern continent. It became the very symbol of Australia. The name came from the language of the aborigines. Not until twenty years after Cook's discovery was the kangaroo formally classified by the Englishman Shaw. Cook, however, did furnish a striking description of the kangaroo's appearance and habits. He spoke of the smallness of the head, chest and anterior

Fig. 56. Man with Kangaroo. Rock painting from
Northwest Australia

extremities, which the animal used only for digging, in contrast to the powerful construction of the lower parts and the heavy tail which was as long as the body. He described the kangaroo's habit of sitting back on hind legs and tail and of moving about in big jumps, using only the hind legs.

Cook's sharp eyes failed, however, to detect something which later on caused even greater astonishment: the fact that kangaroos carry their young in a pouch. Of course, this peculiarity is not so often seen out in the Australian bush as in the picture books. Although the wide-hipped kangaroos seem ideally suited for pro-creation, actually they are not very fertile and their young are very small. The giant kangaroo, which grows to be nearly ten feet long overall, is just over an inch long when he comes into the world and creeps into his mother's pouch.

According to Captain Cook's own report, his expedition shot only one kangaroo, in order to study it. Cook's successors, however, were not so restrained. Whereas the natives killed the kangaroo only for his meat, the Europeans killed him mainly for his skin, which was sold in the trade as imitation sable and skunk. Between the two of them, civilized man and the aborigine nearly exterminated the kangaroo. At the entrance to the Gulf of St. Vincent in south Australia there is an island which, at the beginning of the nineteenth century, was named Kangaroo Island because there were so many of the creatures there. Today not one is left. On the mainland they have become so rare that even the zoological gardens have trouble in keeping supplied.

At the same time it has been shown that kangaroos can be re-settled and bred outside Australia. Successful attempts have been made to acclimatize them in various parts of Europe. They have even been kept alive out in the open in Germany but since the animals do not have enough economic value to be bred on a large scale, they have remained a specialty of Australia. Even there only zoologists and tourists pay much attention to these most famous inhabitants of the land down under.

THE PARADOX OF THE DUCKBILL

One reason why kangaroos have rather fallen out of favour with the zoologists is the fact that there are so many species of them. Including the little tree kangaroo of New Guinea, the kangaroo rats, and their fossil relatives, there are twenty-one known genera including 158 species. The kangaroo can hardly qualify as a rarity; but the monotremes, or egg-laying mammals, are much, much rarer and also more interesting to the scientist. The spiny ant-eater and the platypus or duckbill, to an even greater degree, are considered to be the real marvels of the Australian fauna.

The platypus, a furred animal with a huge duckbill and a voracious appetite notable for its extreme sensitivity to environmental change, has the reputation of being the most paradoxical of all living creatures, in so far as it is the most difficult to place either in the older or the newer taxonomic systems. For over a century the duckbill has been a great trial to the zoologists.

Fig. 57. Duckbill or Platypus. After an old illustration

The platypus owes its discovery to the naturalist Joseph Banks, who accompanied Cook on his voyage to Australia. The very name that Banks used to label the animal raised the question of its classification. Banks called it *"Ornithorhynchus paradoxus,"* that is, "the paradoxical bird-bill." Shaw, classifier of the kangaroo, called the strange creature "platypus" or "flat-foot," and among the English-speaking world this name has stuck. Yet that was not saying much. The external similarity between the platypus and the otter was so obvious that from the start everyone had to assume it was an aquatic animal. Yet in less obvious respects the platypus was fundamentally different from the otter or any other water-dwelling mammal. What, zoologically, was to be done with such an oddity?

To settle this highly controversial question English zoologists sent a stuffed specimen to the German anthropologist Johann Friedrich Blumenbach, inventor of the five human races and, since the death of Linnaeus and Buffon, the greatest authority on all matters of classification. Blumenbach was of the opinion that the platypus could be included among the toothless mammals. This verdict was thrown into jeopardy a couple of years later when the Englishman Home, having studied two specimens of the duckbill preserved in spirits, came forward with the hypothesis that the platypus resembled the egg-laying lizards and so might well be an intermediate form somewhere between mammals and the birds and amphibians.

The following year, 1803, a new answer came from Paris. The youthful Geoffroy Saint-Hilaire, Bonaparte's court zoologist, maintained that a new order would have to be created to give the duckbill its proper place in the animal kingdom. Saint-Hilaire called this group the "monotremes," or the "one-holed" animals. He defined the monotremes as creatures with claws, no real teeth, and a single cloacal opening in the lower part of the body into which both the digestive and sexual apparatus empty. Saint-Hilaire boldly included the spiny ant-eater among the monotremes, though in appearance it differed greatly from the duckbill.

Yet zoologically all the name means is that the alimentary arrangement is similar to that of the birds, which also have a simplified excretory and sexual vent. Indeed, one can hardly claim that the placing of the genital and excretory organs has been any too happily resolved in the higher organisms. In this particular department nature has its own aesthetic laws, which are not like those of man.

It is curious to note that the first serious attack on the Linnaean system of classification should have been based on the sexual organs, which Linnaeus had stressed too much in classifying the plant world and too little in classifying the animal world. Saint-Hilaire's new taxonomic division did not end the controversy over the Australian fauna. A few years later Lamarck came along and questioned the monotremes' right to be listed with the mammals in view of the fact that they lacked the typical breast glands. In addition, they apparently reproduced by means of eggs, worse luck for them. Egg-laying animals could not, of course, be listed among the mammals. Yet they were certainly not birds, for they had no wings, and their breathing apparatus was different, too. Nor did they belong among the reptiles, for monotremes had four-chambered hearts. Well, then, what were they? Banks's choice of a name had been right all along; they were, indeed, a paradox.

Controversy over the platypus and his prickly fellow countryman, the spiny ant-eater, continued hammer and tongs until in 1834 the French zoologist, de Blainville, came out with a conciliatory proposal. The thing to do, de Blainville said, was to apply to the monotremes the old Aristotelian tripartite division according to method of reproduction. De Blainville named the three groups: the Ornithodelphia, or animals which, like the birds, have a cloaca; the Didelphia, or animals with a double uterus, like the kangaroo and other marsupials; and the Monodelphia, or animals with a single uterus and a placenta for the nourishment of the embryo.

This arrangement was well received but the question as to whether the monotremes really laid eggs had yet to be definitively answered. Not until fifty years later did Caldwell send his triumphal cable from Australia to a naturalists' convention being held in Canada. This message, because of its terseness, has become a classic in zoological history: "Monotremes oviparous ovum meroblastic." Which meant: "Monotremes lay eggs characterized by partial cleavage." Even so, a whole generation of careful observation was needed before the Australian biologist, Burrell, was able to show in complete detail how duckbills laid eggs and built nests to lay them in. A century and a half before one might have said, with Buffon, that it was a "humiliating truth" that mammals should reproduce by such a primitive method, but now everyone was more inclined to agree with another of Buffon's dicta, namely that classificatory differences exist only in the taxonomist's head.

THE BIRD PARADISE

Meanwhile the platypus was getting rarer and rarer, until finally the Australian government undertook to preserve a few specimens for posterity. They placed specimens of the platypus and similar rarities in a sanctuary at Healsville, which meant taking away their freedom but providing them with a secure and roomy preserve. Some other famous members of the Australian fauna also needed such protection to save them from extinction, among these the koala, which looks like a teddy bear, and the lyre bird, which zoologists of anthropomorphic bent consider to be the most accomplished actor, singer and dancer among the birds.

Fig. 58. The extinct giant bird Moa which lived in New Zealand probably looked like this

These conservation measures came very late and several of the rarest animals of the southern hemisphere have become extinct in fairly recent years. When Cook first came ashore on New Zealand, moas, giant ostriches over nine feet high, were still found on the South Island. On the North Island, however, they had been wiped out by the Maoris soon after their arrival there, which was probably between the thirteenth and fifteenth centuries—about the same time that efficient European hunters were doing away with the last aurochs. So many remains of the now extinct moa have been found, however, that it is relatively easy to reconstruct this largest of all birds—though it has never had its portrait painted, as has the dodo of Mauritius, famed for its stupidity and last reported alive in 1681.

Foxes and other predators transplanted from the Old World by the early colonists have also contributed to the decimation, and in some cases the complete extirpation, of weaker species in Australasia and Oceania. Before the European arrived, Australia was an immense natural preserve. The only aggressive placental animal living on the southern continent at the time of its discovery was the dingo or Australian wolf dog, as German zoologists call it, which had apparently migrated there from the north in the late Tertiary.

Exactly how the dingo got to Australia is still something of a mystery. An older theory, suggesting that it accompanied the people who migrated to Australia from Asia and became the stock for the first primitive population, has become increasingly dubious since the discovery of fossil dingoes with extinct marsupials dating back to an epoch even before the existence of the Javanese ape man. Some scientists surmise that the dingo may have been an excellent swimmer and by lucky chance eventually succeeded in making his way by water to Australia but this is not very likely either, in view of the fact that dingoes have never been found in nearby Tasmania.

The dingoes, in fact, rather tend to deflate the romantic idea that for millions of years Australia remained isolated from the

rest of the world. In this general connection it is interesting to
note that Australia is the only country where civilized people do
not boast of their genealogy. If they go back more than four generations, they are liable to invite the suspicion of having descended from the deported convicts who formed the first population. Similarly, in the animal world, any animal not dating back
to the early Tertiary or possibly to the Mesozoic, that is, to the
period when the land bridge once linking Australia with Asia is
supposed to have disappeared, must have arrived on the scene
in very recent times. Otherwise the whole theory breaks down.

Fig. 59. Dodo. A sketch by the Dutchman Roelandt
Savery, who was one of the last to see the bird and
who reproduced it in a drawing

Zoo-geographers have given this secluded, sea-girt continent,
a continent cut off from the general evolutionary process, the
name "Notogaea" or "Southland." Notogaea includes the Australian continent proper, Papua as a central part, New Zealand,
Polynesia and Hawaii—five areas in all. If the sea circumadjacent
to these land areas is included, Notogaea is not much smaller than
Asia. Throughout this immense region of the globe nature is supposed to have advanced along the evolutionary scale only as far
as the lowest mammal group. The few highly organized animals,
such as the bats, are assumed to be immigrants.

Notogaea, by common consent, is known as the home of the world's most splendid birds. Some Old World and American families are missing, e.g., the finches, woodpeckers, vultures and pheasants. Otherwise Notogaea is so far superior to Arctogaea and Neogaea in bird life that some have called this southeastern portion of the earth "Ornithogaea," or "Bird Land." Birds not only hold sway in tree and field but have even staked out a claim underground, for in Australia there is a species of bird called the cave parrot. The bird of paradise has been made the emblem of this insular world to the south, a world which the eighteenth-century discoverers thought of as a Garden of Eden.

Experiments with Animals

THE more zoologists studied animals, the more problems they discovered. Yet all along related sciences were trying to make practical use of the sound, though often far from perfect, information yielded by anatomical and physiological research. Animal experiments had been highly developed in antiquity, neglected in the Middle Ages, and in the Renaissance had again become one of the cornerstones of medical research. Both ecclesiastic and secular authorities long resisted the use of human corpses in dissection—Leonardo da Vinci, for example, was driven from Rome on that account—and students had to satisfy their hunger for knowledge with animal material. Thus a science of comparative anatomy arose. This science, incidentally, often worked in terms of premature conclusions based on analogy, not because of any lack of discipline but because this was the only way to forge ahead.

Physiology was even more dependent on animal experiment. Almost all the great discoveries in this field were first made on animals. The very title of Harvey's epochal work on the circulation of the blood shows that his observations apply to animals and the introductory sentences describe the vivisection necessary to explain the movements of the heart. Malpighi's work on respiration was based on experiments with dogs, frogs and turtles. Red blood corpuscles were first observed in a hedgehog—Malpighi, their discoverer, thought they were fat globules. Dogs were used for the first blood transfusions, before risking the introduction of sheep's blood into human veins.

Equally revolutionary were experiments with animals in the field of neural physiology. Indeed, up to the end of the eighteenth century everything generally known or conjectured in this line had been learned from the animal world. Even findings in humans were related to animals, since it was a ticklish matter to express oneself freely on the human nervous system. It was only too easy to be involved with philosophers and theologians in arguments over the question of the soul, which the prudent scientist avoided like the plague.

The use of the adjective "animal," a legacy from Graeco-Roman terminology, steadily increased. In this new context the word "animal" did not mean "bestial" as negatively opposed to "human." An older theory, derivative from the "spirit theory" of Galen the Greek, personal physician of Emperor Marcus Aurelius, saw the life-process as working through three stages: the liver, where nutriment became mixed with the natural spirit, that is, where it was corporeally assimilated. From there the nutrient substances were led through the bloodstream to the heart and there transformed into vital spirit. Finally the animal spirit originated from the vital spirit in the brain. This was the organism's own peculiar spirit, essence of its individuality. By virtue of it the body, via the nervous system, became mobile and capable of higher forms of behaviour.

ANIMAL MAGNETISM

From time to time the newest physical and chemical findings were interwoven into this basic scheme. First it was ferments, which stimulated the vital spirit—wine was said to contain many of them. Then it was specific chemicals, which either inhibited or activated the vital spirit, as the case might be. Then presently another natural force was discovered, a force visibly effective in organic material and not, as had first been thought, limited to certain metals. This magnetic force was first accurately described by the Englishman, William Gilbert, in 1600. Unlike other physical and chemical forces it operated invisibly and at a distance.

It was not a corporeal thing. No strong impact or the like was required for it to function.

This mysterious force, it was suspected, had caused many events that had been regarded as miracles, or transitory mental disturbances, especially the phenomenon of human beings and animals, under certain external influences of a psychic nature, being made to lapse into a trance or sleep-like state. That snakes could be hypnotized had been long known and in the days of antiquity snake-charmers had been among the attractions of the market place. It was well known, too, that fowl could be temporarily paralysed and put into a sleep-like condition; but that the same effect, to the accompaniment of much more curious behaviour, could be induced in adult human beings was not known until the second half of the eighteenth century. This discovery was quite justifiably a sensation in its day.

For a time the Swabian Franz Anton Mesmer who publicly demonstrated the art of hypnosis, first in Vienna, then in Paris, was regarded as a new messiah, particularly after he had achieved some successes in curing hysterical women. Mesmer himself believed that hypnosis was magnetic in nature, and so called it "animal magnetism." An invisible fluid, he thought, pervaded the whole universe and by the use of appropriate methods—which for commercial reasons he kept secret—one person's magnetic influence could be directed on another person, since under favourable conditions everyone is receptive to animal magnetism. Mesmer's materialistically minded followers tried to associate his theory more concretely with the then prevailing ideas on terrestrial magnetism. The most exhaustive text on animal magnetism—for soon a regular science with its own technical periodicals came into being—was D. G. Kieser's work in several volumes. This text was called *Tellurismus*, the doctrine of the earth's influence on its inhabitants.

Since Mesmer, and to an even greater degree his pupils, combined a great deal of charlatanry with their significant discovery, and saw fit to exploit it commercially, the serious scientists would have nothing to do with them. One investigating commission, of which Lavoisier and Benjamin Franklin were members, came to the conclusion that animal magnetism, so-called, was essentially psychic in nature and depended on imitation and imagination, a process in which sexual motives—the contact between the *magnétiseur* and the female patient—were involved. This interpretation, according to which hypnosis was concerned solely with volitional events unrelated to physics or chemistry, came to prevail in science, but far into the nineteenth century the public continued to think of hypnosis in terms of "animal magnetism."

GALVANI'S FROG'S LEG

At about the same time that Mesmer's experiments were arousing such tremendous interest, another mysterious force was reported from Italy, a force that apparently continued to be effective in the organism after death. The Bolognese anatomist, Luigi Galvani, a man worthy of the most serious scientific attention, had observed, in the course of his experiments on the muscles and nerves of frogs, that a frog's leg would contract when an electrical machine was discharged near it. This phenomenon, Galvani believed, might in some fashion be occasioned by external stimuli. Yet the same thing happened when the leg taken from a freshly killed frog was hung on a copper wire and then touched with an iron wire. From this Galvani concluded that the reaction must be electrical in nature, yet at the same time must derive, obviously, from some special kind of electricity, one not identical with that induced by friction.

Galvani supposed that he was dealing with a specifically animal electricity resident in the muscular tissue of the organism and released when the muscle was touched with two different kinds of metal. Of course, the fact that there existed animals which were electrically charged and which could give even human beings a powerful shock had been generally known since Redi's, Lorenzini's and John Hunter's experiments on electric fish. But this was not quite the same. Electric rays had a special electrical apparatus in their heads which enabled them to defend themselves effectively against attackers but in frogs there was nothing of this sort. To produce an electrical reaction in the frog two metals had to be used, and normally frogs did not come into contact with metal. In any event, frogs were capable of making an electric current, but this current was not in the nature of a spontaneous electrical discharge as in the remarkable Mediterranean rays.

Nevertheless, the frog experiments stimulated the scientific world. Galvani travelled all over Europe with his simple apparatus and a container of frogs to demonstrate his discovery to the general public. Although some colleagues made friendly fun of the "frogs' dancing master," on the whole his theory of "animal electricity" was accorded a warm reception. The galvanic theory seemed to explain several previously observed stimulation phenomena in animals, especially in fowls. It also fitted in well with the new theory of the irritability of muscular tissue, a theory introduced to medical science a generation before by the great Swiss physiologist Albrecht von Haller. According to Haller, the body was not exclusively governed by the brain and the vital spirit in control there, since a muscular response could still be evoked in animals whose backbones had been severed.

However, Galvani had an opponent in a fellow countryman and earlier admirer, Alessandro Volta, the physicist. Volta refused to accept the idea that electrical stimulation phenomena in the frog's leg involved any special organic properties. The organic material, he averred, only played the part of a conductor and the same result could be obtained with a substitute material. For its time this was a very bold and novel idea. From it developed the corollary notion of building the famous "pile," that is a series of materials—zinc, copper, damp paper and so on—piled in a certain order one on top of the other so as to produce an electric current. This original combination was soon technically improved on. Batteries after the voltaic model, it was discovered, could most conveniently serve as a source of that electrical force which, at least in the laboratory, could be made to produce a whole series of novel effects.

After Volta's criticism the galvanic theory of animal electricity was for a time thrown completely out of countenance, to the great regret of the physiologists and doctors. From their point of view it seemed much easier to work within the organic world with specifically organic forces than to rely on physical forces coming from without. One of the most important physiologists of the nineteenth century, Du Bois-Reymond, tried to revive the galvanic theory of the "frog current." Animal electricity, although in a different form, finally did again become part of the medical arsenal and as such performed long and yeoman service, for in practical context it is after all not so important that a theory should be absolutely inviolable.

The Force of Regeneration

A third mysterious force which astonished people of the nineteenth century and which caused frightful sufferings to be visited on helpless experimental animals was regeneration. As has so often been the case, a chance discovery provided the jumping-off point. At the beginning it was not clear whether the phenomenon of regeneration was characteristic of plants or animals. It so happened that Abraham Trembley, a natural science teacher from Geneva employed as tutor in the household of Count Bentinck, had put a few plants in a container filled with water. When he looked at the plants again he saw that the stems were covered with little green knobs which pulsed rhythmically in and out as if they had limbs or horns. At first Trembley thought they must be parasitic plants that had somehow settled there. He threw out the water and poured in fresh. Meanwhile, exposed to the air, the parasites contracted even more busily.

Trembley was puzzled. What sort of organisms could they be? Were they plants or animals? He knew that many plants lived after being cut into two, but he assumed that with animals this was impossible. To test his specimens he cut diagonally through the green heads, carefully taking note, as he did so, of the date, which was 25 November 1740. Nine days later the green things had doubled in number, a whole organism having grown again from each half. Therefore they must be plants. He observed, however, that the halved objects had moved about, which would make them animals.

To get advice, and at the same time to report his experiments, Trembley wrote to Réaumur, then the grand master of French experimental science. Even before the answer arrived Trembley himself had found the solution. He had observed that the green organisms caught tiny insects with their "arms." The case was clarified; the organisms were animal. Réaumur himself came to the same conclusion. He named the mysterious animals fresh-water polyps, because their horns, from Trembley's description, were similar to the arms that marine hydra use in seizing their prey. Encouraged, Trembley continued with his experiments. He cut up the polyps into several pieces and a whole animal grew out of each piece. When he cut pieces off their heads, they grew new heads, and when he cut the head off partially, several heads appeared, like the hydra of Greek legend. But the polyps had even stranger characteristics. Various parts could be grafted together at will. Place the head on the hinder part, even on the hind part of another individual, and in half an hour the two would grow together.

This property of regeneration in polyps created a furore in the scientific world. Zoologists seized on Trembley's discovery and hastened to test it out on other animals. The Swiss entomologist, Charles Bonnet, experimented with fresh-water worms, having no polyps at hand, and achieved the same success. If the worms were cut into two, the headless half sprouted a new head and the tail-less half a new tail. Bonnet's zeal went even beyond Trembley's He hacked worms into as many as twenty-six parts and most of them became regenerated into complete organisms. Even when regenerated animals were again cut up—Bonnet experimented six times with the same unfortunate worm—each time the parts grew into wholes. Other investigators tried their hand with other invertebrate animals. Pierre Lyonet, a lawyer who later made a name for himself with a book on caterpillars, experimented with dragon-fly pupae, and Réaumur with flatworms. In Rome Father Mazolleni busied himself with the same problem. All these people got the same astonishing result: nature was able to form a whole out of any constituent part.

The question as to how far this capacity for regeneration extended in the animal kingdom was still open. Was regeneration peculiar to the lower orders, or was it a natural force of general application? The fact that even in somewhat larger and more highly organized animals certain parts of the body grew back after being severed either by accident or surgical intervention had long been known. Regeneration, however, was often only apparent. Thevenot had observed that even though the regenerated tail of a lizard looked externally like the original tail, actually its bony structure was not identical. Réaumur had experimented with regeneration among the crustacea. When he cut off the legs of little fresh-water crabs, they grew new legs, but with salt-water crabs the experiment failed. Did fresh water, then, have something to do with regeneration? Did regeneration depend on how and where the limb was severed?

René-Antoine de Réaumur, though inclined to be rather credulous, was a man of ingenious ideas. He was called the "Pliny of the eighteenth century," and not entirely without reason. Réaumur's controversial question was submitted to Spallanzani, greatest physiologist and most skilful experimenter of the time. This professor of natural history at the University of Pavia, a man of universal learning and indisputable seriousness, had already solved many of the mysteries of generation and growth. He had, for example, been the first to succeed in artificially fertilizing frogs' eggs. Undoubtedly Spallanzani would be able to clear up the problem of regeneration. He began by cutting up earthworms and announced that, with some qualifications, he had confirmed observations previously made on aquatic worms. Then he proceeded to slice up a salamander. He tore off the salamander's legs, feet and jaws, and they all grew again, showing the same proportions they had had before being excised. Nature did not create many parts out of one part according to her whim, but restored what was missing and what belonged to the animal in question according to the Creator's plan. Nature would not be robbed or diverted from her preordained course. Every organism was preformed in the egg before birth, indeed before fertilization, which after all was only a stimulus. This form, predestined by nature, persisted until death. Regeneration was logically explained by the preformation theory. As for preformation, Father Spallanzani, like so many other scientists of his day, was absolutely convinced of it.

Yet the great mystery remained. Why did a worm's head or a salamander's foot grow again when cut off in the laboratory whereas if the same organs were severed from a dog or horse, let alone a human being, there was no regeneration? Nature simply wants things that way, and so it is and always will be. The results of Spallanzani's experiments were rather disappointing, especially for the surgeons, who had been hoping that a type of artificial regeneration useful in practical medicine might come from experiments on lower animals. But even negative results have their value.

THE FIRST FIRE-BALLOON PASSENGERS

Scientific knowledge has cost countless animals their lives. For the most part the animals have been the kind ordinarily spared by man, since they serve to provide neither food nor clothing. These experimental animals have literally died a martyr's death, for the Greek word *martys* means "witness." That they might bear witness to certain causes and effects suspected by the experimenters animals have had their limbs cut off, their spinal columns destroyed, their sight taken from them. They have been subjected to slow death by suffocation and poisoned with biting caustics, the better to observe their death agonies. One might almost say that the ones that have had their heads chopped off, to see how long reflex movements would continue thereafter, have had the best of it. With others the torments have often lasted for hours and days, even weeks, if the animals endured.

Animals have had to bear the brunt of every experiment man could think of and yet feared to try out on himself. Guillotin, the French physician, tested his guillotine on a sheep. There were less gruesome experiments, however, and the happiest of them during this intensively experimental period was carried out not in the laboratory but before the eyes of a vast crowd. It was the first flight of a hot-air balloon.

Fig. 60. "The Great Steam-duck." American imaginary
drawing of a jetplane (1841)

For thousands of years man had nursed the hope that some day he would be able to fly like the birds. Some thought this could be done by using wings, as in the Daedalus legend of the Greeks, others fancied that birds could be used as regular trans-port animals. In perfect seriousness fantastic drawings were made of aerial cars drawn by four eagles or other such feathered crea-tures. Passengers had only to sit back and steer.

Now the problem had been solved in a different way. By chemistry, rather than by physics and observations of bird flight, man had at last succeeded in constructing a machine that would bear him through the air. It was not the kind Leonardo da Vinci had visualized, which was to become a reality four hundred years after his time, but a large hollow sphere made of the lightest sort of material with fire built under it to thin the air inside and cause the sphere to rise. Surprisingly enough animals had contributed nothing to the technical solution. Even the bag of this first balloon was made of paper, rather than silk, as later became the common practice. The Montgolfier brothers, inventors of the hazardous contraption, manufactured wallpaper, and paper was closer to their hearts than silk.

Few ideas were as quickly put into effect as that of the lighter-than-air hollow body. The first "montgolfier" ascent occurred in June 1783 at Annonay, in the south of France. There were no passengers. Then, a few weeks later the experiment was repeated in Paris. All went well until the balloon came down some twenty kilometres away in open fields. At first the peasants thought the moon had plunged to the earth. After they had got over their scare, they ripped the balloon to pieces, tied the shreds to a horse's tail and had him drag them through the surrounding villages to signalize their victory. Thereupon the government issued a proclamation explaining to the people that a balloon was not an unsettling natural phenomenon but a perfectly harmless apparatus "which someday is expected to be of use in filling social need."

To find out whether life could be sustained on aerial flight, a wickerwork basket was hung from the balloon for the next ascent, and in it were placed a sheep, a hen and a duck. With these peculiar passengers on board the montgolfier took off at Versailles, 19 September 1783, with the whole court looking on. The flight was not so long as the previous one but went off without accident. After the straw fire under the bag had burned itself out, the paper balloon came down in the nearby wood of Vaucresson. The basket cage made a safe landing, and amid general rejoicing the animals, too, were found to be safe and sound. Their limbs were whole and their breathing apparatus had not been damaged by rapid movement or ascent into celestial regions.

So it had been proved that creatures who seemed unfitted for it by nature could go high up into the air without being harmed.

From now on it was only a question of courage as to whether human beings would expose themselves to the same danger that had been laid upon the animals: whether they would allow themselves to be borne aloft by means of a straw fire under a large bag of paper. Certain young aristocrats did not hesitate to take the risk and they implored the king to let them experiment. And so, two months after the sheep, the hen, and the duck, Pilâtre de Rozier and the Marquis d'Arlande made their historic balloon ascent over Paris and the following year a balloon crossed the English Channel for the first time. Still, the fame and the glory of pioneering lighter-than-air flight must go to the animals.

CONFLICT OVER VIVISECTION

The ceaseless hit-and-miss experimentation with animals understandably enough evoked some protest. Antivivisectionists came from many different camps. In part they were diehard reactionaries who considered it sinful for scientists to pry too deeply into life's mysteries. They believed science was getting out of hand when it tampered with problems that had been settled once and for all by religion. On this issue the orthodox were at one with the sceptics who even a hundred years before the great physiologist Du Bois-Reymond coined the phrase *"ignoramus ignorabimus"*—"We don't know, and we never will"—had seriously doubted that experiments on living creatures would ever lead to any notable advance in knowledge.

There were also a great many well-meaning people who rejected all forms of vivisection out of pity for the animals. They wanted no part of it—from the harmless injections to the brutal operations in which legs were cut off, bowels drawn out, the skin pulled off the living creature. In this group there were several shades of opinion. Some were out-and-out sentimentalists, others were utilitarians, who fought vivisection because they could see no immediate good from it. These people were willing to condone experiments on animals if they benefited medical science, say by testing new drugs. Yet in cold fact, the vast majority of seventeenth- and eighteenth-century experiments advanced physics and chemistry more than practical medicine.

It is true, of course, that medicine cannot forge ahead without concurrent advances in other branches of science. Even so, there is a big difference between experimentation for the sake of pure knowledge and the experiments with antitoxins carried out by Pasteur and his students. Savants of world reputation, such as Blumenbach, insisted on this distinction. Blumenbach urged that vivisections be carried out publicly in large auditoria so that as many doctors as possible could benefit from the one operation. He pointed out also that fewer animals would have to be sacrificed.

However, this arrangement was not feasible in many cases where a long series of experiments was necessary. Also, many experiments did not lend themselves to being carried out in a large auditorium. In any event, the demand for public control over vivisection attracted vigorous support. In England and several other countries the antivivisectionist movement finally succeeded in getting an official licensing system to cover all kinds of experiments using animals, with the exception of those involving mere training.

Among the arguments adduced in favour of vivisection is one that had scarcely any meaning in the humanitarian times of the last century, but which has again acquired a sad actuality since the horrors of the Nazi concentration camps—that experimenting with animals is in many ways a substitute for human experiment. At the same time the usefulness of substituting animals for humans depends on the physiological process or disease under investigation. Even in the eighteenth century scientists were inclined to be sceptical in this general respect, and Buffon's theory of the unity of all living things did little to alter their outlook. The scales did not tip the other way until Jenner had demonstrated the relationship between cowpox and smallpox. It will be remembered that Jenner's experiments led to prophylactic inoculation, a method long known in the Orient.

Being used as experimental subjects at least connoted an improvement in the animals' social position. In former times, with the exception of a few courageous doctors who tested their theories and therapies on themselves, criminals, slaves or outlawed races had taken punishment as laboratory guinea pigs. In ancient Egypt and Persia condemned prisoners were often turned over to the physicians for experimental use. This custom was often in the nature of a reward for the king's personal physician. In certain circumstances, it was a reprieve for the prisoner, too. A few such cases are known from the Middle Ages; for example, the bowman of Meudon, whose life was saved, after he had been condemned to death for murder, by handing him over to a doctor who took out one of his kidneys.

A variation on the theme of vivisection was the office of court taster, who had to sample all dishes and drinks prepared for the lords and ladies of the realm. During the Italian Renaissance, when murder by poison flourished, the profession of taster entailed painful risks. During this period many an experimental subject lost his life. Even as recently as the times of Louis XIV it was common to practise operations *"in anima vile"* or "on vile souls," before tackling more illustrious patients. In a sense, therefore, using animals for similar purposes was a sign of the general tendency to equalize the rights of man and beast, rather than of low regard for the animal world.

ANIMAL PROTECTION AND VETERINARY SCIENCE

The fight against vivisection was only the most vociferous symptom of a wider movement on behalf of animals. The humanitarian philosophy which, in the second half of the eighteenth century, had cropped up in many departments of life also benefited the animals. A feeling arose that they should be protected from brutalities, accidents and sickness. The organized movement for protection against cruelty to animals began in the first decades of the nineteenth century, though the seed had been sown one or two generations before. The wilful abuse of draught animals by teamsters and particularly the torturing of animals by children became subjects of hot debate. Teachers became interested and protection for animals was soon part of the programme of modern pedagogy. Jean-Jacques Rousseau even went so far as to preach against hunting since it hardened men to cruelty and bloodshed.

The most significant practical result of this animal-loving epoch was the training of competent veterinaries. This profession, remarkably enough, had never been legally recognized or controlled. In certain countries there were regulations for blacksmiths but treating sick animals was not considered to be a profession of its own. It had never been subject to the old guild regulations, nor had it ever required university certification. Anybody was deemed capable of going to work on an animal.

Far back in the third century B.C. the Buddhist King Asoka of India had built animal hospitals and made it obligatory for doctors to help sick animals as well as sick people. In western history such care had been unknown. Though a stall was set aside for horses with infectious diseases in the military stables, if the horse did not get well quickly he was shot. Since the sixteenth century veterinary science had made great strides and there were bulky and excellent treatises on the subject, the best being of Arab origin, but pure chance dictated whether anyone acquainted with the literature was on hand when needed. Naturally a few experts were attached to costly royal stables and others were thinly scattered throughout the army, but out in the country, even on the great estates, there was practically no one who knew anything about handling sick animals beyond applying a few rule-of-thumb remedies.

A change in this situation first came about after severe epidemics had destroyed a considerable part of the animal population of western Europe during the 1740s. The real founder of modern veterinary science was a French stablemaster, Claude Bourgelat, who started the first school for veterinaries in his home town of Lyons in 1761. Similar attempts had been made before in

Prussia, Holland and Switzerland but these did not get very far. The school in Lyons, however, quickly won international fame, and by the end of the century almost all the large European countries had special schools for the training of veterinaries.

Fig. 61. Veterinary surgeons and their remedies: syringes for enemas, apparatus for opening the mouth, etc. (copper engraving, 1701)

The term "veterinary medicine" should really be qualified. It would be more accurate to call veterinaries "doctors for domestic animals" for, with the exception of a few specialists employed at zoological gardens or at snake, crocodile, seal or ostrich farms or the like, veterinaries practise only on a dozen or so domestic animals. The horse has long been the veterinaries' prime interest, followed by animals providing meat, milk or wool, that is, horned cattle, pigs, goats and sheep. In southern countries donkeys and mules must be added to the list, and in North Africa and Asia Minor veterinaries are often called in to tend sick camels, llamas in Peru and reindeer in Finland. American poultry farms are regularly inspected by veterinaries, and rabbits, too, belong to the realm of veterinary art. In the big cities dogs and cats are the veterinaries' stock in trade.

With this the list is nearly complete. There is not therapeutic science for the vast majority of animals, not even for the most harmless ones most gladly tolerated by man. A few zoologists or private collectors may do a little, but that is about all. Veterinary science, leaving aside the treatment of animals kept for pleasure, is an auxiliary branch of animal husbandry. In this it is basically different from medicine as practised on human beings. Man bothers with sick animals only in so far as they are useful to him or if, as with dogs, they are part of his household. Yet the fact that even so much has been accomplished may be regarded as one of the greatest boons owed by the animal world to human egotism.

PART FIVE

THE MACHINE AGE

🔯 XX 🔯

Fear of Hunger

In spite of the advances made by western civilization after the Renaissance in the most varied fields of science and technology, and above all in medicine, one fact persisted as if unalterably determined by natural law—there was no substantial increase in population. About the middle of the eighteenth century the total population of Europe was not much greater than it had been at the beginning of the fourteenth century, that is, before the Black Death, in 1348, carried off a quarter, or perhaps even a third, of the people. A count of the victims of the pest ordered by Pope Clement VI gave a score of 42,836,486 dead.

The losses resulting everywhere from this frightful epidemic were made good fairly quickly but thereafter population growth slowed down. The Hundred Years' War devastated France and the Thirty Years' War did the same to Germany. Nor were there any long interludes of peace in other European countries. Wars civil or foreign everywhere hindered an increase in the population, not so much on account of losses on the battlefield as of losses from epidemic diseases and chronic hunger. Humankind became so used to these periodic decimations that they held them to be part of the divinely decreed order of the world. Some statisticians sought to prove that the number of humans must double every twenty or twenty-five years. The learned Sir William Petty even conjectured that this doubling occurred every ten years, and by means of ingenious calculations demonstrated the rhythm of increase in world population since the time of the original eight people who came safely ashore from Noah's Ark. But speculations of this sort obviously had little to do with reality. Actually there seemed to be strict, fixed limits to the growth of humanity.

In the second half of the eighteenth century, when so many traditional "laws" went by the board, this one, too, began to waver. As the epidemics waned, the population of several countries began to increase at an unprecedented rate. This sudden spurt was most apparent in England. There, despite severe wars, in a space of fifty years the number of inhabitants had increased by half. At the same time the masses became even poorer, which appeared to lend support to the maxim that in this world man is born to sorrow. The poor, who were now crowding into the cities, might work for a time in the factories and earn a pittance and when they could toil no longer they might eke out their respite by vegetating in blank misery as charges of the state. Yet sheer physical degradation and disease made it a certainty that their pangs would not last forever. Such was the prevailing opinion.

MALTHUSIANISM

In 1798, the year in which Jenner published his epochal work on inoculation for smallpox, another thin book came out in London, showing the dangers of over-population. The author, who for a time remained anonymous, was a completely unknown country pastor called Thomas Robert Malthus. His basic thought was by no means new. Of the great political economists of the seventeenth and eighteenth centuries there was hardly one who had not declared that human beings, like all other creatures, tend to propagate to the very limit of the available food supply, but until Malthus no one had ever expressed the idea so pointedly. He translated the so-called law of human economy into arithmetical terms and brought it into a biological frame of reference. At best, Malthus said, the food supply increases in arithmetical progression—1, 2, 3, 4, etc.—whereas sexual drive and reproductive apparatus make it possible for human beings to increase in geometrical progression—2, 4, 8, 16, etc.

Such is the human dilemma, Malthus averred, and the most grandiose laws in favour of the poor cannot resolve it. Nor, on the other hand, can the problem be solved by creating a larger food supply, since more food would only result in further increases in the population. The only way out, according to Malthus, is to adjust population to the food supply. In the first edition of his book Malthus contented himself with the painful conclusion that only suffering and vice could bring about equilibrium, but after getting deeper into the problem, he counselled his fellows to practise "moral restraint," that is sexual continence. "If we could persuade the hare to go to sleep," he said, "then the tortoise might have a chance to overtake him."

The marked sexual tone which Malthus gave his theory, albeit in a perfectly proper way, was undoubtedly the main reason why a truism suddenly became a sensation. In Malthus's formulation, the population problem ceased to be a matter for discussion behind closed doors by statesmen and specialists and became everybody's concern. Every enlightened human being had the right, indeed, the moral obligation, to contribute something to the solution of the over-population problem by inhibiting his lusts.

Although the Malthusian theory, like all theories concerned with sex, at first evoked a storm of protest among the general public, it soon became part of the credo of political science. Even in prosperous circles least affected by population pressure—Malthus preached continence only for the poor—his advice was sympathetically received. He was made a professor, with a handsome salary, in a school where the East Indian Company trained its officials. The French Academy of Moral and Political Sciences and the Prussian Academy of Sciences named Malthus a corresponding member, and in England the name of Malthus was ranked among the mental giants of history.

Indeed, many saw a new Descartes in Malthus, one who had

determined the bounds between man and the animals in a much
more plastic way than his French predecessor. Apparently it was
in the sexual sphere, where man's animality had been thought
most pronounced, that the difference showed up most clearly.
For, according to Malthus, the reproductive process in animals
is governed by instinct. Animals propagate automatically, like
machines, but human beings, thanks to their higher intelligence,
can curb life's primitive forces and thus escape the punishment
which nature visits upon all creatures who carry sex and reproduction to extremes. In contrast to the neo-Malthusians, who
recommend a non-ascetic birth control independent of the human
will, Malthus himself classed sexuality and reproduction together
and held that it was immoral, in practice even criminal, to separate the two functions.

Essentially the Malthusian doctrine was as monkish as anything from the Middle Ages. Nature punished mankind for its
concupiscence with misery and hunger and conversely rewarded
the chaste. However, this ascetic theory was presented in such a
logical way that at first sight it looked like an economic cure-all.
Bring fewer children into the world and there would be no more
hunger. The poorest would have all they needed to eat. The entre-
preneur class agreed heartily with Malthus, though they realized
it included the possibility of a short labour supply in the more
or less distant future, which would cause a rise in wages. At all
events, this alternative seemed preferable to the costly English
poor laws, and even more preferable to such hunger riots as had
been characteristic of the French Revolution.

POTENCY AND FERTILITY

The natural scientists, too, were pretty much in agreement with
Malthus. Certainly in the history of America and other new countries there were some examples of a marked increase in the food
supply such as the offspring of the pigs which Columbus had
transplanted on Santo Domingo. But on the whole the theory

WARE CONTRAFECTVR EINES LAMPELS MIT
Dreÿen Leibern und einem Kopff So im versch:
inen Monat Julÿ dieſzes 1620 Jahrs Zue Claußenburg
in Hungarn von einem Schaff allſo geſtaltet geш.
orffen und uon Furnehmen herrn geſehen·
Worden.

Fig. 62. Three sheep with one head (engraving of the seventeenth
century)

265

that there was neither enough food, as a rule, to meet current need nor enough living space, in the physical sense, to permit the human race to expand seemed to be confirmed.

The newer microbiology had lately furnished proof of this by opposing potential and effective increase. It is true that the decisive obstacle does not lie primarily in the discrepancy between physiological reproductiveness and potential food supply for the newly born as in what, from the human economic standpoint, is the tremendous wastefulness of the fertilization process. The male and female germ cells, in a quantitative sense, are utterly out of proportion. The vast majority of the male gametes must die without contributing anything to the preservation of the species.

A female herring spawns something like 40,000 eggs, a turbot 9 million and a salmon 28 million, yet of these only a small portion are ever actually fertilized. The number of eggs spawned by an American oyster varies between 15 million and 150 million, and an oyster can spawn this number of potential offspring five times annually. During the three years of her prime a queen bee lays 5 million eggs. A frog spawns 6,000 eggs a year and theoretically can generate 54 thousand million frogs in three years. Actual observation shows, however, that the frog population, even where the terrain favours its increase, remains stable.

The discrepancy between potency and actual fertilization is greatest on the human level, with the difference that here, as is the case with all higher animals, the male sperm is the mass product. A normal discharge of semen—and during his lifetime a healthy man has several thousand discharges—contains more than 200 million spermatozoa. Therefore one male individual, if every one of his sperm encountered a receptive ovum, could produce progeny a thousand times more numerous than the present world population. The limiting factor is the female's ability to conceive. During her sexual maturity a woman produces only a few hundred ova. Since additional fertilizations during pregnancy are extremely rare, eighteen to twenty conceptions are the general physiological maximum. Only a single sperm out of hundreds of millions is actually involved in the reproductive process. The remainder never come to perform their physiological function. It is the same in those animals which man uses as food.

Compared with these purely physiological losses the discrepancy that Malthus tried to illustrate by the difference between an arithmetical and a geometrical progression seemed trivial. Biological propagation is marked by a tremendous waste of reproductive material. Modern animal-breeding programmes try to attack the food supply problem from this angle and endeavour to correct in some degree nature's irrationalities in the process of reproduction.

THE ART OF CROSSBREEDING

Malthus's contemporaries were mainly concerned with the problem of space, of land enough for pasturage and agriculture so that man could have more to eat. Malthus himself firmly believed that there was no permanent solution, indeed not even a provisional one good for a few generations. On the other hand the solution he recommended, that is, a voluntary adjustment of reproduction to available food-producing areas, proved to be unworkable. The poor people whom his theory was supposed to benefit simply paid no heed. They may not have been particularly anxious to have large families but their sexual drive was too powerful to be inhibited by poverty.

The alternative was to make better use of available food-producing facilities. There were various ways of going about this, the easiest being, it would seem, to have people migrate to thinly settled countries. Three-quarters of the habitable earth's surface was undeveloped, or so William Godwin, English champion of land reform, had reported at the end of the eighteenth century. The Irish, most bitterly plagued by hunger, migrated in droves to America, but despite material pressures the English workers were reluctant to leave job and country. This was a lucky thing for England, since a dense population was needed to tend the machines and help consume their products. Godwin himself had maintained that even in England everybody could have enough to eat if the land was worked more efficiently and the distribution of food more fairly regulated.

The technical possibilities of better land yield had already been tested. At about the same time that English machinery manufacturers were revolutionizing the industrial world, a few English farmers were also introducing revolutionary changes into their own sphere. The pioneers in improved farming methods were two owners of large estates in Great Britain. Thomas Coke, who in 1837 was made Earl of Leicester, improved farm practice to a point where the yields from his land increased tenfold. Robert Blakewell became the founder of modern animal breeding. He created the New Leicester sheep and the longhorned Dishley cattle. He crossbred horses until he got a sturdy farm horse ideally suited for work in the fields. He experimented with grasses and sowed his improved grains on new land so that his livestock might have the best of fodder. As a result his beef cattle doubled in weight and his sheep tripled.

The work accomplished by these two pioneers attracted a following. Even while outsiders were marvelling at the towering chimneys of English factories and the gearwork of their machines —innovations which gave the impression that England had become solely an industrial country—English agriculture was in fact experiencing an unprecedented upswing. Even as late as the beginning of the 1840s the land was producing enough grain to supply the country, though the population was then three times as great as it had been a century before. This was striking proof that Malthus must be wrong. English cattle were rated the best in the world. As it turned out, however, the urban population grew so rapidly that even the most highly rationalized agriculture could not keep pace. Farm prices, supported by protective tariffs, were high. The factory owners pressed for the free entry of foreign food products and the release of farm workers from the land.

A new division of labour was indispensable, since it was impossible in such small space to build up the greatest industrial plant in the world and at the same time supply enough food for the working class from domestic sources alone. The factories turned out clothes, but nothing to eat. That was the dilemma, and it did not arise from sex-induced over-population as predicted by Malthus.

The Settlement of the Pampas

In some instances animals, rather than human beings, were the emigrants. A selected number of the best English breeding cattle was shipped across the sea to Argentina, Australia and the still completely unsettled islands of New Zealand. Australian sheep, however, are of Spanish origin. The parent stock consisted of the twelve ewes and a ram imported in 1801 by Captain MacArthur from South Africa, where merinos had been introduced a generation before by Colonel Gordon, a Scot in the service of the Dutch. In Argentina, on the other hand, English breeds of sheep dominated. English breeds of beef cattle were also most in demand everywhere throughout the southern hemisphere. In Argentine history the arrival of the English Lincoln sheep in 1840 and that of the first Shorthorn bulls in 1848 are celebrated as important historic dates.

In lands washed by the south Pacific English settlers reared livestock much as they had done at home, but in the pampas the experiment was not so safe. A nomadic herdsmen folk, the Gauchos, had arisen on the plain of La Plata in the eighteenth century from a mixture of Spanish Creoles and Indians. In some respects these Gauchos resembled the Asiatic horsemen of the Middle Ages. Culturally, at any rate, they were not much more advanced, but were extremely individualistic and so harder to organize. They were theatrical in their gestures, aggressive and expansionistic. For several decades politicos of Gaucho extraction sat in the driver's seat in Buenos Aires and used their political power to commit all manner of violence. In South America the

name of the super-Gaucho, Juan Manuel de Rosas, has the same
dread aura as that of Genghis Khan in Europe.

Yet it was under the infamous régime of the *caudillo*, Rosas,
that English beef cattle were introduced into Argentina. It
seemed extremely doubtful that an orderly, modern form of animal husbandry could ever develop there. Looking back on history's course as it unfolded in this lower South American region,
one might almost say that here animals formed man rather than
the reverse. In time the romantic, gypsy-like Gaucho type virtually disappeared. A few untameable elements retreated with
their herds into the mountains. English cattle became dominant
on the pampas and the Gauchos adapted them with exemplary
care. The owners of the great Argentine estates bred livestock
with the same sporting zeal as the English landlords, and with
even more commercial acumen.

On the *estancias*, the ranches of the pampas, the descendants
of the English breeding stock increased by tens of thousands.
Towards the end of the nineteenth century there were five million
people in Argentina, as against twenty million beef cattle and
eighty million sheep. The vast majority of this livestock stemmed
from the English counties of Durham, Hereford, Lincolnshire,
Hampshire, and so on. The human population had likewise multiplied quickly in this new Garden of Eden, but by no means as
impetuously as Malthus had prophesied. Indeed, there was a
huge surplus of meat for export.

FROZEN MEAT

For several decades the progeny of the four-legged immigrants
made the return trip to the land of their forefathers jammed together in narrow ships' holds and, once home in England, suffered
the slaughterhouse fate decreed by their human masters. Transportation costs were high, however, and a more efficient method
of shipment was badly needed. The Argentinians dried and salted
meat and shipped it across the equator as far away as Cuba; but

Europeans did not take kindly to this primitive way of conserving food.

A more rational process resulted from Liebig's physiological investigations. He was far ahead of his time in stressing reduction in weight. Shipping carcass meat, Liebig pointed out, meant shipping water; but the nutriment and even the taste of meat could be retained if it were dehydrated and kept in cans. Liebig's meat extract proved to be a partial solution for the Argentine livestock industry at a time when the export market was critically threatened. Yet it was not the final answer. Europeans wanted meat that looked like the real article. They simply did not take to powdered extracts, even though they were just as nourishing and recommended by doctors. Meanwhile the canning industry had been experimenting along other lines. Meat was conserved first in glass, then in iron containers and finally in tins made of zinc. Yet none of these processes proved to be satisfactory for the shipment of big quantities on long sea voyages through the tropics.

The real problem was to find a way of eliminating heat. To keep the meat fresh it had to be frozen and kept frozen no matter how hot the weather. Since the beginning of the nineteenth century refrigeration technique had been in the process of theoretical development in France and on a practical basis in the United States. Still it was one thing to transport frozen meat by rail from Chicago to New York, and another to carry it unrotted across equatorial seas. A rich Australian, Thomas S. Mort, sank his whole fortune into developing a freezer in Sydney. He had ice-making machines brought from the United States to equip a freezing plant there but, just as he was on the point of sending his first shipment of frozen meat to England, a French engineer, Charles Tellier, beat him to it.

In 1877 the first refrigerated steamship was sent from Rouen to Buenos Aires and after a round trip lasting a hundred days returned with a well-preserved cargo of frozen Argentinian beef.

This was a great event in the business of supplying food to industrial countries. Once the Frenchman had shown it could be done, refrigeration technique was rapidly improved. While the Tellier process kept the meat only one or two degrees below freezing point another method was soon devised to freeze the meat solid. The first freezer factories were built in Argentina and Australia at the beginning of the eighties. Soon there was a whole fleet of special vessels for the transport of frozen blocks of meat.

Although the Prince of Wales tried Australian frozen meat and gave it an enthusiastic recommendation, other connoisseurs of good food were more reluctant to praise. In normal times frozen meat was eaten mostly by the poorer class. Even so, the new process made it possible, especially in England, to provide millions of people with a better diet. The endless debates in the British Parliament on what could be done about the meat scarcity came to an end. Certainly no absolute solution had been found for a social problem that had troubled political economists and humanitarians since the beginning of the machine age, yet the machine itself had at least done something towards easing the lot of the poor.

Horsepower

AFTER James Watt had built his steam engine, he wanted to find out how much work his machine could accomplish. The most impressive way of measuring work done was by comparing the engine's output with that of a horse. Physiological experiments revealed that a horse could work constantly at the rate of 22,000 foot-pounds per minute. This figure was arbitrarily increased to 33,000 foot-pounds per minute and called a "horsepower."

When the French introduced the metric system they corrected the power unit by scaling it down a little. Henceforth on the Continent a *"cheval-vapeur"* or *"force de cheval"* was understood as equivalent to the energy necessary to lift seventy-five kilogrammes one metre in one second. The English, however, continued to use the older definition. As a result, two systems of reckoning, differing by almost 1.5 per cent, have been in use thoroughout the world ever since.

The horsepower was an honourable memorial that the masters of steam dedicated to the animal kingdom. Many thought it would be a sort of tombstone for the horse, but such thoughts were rather premature. For half a century the steam engine actually had little adverse effect on the animal world.

Wheels were soon turning by steam power in hundreds of factories, but James Watts's machine replaced only human workers, not horses, oxen, donkeys and camels.

An early attempt in 1770 by Cugnot to use steam as a source of tractive power did not get very far. His colossal steammobile, which had wheels as high as a man and a body longer than a modern locomotive—Cugnot had designed it to haul cannon—

Fig. 63. A caricature of new machinery: a "beardshaving mill" shaving
a dozen men at the same time (about 1754)

evoked wonderment in Versailles but little else. Since Cugnot's
machine could go at only about two and a half miles an hour, the
experiment was abandoned. Then along came the montgolfier and
overshadowed all other technical novelties in France. The marvellous ascents of the hot-air balloons made such laboriously contrived land vehicles seem almost old-fashioned.

POST-COACH AND RAILWAY

The English were more persistent and had a more practical
bent. Yet in England, too, a generation passed before anything
usable developed from experiments with steam locomotives.

Meanwhile intensive industrialization had made the transport question critical. The highways connecting the large cities were clogged by horse-drawn vehicles. Accidents were almost as common as they are today in the automobile age. Then, too, the military needs of the Napoleonic wars were an extraordinary drain on the supply of draught horses. All in all the times were ripe for a basic change in the transportation field.

It has been said with some justice that the invention of the railway was more an organizational than a technical innovation. Both the steam train and tracks to run it on were already in existence. All that needed to be done was bring the two together. Trains of horse-drawn trucks running on rails had been in use in English mines since the seventeenth century. At the beginning of the nineteenth century horses had been replaced by a locomotive in a Welsh coal mine, though in fact the engine moved so slowly it could be used only for hauling material.

Stephenson's innovation a quarter of a century later consisted primarily in building a faster version of the already existing loco-

Fig. 64. An engine patented in England 1829; it was meant to be driven by one harnessed horse

motive. Actually Stephenson's machine did not at first offer much greater speeds than conventional means of transport. The first passenger line was built in 1830 and ran between Liverpool and Manchester. The locomotive could go at about 15 m.p.h. In 1814 French post-coaches were regularly averaging 8¾ m.p.h. over much longer distances and expresses went twice as fast. As early as 1750 an English sportsman, the Duke of Queensberry, set up a record of nearly 19 m.p.h. using four racehorses hitched to a vehicle weighing only 330 pounds. The duke drove these horses at a steady trot over the highway. In any event, it was held that the "steam horse" could never keep up with a fast rider on horseback. A year after the first railway line was dedicated, a famous gentleman rider by the name of Osbaldeston made a bet of a thousand guineas that he could cover two hundred miles in ten hours. Using twenty-eight different horses he galloped the course in eight hours and forty-two minutes, averaging over 23 m.p.h.

Not everybody, of course, was able to make such fast time, but by frequent and rapid change of horses even the regular postal service was speeded up to a point where a letter could be brought from Lyons to Paris in two days, a feat at one time considered impossible. The steam railways developed in giant strides, however. Soon there were trains that could travel at over 25 m.p.h., a speed approaching that of bird flight. Certainly no four-footed animal could any longer compete.

The horse's first reaction to his iron competitor was psychological: when he saw a locomotive he shied. The many accidents, however, may have been due more often to the driver's or rider's fright and awkwardness than to the horse's nervousness. Had not such an intelligent man as Thiers, historian and French Minister of State, solemnly predicted a quick end to railways, since the mere sight of machines travelling at such unheard-of speeds would drive people out of their minds? Thiers's prophecy was not quite so absurd as it came to sound later on. For several decades the business of horses rearing up at the sight of a train, and the complications resulting therefrom, provided an inexhaustible theme for humorous publications.

The railways' effect on the number of horses was less spectacular. Although after the middle of the nineteenth century coach horses were used less and less in the most technically advanced countries as a means of overland transport, the horse, both as a riding and a draught animal, long continued to rule urban communications, and this alone sufficed to ensure his continued existence. There was no sudden decline in the equine population, as there was later after the appearance of electric trams and motorcars. In fact, the number of horses actually increased in spite of the railways. The new horse-raising countries, such as Argentina, had to help to cover the European demand.

The Patriarchs of the Thoroughbred

Although the horse lost a good deal of his importance as a draught animal he lost none of his glamour otherwise. Indeed, as time went on the horse went up in social estimate. It was almost as if man did not want to admit that mechanical wheels were faster than horses' legs. At just about the time that railway tracks were encircling the globe, a real passion for horse racing sprang up all over the world, and most violently in England, birthplace of steam trains.

Horse racing is a very old sport. Some historians maintain that horses were raced in Britain even before Roman soldiers crossed the Channel. History records that Englishmen under Henry II in the twelfth century were amused by horse racing, at a time when such doings were still regarded as unchivalrous on the Continent. Yet the actual birth certificate of English horse racing is from an ordinance passed by the city council of Chester in 1511, permitting races to be held annually. Until the seventeenth century, however, racing was an artistocratic sport, a court diversion. Those wealthy members of the middle classes who tried to keep up with court society also laid stress on avoiding anything that smacked of money or business. In this respect the English were even more conservative than the Greeks of heroic times. Winners were awarded gold or silver cups or salvers. Those who took part in the races were obliged by custom to furnish the next year's prizes.

It is interesting to note that horse racing became a popular sport in England at the same time that bullfighting became a mass entertainment in Spain. Up to the first half of the nineteenth century horse racing in England, like the *corridas* in Spain, remained a markedly national sport that failed to catch on in other countries. As in the case of bullfighting, horse racing, with more or less justification, likewise provided an excuse for improvements in breeding. Sporting contests, it was claimed, would make for finer animals.

But nature did not equip either country, England or Spain, as well for this breeding as the sporting people would have wished. As a result animals were imported to satisfy the demands of racing or exhibition and came to out-rank domestic strains. In both Spain and England it was the near east that supplied the west's deficiency. Like the best Spanish fighting bulls, the outstanding English race horses came from the Mohammedan world. The foreign strain in race horses came to be even more pronounced than in the bulls. The immigration took place in more recent times, and Englishmen were shrewd enough to make no bones about the fact that their long-legged racers were of eastern origin.

The three great thoroughbreds who founded English horse racing had western names but their eastern origins are definitely known. The most illustrious of these three patriarchs was the Arabian stallion Darley, who sired the even more famous stallion Eclipse, wonder horse of the eighteenth century. During the twenty-three years of his glorious career Eclipse won twenty-six important races, and took the much-coveted Silver Cup eleven times. Indeed, Eclipse was never beaten. An even more enduring monument to his memory is the fact that among his children and grandchildren there were 344 successful racers, who, all told, brought their owners some £158,000.

Village circus, about 1820

"Dancing Bear," lithograph by Otto Speckter

Gottlieb Daimler

James Watt

The victors over horses

Besides the progeny of the Arab Darley, who started the Eclipse line, there were the Matchem and Herod lines, which cut a more modest, though still very impressive, figure. The Matchem line was originally sired by the Berber Godolphin, who was discovered by Coke, the breeder, drawing a watercart in Paris. The third horse of this famous trio was a Turkish stallion named

Fig. 65. Patent "Impulsoria" (1850), one of the last attempts to prevent the replacement of horse power by steam power

Byerly, who served in the army in Ireland before siring a whole series of famous race horses, among whom the stallion Herod shines with especial brightness in turf annals. A grandson, the brave Diomed, was winner of the first Derby. Modern research has disclosed that Herod left his descendants an unpleasant legacy in that they frequently suffer from nose bleeds. However, this weakness has not impaired their success at racing.

HORSE RACING AND BETTING

While these immortals of the turf were doing their famous deeds, their human owners and admirers were creating the institutions which have given English horse racing a world-wide reputation. The Jockey Club was founded in London in about

1750 and became the model of countless imitations which, in other countries, served social and political as well as racing interests. Thirty years later the twelfth Earl of Derby, in the little county town of Epsom, started the race that bears his name. Thereafter the fame of Newmarket, long the turf centre of England, was somewhat dimmed.

Fig. 66. The defeat of the horses is complete: mechanical tramway disguised as horse carriage

The old aristocracy's interest in horse racing moved the newly rich to emulation. Owning a racing stable came to be thought of as a sign of social rank and high ambition, if not as an outright privilege. Military considerations moved the young Bonaparte to imitate the English example. When his brother Lucien, then Minister of the Interior, proposed to revive the Olympic Games in. antique costume in celebration of the Fourteenth of July, the new monarch replied in a letter: "Chariot racing may have been all right in Greece where they were attacking each other from chariots, but with us it means nothing." The fraternal argument ended in a compromise. Chariot races were held but the drivers wore modern English jockey costumes. Napoleon himself was all for horse racing and offered prizes for the best French studs. Under the old régime there had not been much racing and for that little English horses had been used. In a sense Napoleon may be considered as the founder of the modern turf sport on the Continent.

After the fall of the empire, French racing went into a decline. Not until the "dandy" period in the 1830s was the sport revived. The first horse races in Germany were held during this same period. By the middle of the century there was hardly a country without its own stud farms, race tracks and regular racing seasons. The race became the great social event. Under Napoleon III the new track at Longchamp was the meeting place for European high society. Oddly enough, it was the railway companies that backed the Grand Prix at Longchamp, biggest money race on the Continent. The Duc de Morny, the emperor's stepbrother, was the great French patron of the turf. In west European countries, as in ancient Byzantium, no sport was enjoyed more than horse racing by aristocracy and masses alike.

It was not the public's desire to be entertained, still less any interest in breeding fine horses, that made racing so popular. The associations that organize races may claim as much as they like that their only purpose is to improve the quality of the equine race. Everybody knows that horse races are an excuse for betting. Throughout the world the totalisator is the little man's stock exchange. All the bettor needs is a little stake to try his luck and to have the heady pleasure of imagining himself engaging in speculations based on deeply grounded information, but in fact most bettors have never seen the horses on which they place their bets, nor have they the least inkling of their real racing abilities. A comprehensive technical literature filling whole pages of the daily newspapers takes the place of first-hand knowledge. The telegraph makes it possible to bet on foreign races. Millions of pounds are wagered all over the world on the Derby at Epsom and the Grand Prix at Longchamp.

Betting on the races was democratized during the nineteenth century. Prior to this racing had been a sport largely limited to the rich and great; betting stakes had been very high, but the number of bettors small. The custom in English clubs of wagering between two gentlemen in time developed into a system of group betting. If enough bettors took part, each gambling on a different horse, one of the group took over the responsibility of keeping books to divide the winnings according to the proper ratio. In the clubs the post of "bookmaker" had honorific significance. Outside the clubs, however, bookmaking became a profession held in low regard. When some public bookmakers became very rich —in Paris many of them earned more than a million gold francs a year—society began to see them as respectable people who carried on their betting business with all the dignity and dependability of a banker.

Horse racing in England for some time continued to be characterized by certain social rituals. The Derby was long considered by high society to be a sporting event for gentlemen alone. Two days after the race at Epsom the ladies attended another race called the Oaks, founded concurrently with the Derby by the Earl of Derby, and named after his estate, "The Oaks." It was not considered good form for the female turf fans to bet money on the horses: instead they wagered dozens of pairs of gloves, though eventually this affectation went out of fashion. In time betting became big business, with a turnover no horse market could hope to match. Bets could be made on the Derby a year in advance, and hundreds of thousands of people found pleasure in speculating on this or that horse's odds.

The newer sports, especially soccer, have drawn away part of the racing crowd, while at the same time developing a betting complex of their own. Moreover, in England, at least, the dogs

offer the horses strong competition. In dog racing trained greyhounds or whippets chase an "electric hare," a mechanically
driven contraption that sweeps round the inside of the track. In
late years the sport of dog racing has grown to such proportions
that the English Parliament, in the interest of the national econ-

Fig. 67. The superseded cart horses are compelled to earn their living
in this melancholy way (caricature of 1834)

omy, has set legal limits to the number of tracks authorised. In
London alone there are fifteen miniature courses, and throughout
England fifteen million bets are made annually on the dogs. A
highly specialized twenty-four page newspaper keeps the fans
posted on the races and supplies technical information.

CIRCUS AND ZOO

The dangerous and virtuoso sport of the animal circus developed parallel to the relatively harmless sports in which animals
race against each other. Here, too, the tradition is a thousand
years old. Even during the Middle Ages circuses did not die out
altogether, though animal shows in the modern sense date back
only to the seventeenth century. The new equestrian art that had
been tried out in Italy was exaggerated into the acrobatic and
performances were held for the lower classes at the annual fairs.
At about the same time, too, trick riding with two or three horses
came into fashion. The supreme master in this line was Sergeant
Philip Astley, who delighted eighteenth-century audiences by
riding a trotting horse standing on his head on the saddle. Astley
started the first indoor circus, which had both a ring and a stage.

During the first half of the nineteenth century all kinds of stage
spectacles were combined in curious ways. In one of Spontini's
operas an elephant was led on to the stage. Practically any his-
torical-romantic opera worth seeing had to have a scene in which
a pair of horses performed on the stage. Even though stage animals were mostly used only as props in theatres, in shows given
in the arenas they took the leading role. *The St. Petersburg
Courier, Mazeppa* and *The Wild Horse* were circus revues that
no visitors to London dared to miss. Even Shakespeare's *Richard
III* was made into a circus production with equestrian scenes.
Lions, tigers and elephants were gallery attractions but the real
connoisseur of the circus was interested in trained horse acts.

The third kind of modern animal exhibit, the zoological garden,
cloaked itself in science, and this was what made it different from
the old-fashioned menagerie. From their inception zoos have operated under the direction of prominent zoologists. To secure financial backing for their superior purposes these people character-
istically promised more than they could perform. They claimed
that what they wanted to do was to acclimatize strange animals
by means of careful superintendence, much as sponsors of horse

racing professed to be mainly interested in breeding better horses. The Jardin d'Acclimatation in Paris advertises this alleged pro- gramme in its very name. There the French zoologist Daubenton hoped to make the zebra adapt itself to European habitat. If he were successful, a new draught and pack animal would be avail- able, one "stronger than the donkey and, even when naked, more beautiful than the most splendidly bridled horse." But Daubenton's efforts to tame the zebra were in the long run no more suc- cessful than Saint-Hilaire's attempts to domesticate the Asiatic wild ass.

Though zoological gardens may not have contributed much to the domestication of new species, nevertheless there can be no doubt they have contributed much to further natural history edu- cation and still more to the pleasure of millions of spectators. Not so long ago a sensible move was made to please the crowd when the Bronx Zoo in New York, largest in the world, staged open-air acts by the animals at certain hours of the day.

It must not be forgotten that a zoological garden, even though the bars, wherever possible, are replaced by less visible means of enclosure, is still a prison. At first they were death houses for their inmates. Even to acclimatize single specimens a great deal of experience is needed, and this first experience had to be gained the hard way. On the whole the mortality rate in newly opened zoos has been enormously high. The following is a mortality list of birds kept in a recently erected South American zoo: seven out of eight specimens of *Arantinga jandaia* died in the first month, and the eighth forty-four days later; two *Pyrrhura cruentada* lasted about the same length of time; five specimens of *Tyto alba sindara* were dead in eleven days.

Death in the zoo, moreover, is merely the second act in a tragic sequence, for many animals perish while being hunted, trapped or shipped. Of course, in this connection it might be pointed out that the high prices paid by zoological gardens for live animals have been instrumental in saving many lives, since under ordinary conditions the hunter would simply shoot down the quarry to get

Fig. 68. Heraldic menagerie. Political animal caricature, about the
middle of the nineteenth century, by Grandville

skin or horns for a trophy. Such great collecting expeditions as those organized by Hagenbeck in Africa and Asia have indubitably enriched zoological science.

Perhaps the most notable event in Hagenbeck's commercial collecting experience was the capture of specimens of the last wild horses. At about the turn of this century Karl Hagenbeck, a Hamburg animal dealer world-famed for his travelling animal shows and sideshows featuring natives from the wilds—for they were all the same to him, exotic animals or exotic people—organized an expedition to the Gobi desert to attempt to bring back some of the wild horses that roamed this area. Two decades before, the Russian explorer, Nikolai Mikhailovitch Prjevalsky, had reported the existence of real wild horses in western Mongolia, dark ponies with broad heads and slanting eyes apparently not unlike the horses ridden by the hordes of Genghis Khan. The discovery of this hitherto completely unknown animal had evoked great interest among zoologists and others. *Equus prjevalsky* might or might not be the lineal ancestor of the modern horse but in any case he was a living anachronism out of prehistory.

So Hagenbeck set about capturing some specimens of this witness from the past. Hagenbeck was one of the great merchant princes of his day and anything he did was in the grand manner. A few years before, in 1897, he had appeared at the Chicago World's Fair with an exhibit of one thousand animals. Now he commandeered two thousand Kirghiz tribesmen to help him get hold of some of these shy, fleet wild horses of Asia. The animals lived in small herds under the leadership of a stallion who galloped off with his companions in his wake at the first sign of danger. Hagenbeck's army, however, succeeded in catching thirty-two specimens, enough to supply all the large zoological gardens in the world.

The young horses from the steppes got accustomed to life in captivity in an amazingly short time. Soon they were following their keepers about as submissively as dogs. To everybody's satisfaction, they propagated industriously. They fitted in so well, however, that they lost some of their original glamour, for every-body had rather expected animals so exotic to have peculiar habits. For a brief interval they were a sensation, thanks less to their appearance than to their prehistoric past and Hagenbeck promotion. Thereafter these unpretentious Mongols became lost among the shadows along with the rest of the commonplace animals and were replaced as stars of the zoo by the Ethiopian giraffe and the Tibetan panda.

🔲 XXII 🔲

The Darwinian Revolution

AT JUST about the time that the new technical inventions were widening the gap between human beings and animals, when even the most useful animals were losing their utility and becoming mere playthings and curiosities, zoological science came to the rescue and connected man and animal through a common genealogy. Though there may be some justification for thinking of Darwin's *Origin of Species*, which appeared in 1859, as a turning point in the history of ideas, it must not be imagined that Darwin was the first to create or formulate or even bring into circulation the modern idea of evolution.

By the middle of the nineteenth century no open-minded natural scientist any longer seriously believed that the earth, with all its appurtenances, vegetable and animal, had always looked as it did in modern times. The earth's crust and all living things on it were in constant movement and change. Even in liberal arts circles the evolutionary idea had long since been familiar and no one had formulated the concept more clearly than Hegel, the most influential thinker of his epoch. The evolution of the physical world, in his opinion, was not as creative as that of the spiritual. Yet physical evolution, he said, is a fact, a natural necessity in the deepest sense.

"Development, however, is also a property of organic objects," Hegel wrote. "Their existence presents itself, not as an exclusively dependent one, subjected to external changes, but as one which expands itself in virtue of an internal, unchangeable principle; a simple essence—whose existence, that is, as a germ, is primarily simple—but which subsequently develops a variety of parts that become involved with other objects, and consequently live through a continuous process of changes—a process, nevertheless, that results in the very opposite of change, and is even transformed into a *vis conservatrix* of the organic principle, and the form embodying it."

Fig. 69. "A Runaway War-horse" by Adolph von Menzel (1840)

Hegel saw change in nature as cyclical and thus "evolution," for him, was pretty much confined to the development of the individual. However, Hegel's followers made this developmental principle apply to the species. As early as 1819 the zoologist Oken made an attempt to describe the human skeleton in terms of development from animal forms. It may be that the Hegelian philosophy, sliding off as it does into the purely speculative, increasingly discredited the evolutionary idea among naturalists. At the same time, when August Weismann, thinking to honour his teacher, Charles Darwin, said in effect that the evolutionary idea had been forgotten after 1830 until Darwin's advent, he was grossly exaggerating. All along the concept was alive and working in people's minds. Yet there was no plausible explanation to show why and how evolution had followed the pattern suggested by the findings of comparative anatomy, physiology and—above all—the new science of palaeontology.

SCHOPENHAUER'S THEORY OF DESCENT

The fact that the biogenetic principle, as originally formulated by J. F. Meckel and later reaffirmed by Haeckel, came to be widely recognized among zoologists in itself argues against the supposition that all belief in evolution, except in so far as it had been kept alive by Darwin, had died out in the last decades before the appearance of the *Origin of Species*. The biogenetic principle, which states that the embryonic development of the individual recapitulates the evolution of the species in question, would make no sense if the evolution of the species were not taken for granted. In any case, the development of the foetus itself showed the evolutionary sequence that Darwin attempted to reconstruct in another way.

The question of how the transition from one species to another had come about was hotly argued. All sorts of intricate theories were advanced. Harvey's old theory of *generatio aequivoca*—that procreation can result only in offspring like the parents—was countered by another theory claiming that offspring can differ specifically from the parents. According to this view, nature can make saltations in a single generation not only engendering the small changes that later became known as "mutations" but radical transformations as well, thus giving rise to entirely new species.

This bold, though quite unsupported, theory was most strongly championed in work published anonymously by the English geologist, Robert Chambers, which created quite a stir. On the Continent the most fertile and daring philosophical mind of the period, Arthur Schopenhauer, seized on the idea and developed it into a fantastic yet closely argued theory of evolution. A few months after the publication of Darwin's chief work Schopenhauer wrote:

"Why should not each new and higher species have originated by virtue of the foetus form having suddenly advanced one step above the form of the mother bearing it? It is the only rational, that is, the only thinkable way that the species could have come into being. We have pictured this advancement not as proceeding along a single straight line, but rather as proceeding along several concurrently ascending lines. For example, on one occasion an ophidian came from the egg of a fish, again a saurian from another egg. And at the same time still another fish gave rise to a batrachian, and this in turn to a chelonian. From a third fish came a cetacean, or perhaps a dolphin. Later a cetacean bore a porpoise, and finally a porpoise bore a walrus. And it may be that the duckbill came from a duck's egg, and from the egg of an ostrich some large mammal species."

As a true philosopher who never shrank from the consequences of his logic, Schopenhauer immediately added a history of human descent to his theory. He did not doubt that *Homo sapiens* descended in a direct line from the apes, indeed, by race and region from various species of apes in existence today. "We must not conceal from ourselves the fact that according to this view the first human beings in Asia are to be thought of as descended from Pongo (whose young is called orang-utan) and in Africa from chimpanzees, not as apes, but forthwith as men."

These amazing sentences were written in 1859 by one of the most intelligent and best-read men in Europe. Schopenhauer died the following year, apparently without ever even laying eyes on Darwin's *Origin of Species*.

Although Schopenhauer's bizarre theory succeeded only in bringing a superior smile to the lips of zoologist and embryologist—in the Darwinian literature Schopenhauer has not been honoured by as much as the mention of his name—nevertheless his views give us an excellent idea of what the intellectual climate was like when Darwin stepped before the public. Two conclusions could be drawn from the Schopenhauer theory: that one species arises from another species and that man is no exception to this rule. This line of thought was nothing new to the learned. It was the "how" of evolution that was the unsolved riddle.

The only theory of descent that attempted to give a causal explanation of the evolutionary process was still the theory of external influences, the use and disuse of organs, etc., which Lamarck had postulated half a century earlier. Lamarck held that organic nature is like a wax tablet on which environment has left lasting impressions. Lamarck's arguments were imaginative and illuminating, yet in some respects rather childish, too. For example, he claimed that the giraffe had such a long neck because his ancestors had had to stretch so far to get at the branches of tall trees. The objection later raised to Lamarck—namely, that acquired characteristics are not hereditary—at first played no important part in the discussion. Up to a certain point Darwin and his original followers were Lamarckians. None of them disclaimed the importance of environment in originating the species. Haeckel's *Generelle Morphologie der Organismen*, published in 1866, closely followed the Lamarckian line.

But Darwin introduced into the debate an idea never before clearly expressed. Each species, he said, had to struggle for its existence or perish. Struggle is necessary in nature. This aggressive, activist approach, even to the peace-loving folk of the nineteenth century, said more than Lamarck's passive theory of adjustment to external influence. The phrase "natural selection" —of the good fighter and the most adaptable in the struggle for existence—fascinated such keen and independent minds as Thomas Huxley. Overwhelmed, like a converted sinner, this most zealous of Darwinian disciples wrote: "My reflection, when I first grasped the central idea of the *Origin of Species* was: how extraordinarily dense of me not to have thought of it myself!"

The Case of Wallace

Charles Darwin, as a matter of fact, had not been the first to think of natural selection. At least one other, the zoologist Alfred Russel Wallace, had hit on the idea about the same time. It is not uncommon in the history of ideas for several people, quite independently of each other, to make the same discovery or invent the same thing at about the same time. Yet there is no stranger instance of duplication than Darwin's and Wallace's discovery—or invention—of the principle of natural selection. Both got the idea while reading Malthus. Darwin discovered Malthus in 1838, soon after his return from his long trip to South America and Australia, when he picked up the *Essay on Population* to read it, in his own words, "for the pleasure of it." Wallace came into contact with the same work twenty years later, while prostrated by fever on a small Malayan island.

The external stimulus to this discovery alone is very remarkable. For although Malthus used the expression "struggle for existence," there is nothing in his work pointing to evolution as understood by Darwin or Wallace. Malthus's population theory is concerned solely with a quantitative problem, whereas Darwin and Wallace are interested solely in qualitative changes in the species. Had not both of them cited their debt to Malthus, it is probable that none of their biographers and commentators would have ever dug up this intellectual fatherhood. Even more astonishing, actually, is the fact that Wallace, in 1858, in the first outline of his theory of natural selection, should have followed the same train of thought and even used the same expressions found in Darwin's much earlier—although then as yet unpublished—outline for the *Origin of Species*.

Had not Wallace, as vouched by all who knew him, been such a completely honest and modest man, one would have assumed that somehow, despite his long stay in the Malayan archipelago, he had got wind of Darwin's theory; but Wallace could not have consciously plagiarized, for he notified Darwin of his discovery post haste, with the remark that he might find it as new as he did himself and that it might prove useful in his studies on the origin of the species.

For two decades Charles Darwin had been occupied with leisurely research at his country place in Downe, piling up ever more material to buttress his theory. He was anything but a vain or ambitious man but he was rather frightened by the thought that priority of discovery might slip from his hands. The situation was very similar to the one two hundred years before, when

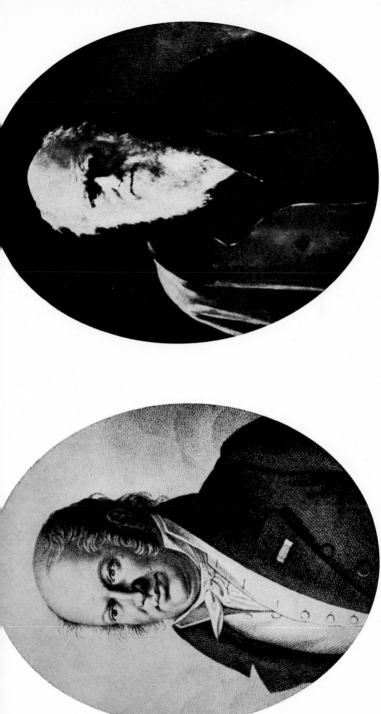

Etienne Geoffroy Saint-Hilaire

The theory of evolution in the nineteenth century

Charles Darwin

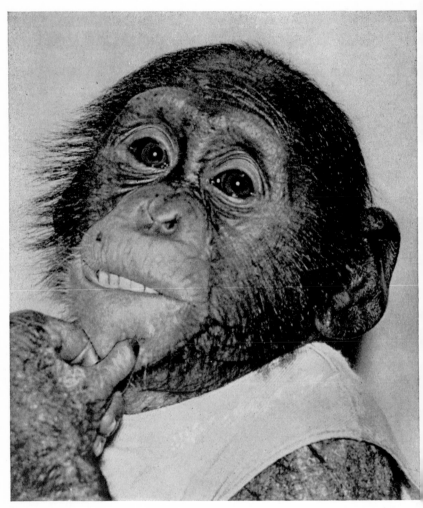

The ape problem

Newton, having learned that Leibniz had invented the same mathematical method, decided to make his differential calculus known as quickly as possible. This time, however, there was no disgraceful squabble over who came first. The problem of the fame of discovery was skirted in elegant fashion. The great geologist, Lyell, then regarded as the highest authority in English natural science, sent Darwin's older outline and Wallace's more recent one to the Linnaean Society for simultaneous publication.

No one was more delighted with this solution than Wallace. Never in his most fevered dreams had he ever hoped for such an honour. Wallace was a poor man who, on behalf of his studies, had lived a laborious hand-to-mouth life in the tropics. He had financed his risky explorations in the then unexplored Amazon region by selling rare butterflies and birds to a London animal dealer and had spent eight adventurous years on the islands in the Indian Ocean collecting six thousand insect species. But Wallace was more than just a collector, as later came to light. In native intelligence and scientific training he had all the qualifications for a great naturalist. Yet never did Wallace cast doubt on Darwin's priority once he had learned about the other man's work. Indeed, he became and remained a faithful Darwinist.

Meanwhile, news of the duplicate discovery moved the fifty-year-old Darwin at last to call a halt to preparation and get the results of his life's work down on paper. He retired to the Isle of Wight and there, in fourteen months, wrote the book that heralded a new era in natural science.

THE BATTLE OF THE APES AT OXFORD

The popular success of the *Origin of Species* exceeded all expectations. It is hard to say what the magic was but on the first day of publication the whole edition of 1,250 copies was sold out. Darwin realized full well that his struggle for existence had begun in earnest. With his zoological work on coral reefs and his thick book on fossil mollusca Darwin had already made a name for himself among the professionals, but he had always lived outside university circles and the general public had never heard of him. Yet his theory of evolution was intended to convince the general reader, as well as the specialist. The very way he had formulated it revealed that it was aimed at wider circles in the hope of reshaping general opinion on the origins of the animal world.

There is a picture of Darwin dating back to the period shortly before the publication of the *Origin of Species* in which he is shown poised as if minded to challenge the whole world to do battle with him. At this time he had not yet grown the flowing beard which became the characteristic feature of standard Darwinian portraits in later years. Here he has a smoothly shaven face, bushy eyebrows under a powerful forehead, a bald head, side whiskers, a stern look. He appears to be a typical John Bull as known from the cartoons. The face could have belonged to a hardheaded factory owner or to a virile politician of liberal persuasion; but the truth of the matter is the picture just goes to show how little can be proved from physiognomy.

This man, who had made the idea of the struggle for existence into a life principle, was himself anything but a fighter. Fate had been kind to him. Unlike Linnaeus and many other of his professional colleagues Darwin had never had to fight to keep alive, worry about where his next meal was coming from, work his way through school, arrange books in other people's libraries, blunder his way along as private tutor, lick fine boots to get a professorship or the like. He had been spared all the insecurities that had dogged so many other natural scientists in their youth. He was not from a wealthy home, but his family had been sufficiently well off to provide him with a comfortable upbringing and a broad education. Also he came from a family with intellectual interests, and since earliest childhood had heard biological problems discussed. His grandfather, Erasmus Darwin, had made a name for himself by writing didactic poetry and a book on the laws of organic life. Many now consider him, with Lamarck, to be one of the great originators of the evolutionary idea. Darwin's father, a prominent physician in Shrewsbury, had a sympathetic understanding for his son's none too practical inclinations and raised few objections when Darwin broke off his studies at Cambridge to take part in the rather adventurous expedition to Tierra del Fuego and the islands of the South Seas under Captain Fitzroy.

The five-year voyage on the *Beagle*, a three-master of 255 tons equipped with seven cannon and twenty-two chronometers, gave young Darwin an opportunity to store up a tremendous amount of zoological, botanical and geological information. However, his long stay away from home did not make him like adventure. When, in October, 1836, he returned to England, in his own words "in a dead and half-alive state," he had been cured of his wanderlust for good. From then on there was only one kind of life for him—a snug house, a sofa, books and walks in the immediate neighbourhood. His classic description of his trip, *The Voyage of the Beagle*, got him the honorary position of secretary of the geological society, but he hated the pattern of life in London—not only the city streets with all their dirt and noise but also the doings of the scientific societies, "where the members were snarling at each other in a manner anything but like that of gentlemen." By the age of thirty he had become a solitary, content to live in his family circle with a few chosen friends. Indeed, he was retiring to a point where he began to feel unwell and made himself out to be more of an invalid than he really was.

Darwin's inner seclusiveness had a retarding effect on his scientific production. He was shy and over-critical of himself. The more arguments he found to back up his basic idea, the less secure he felt. He was constantly oppressed by the thought of what Lyell, the geologist, would say, as well as the host of opponents that would assuredly rise up to contend with him. When he finally let himself be convinced by friends that he should write a book recording his ideas on the origin of the species, he felt as if he had been forced to do it against his better judgement. Before the book got to the booksellers, he sent copies to a few of the best-known naturalists in England and France, apologizing to each for his presumption. He told his old teacher, Henslow, that the work was only a preliminary study, and that he planned a larger one on the same subject. To one of his friendly critics he wrote: "I feel sometimes a little frightened whether I may not be one of those monomaniacs."

A man who talks like that is certainly not a real revolutionary. Darwin wanted to change the order of things, but to do it without hurting anybody's feelings. So as not to offend the orthodox he deliberately avoided mentioning the human line of descent in his *Origin of Species*. Yet he was convinced that man is subject to the same vital principle as other creatures; that the human species has descended from some other animal species by way of variation. Even while he was still writing the book, in a letter to Lyell he openly expressed his misgivings about the public reaction. Lyell should tell the publisher that the book was not as unorthodox as the subject matter might suggest. The publisher should know that he, Darwin, had not delved into the origin of man. He had not tried to drag Genesis into the debate. Indeed, he had presented facts and no more and from facts had drawn such conclusions as seemed fair to him.

Caution availed nothing. The specialists were content to attack him on the ground that he had brought forward no definitive evidence for his theory; that he had replaced the concept of "species" with the even more questionable one of "variety"; that he had anthropomorphized nature, making her appear like a sort of cruel cattle breeder. These scientific objections, however, paled into insignificance beside the storm of protest raised by the "monkey question." Darwin's straddling got him into more hot water than if, like Lamarck and many others, he had faced up to the question squarely.

The orthodox demanded a reckoning. Of course, in these days there was no Inquisition, and England was a land of intellectual and civil freedom, but anyone who attacked publicly had to defend himself publicly. The battle would be fought on holy scientific ground in the Museum of Oxford University. The leader of the counter-attack was Wilberforce, Bishop of Oxford, reputedly an excellent mathematician. Darwin himself was not present. As spokesman he sent his "bulldog," Thomas Huxley.

Scientific argument, it is fair to say, had very evidently not kept pace with the scientific achievements of the past century. In comparison with the insults hurled back and forth at Oxford, the exchanges of La Mettrie's day were mere pit-pats, the polemics of Descartes v. Gassendi models of politeness. There were no knightly daggers here. It was a case of grab a club and smash away. Thinking to lay his adversary low, the dignified bishop yelled: "I should like to ask Professor Huxley, who is sitting by me, and is about to tear me to pieces when I have sat down, as to his belief in being descended from an ape. Is it on his grandfather's or his grandmother's side that the ape ancestry comes in?"

The learned audience greeted this sally, later often to be repeated without being improved in the telling, with shouts of laughter. Whereupon Huxley rose to his feet and proceeded to land a smasher on the bishop's chin. "I asserted—" he said, "and I repeat—that a man has no reason to be ashamed of having an ape for his grandfather. If there were an ancestor whom I should feel shame in recalling, it would be a man—a man of restless and versatile intellect, who, not content with success in his own sphere of activity, plunges into scientific questions."

The bishop reeled. The mood of the whole gathering suddenly changed. The Darwinians had won the day. Of course it was not a final victory but henceforth the evolutionary movement attracted lively support. Beyond this, Darwin himself had a stroke of luck. In his book on orchids, which came out immediately after the *Origin of Species,* he said there must be an insect, as yet unknown, able to fertilize the giant orchids of Madagascar. Shortly afterwards a huge hawk moth actually was discovered on Madagascar, one with a proboscis that exactly fitted the dimensions of the giant orchid. This was almost as great a scientific success as the discovery twenty years before of the planet Neptune, after its existence and position had been adumbrated on the basis of the Newtonian theory. At the same time a correct prediction of the existence of the giant moth was no proof for the transformation of animal species. Indeed, precalculations of this sort fitted rather more readily into Lamarck's scheme than into Darwin's, but since Darwin had made it, it was a personal triumph for him. Even the sceptics told themselves that the teachings of a man with such a precise knowledge of nature must have something to them.

VICTORY OF EVOLUTION

Large and aggressive pro-Darwinian groups sprang up among the younger naturalists, and even more among laymen. Even in the highest and most influential circles the Darwinian theory became accepted. Lyell, to Darwin's chagrin, had not accorded the theory of zoological evolution complete recognition and so Darwin must have found it rather comforting when, in 1864, Lyell had a conversation with the Crown Princess of Prussia, daughter of Queen Victoria, and found she was an enthusiastic Darwinian. Even among men of the cloth a change of attitude began to appear. Cuvier's four successive "creations" did not exactly agree with the Biblical story of the Creation, yet no one any longer took offence because of that. Why should the Darwinian theory be handed over to the atheists for use as propaganda material?

Darwin stayed apart as much as possible from movements which would have made a universal philosophy or even a religion out of his theory, but he could not indefinitely avoid coming to grips with the "monkey question" when, against his wishes, it had become a fighting phrase. In order that he might not be suspected of trimming, eleven years after the *Origin of Species* Darwin brought out his famous work *The Descent of Man*, which, however, added little to what had already been written in the meantime by his followers, Huxley and Haeckel. In any event, he had eased his conscience and completely clarified his position. Still the Anglican divines decided that Darwin did not merit burial in Westminster Abbey.

The Darwinian revolution had conquered the world in an amazingly short time. Now and then some determined counter-revolutionary rose up and tried to free mankind from the shame of having a prehistoric—if not a contemporary—ape for a grandpapa. The most curious attempt to save man's face occurred in the United States in 1925. In Tennessee, before a regular court, legal proceedings were instituted against all forms of the theory of evolution and a high school teacher was heavily fined for having taught that man descended from the apes. In several other states the theory of evolution was eliminated from biology courses and to this day remains under ban. In a short history of the Civil War dating from this same period we find the following edifying thought: "Unless there is a new secession in protest against the theory of evolution and the godlessness of the Northern universities, the Union seems no longer in danger."

Battle Against Sickness

THE railway and the steamship narrowed the spaces of the world. People and animals could move more rapidly from one country to another and the new economic philosophy demanded that their way be smoothed, and formalities at frontiers be held to the minimum. Yet travellers carried their diseases with them, and epidemics spread faster. Instead of the pandemics which, in earlier times, had decimated the inhabitants of the earth, there was now an almost unbroken chain of small epidemics. Diseases once rare became international in scope.

Among the animal diseases the most feared was anthrax. All kinds of livestock, beef cattle, sheep, goats, pigs, horses, camels and dogs were subject to it. Nor were human beings immune. However carefully the stricken animals were handled, the disease could still be contracted by people handling hides, hair, or by-products coming from anthracic animals. No malady was more treacherous. Anthracic animals would suddenly collapse and die after an hour of frightful agonies. Alternatively they would suddenly break out in pus-filled swellings and run a high fever. If, after a few days, their temperature dropped, this was not a sign of a turn for the better but a forewarning of death.

Anthrax, splenic disease, wool-sorter's disease, as it was variously called—also *Milzbrand* from the German and *charbon* from the French—was a constant menace to animal husbandry. In France alone anthrax was costing the farmer twenty million gold francs a year. There was no effective remedy for it, though doctors had been seeking one for two thousand years. Nor was the cause of the disease at all clear. Because it attacked its victims like a consuming fire, burned them up, as it were, the Greek and Roman doctors had named it "anthrax," the Greek word for coal. This name has been retained in English and literally translated into "*charbon*" in French. The German name, "*Milzbrand*," from "*Milz*" meaning "spleen" and "*Brand*" meaning "inflammation," indicates that the disease often entails an enlargement of the spleen. It also serves to show how little was once known about its real origin.

Anthrax is a highly infectious disease. So much had always been obvious. But what was the cause of the infection? The theories then in circulation sounded more learned than earlier ones but actually were even farther from the truth. In the sixteenth century the Veronese physician, Fracastoro, had surmised that all contagious diseases must originate from specific germs. This theory had been shelved. Indeed, there seemed to be no sense in sticking to a theory that could not be proved and which was not, on the other hand, a working hypothesis leading to practical results. In 1840, however, Jakob Henle, the great German pathologist, revived Fracastoro's claim that infectious diseases were caused by specific micro-organisms. Yet he was unable to prove the hypothesis and, after having long searched in vain for corroborative evidence, he was forced to fall back on the explanation that disease germs must look so much like tissue that the two could not be told apart under the microscope.

Only nine years later another German doctor from Wippenfurth, by the name of Pollender, found chains of remarkable rod-shaped micro-organisms in the spleen of animals that had died from anthrax. The same microbes were also shown to be present in living animals in the last stage of the disease. During the sixties the French investigators, Davaine and Reyer, were able to isolate and culture the bacillus. The microbes under glass grew like little plants, yet the prevailing opinion remained that the rod-shaped things were merely secondary symptoms of the disease, the products of decomposition rather than the actual causal agent. It was only when Robert Koch, a completely unknown doctor in the German province of Posen, systematically demonstrated in 1876 the development of the anthrax bacillus and produced experimental evidence to show that the disease could be artificially induced, that the sceptics were finally forced to admit that science was at last on the way to solving a great mystery.

The Miracle in the Sheep-fold

The three decades needed to discover and identify the anthrax bacillus was a time of revolutionary progress in the sciences. Louis Pasteur, who typifies this period, was more of a clairvoyant than an experimenter. He was obsessed by the belief that there was a microscopic underworld from which came all good and evil in nature. He saw the influence of bacteria at every hand, and from this premise went directly to therapy without the pedantic inhibitions torturing other savants. Pasteur was a born healer, although he never sought a medical degree. No matter what he turned his hand to—and his interests were constantly changing—he was able to effect cures, and his remedies were successful, almost miraculous. He cured diseases in wine, beer and milk, in silkworms and hens. The theory on which he leaned was neither new nor profound. His techniques were rather slapdash, a weakness for which he was soundly rebuked by the painfully correct Robert Koch. None of this matters; Pasteur was a man of intuition, a genius at grasping essentials and, where he thought necessary, at constructing relationships.

Wide and varied as Pasteur's works may be, in essence they all represent the application of two principles, which were well known before his day: that bacteria can be killed by moderately high temperatures; and that human beings and animals can be protected from contagious diseases by injecting into them small doses of the infectious material, that is, attenuated living germs, killed germs or germ products. The first of these two principles, as well as the organic nature of fermentation and decomposition, had been established by Schwann long before Pasteur, and in France Cagniard de la Tour had got the same results. The need for asepsis in medicine had been recognized by the Hungarian physician, Semmelweiss, a generation before Pasteur.

The idea of preventive inoculation was even older. It went back to Edward Jenner, the English physician of the mid-eighteenth century. Actually the glory of the discovery should go to Lady Mary Montagu, wife of the English ambassador to Constantinople, who in 1717 described inoculation methods in common use in Turkey and later worked hard to get them accepted in England. She was not, however, very successful, and even Jenner ran into powerful resistance. Nevertheless, by the time Pasteur began his experiments in prophylaxis, inoculation against smallpox was already obligatory in many countries.

As an intellectual personality and a scientific thinker Pasteur does not compare with his great rival, Claude Bernard. Indeed, during the eighteenth and nineteenth centuries France produced so many biological experimenters of scope and originality that it may be asked why popular opinion should have ranked Pasteur so much higher than any of the rest. Even during his lifetime Pasteur was honoured like a national saint. The explanation for this lies mainly in the fact that Pasteur, unlike so many other French savants, always tended towards the practical, that even before he turned his attention to saving human lives, his scientific work had saved the livestock people a great deal of money. Besides, Pasteur was a master in the art of self-advertisement.

His famous cure of the sick sheep of Pouilly-le-Fort in 1881 was staged like a play. The *mise-en-scène* was a cowshed on an estate southeast of Paris. The agricultural society of Melun had placed fifty sheep at Pasteur's disposal, likewise a goat and several cattle, so that he might carry out a public test of the effectiveness of his inoculation against anthrax. The demonstration, it was later claimed, probably to romanticize the story a bit, had been originally instigated by one of Pasteur's opponents, for on the basis of rather limited laboratory experiments Pasteur had made a hard-and-fast claim that animals could be protected from the dread disease of anthrax by one or two harmless inoculations. Now he had to make good this claim.

Pasteur did not have to be asked twice. On 2 May 1881, he arrived at Pouilly-le-Fort accompanied by two assistants, and there, in the presence of farmers, veterinaries, journalists, senators and other honoured guests, inoculated half the animals with a weak injection of anthrax bacilli. Twelve days later he repeated the injections, this time using a somewhat stronger dosage. On 31 May came the main experiment. A normally lethal dose of bacilli was injected into all the animals, those previously inoculated and those not. This time it was a case of life or death. Patiently the animals awaited their fate. No antivivisectionist dared lift his voice in protest against this mass experiment. If only twenty-five animals died to save the lives of thousands, the victory over anthrax would not have been too dearly bought.

Two days later the whole audience reassembled at the agreed hour. The outcome was successful beyond all expectation. Every one of the inoculated animals was alive and apparently in perfect health, whereas all but two of the uninoculated animals lay dead, and these two, bleeding from nose and mouth, were writhing in their death throes.

It was an unheard-of triumph of science over death—and yet only a laboratory success. If the vaccine were administered by unskilled hands, the results, it was discovered, were far less favourable. Also, the vaccine that Pasteur now hastened to supply in great quantity was anything but dependable. Inoculation was not only often ineffective but in many cases resulted in serious sickness and death. On the whole Pasteur's fight against anthrax was, and continued to be, inconclusive. The results were certainly not quite so disappointing as in the case of tuberculin, which a decade later Koch thought was the answer to tuberculosis. Yet neither vaccine yielded results positive enough to justify the risks involved. It was not until thirty years later that Dawson perfected the prophylactic technique to a point where the contingent dangers, at least, were obviated. Even then the protective effect remained dubious.

MAD DOGS

As always, when Pasteur thought he had won a great victory, he left the field of battle to his students and himself turned to other things. Once more he came to grips with his sworn enemies, the bacteria which were dangerous to animals, and through them to man. Obsessed with a penchant for the dramatic, he picked out the most spectacular, if not the most important, infectious disease, rabies. Plainly all dogs could not be inoculated just because of a few rabid ones, and human beings were even less willing to submit to prophylaxis. Here the only help was therapy.

Pasteur, already in his sixties, began to study rabies systematically and moved more carefully than was his wont. Since rabies was obviously a disease affecting the nervous system, the vaccine, he decided, would have to be introduced into the animal's central nervous apparatus. To do this, a kind of vivisection was necessary from which even Pasteur, who in his time had done away with many hundreds of animals for experimental purposes, recoiled. The experimenter would have to chisel open the skull of a healthy dog and inject into the healthy brain diseased material from the brain of a rabid dog. Pasteur's pupil, Roux, refused to be swayed by the older man's sentimentality. Roux carried out the experiment countless times on dogs, then on rabbits. At last Pasteur and Roux obtained a vaccine from the spinal cord of artificially infected animals able to immunize other animals against rabies. With truly mystic zeal they gave each animal fourteen injections exactly. Fourteen was the correct dosage, no more, no less.

Yet the experiment on human beings, to which all the others had been merely preliminary, had yet to be made. Pasteur toyed with the idea of testing his vaccine on himself, a vaccine which at this point he still thought of as a preventive rather than a cure. It happened that a desperate Alsatian woman brought Pasteur her child, who had been almost torn to pieces by a mad dog, and begged the aging miracle doctor to help her. Even before the cinema got hold of this story, the cure of little Joseph Meister had been romanticized into a touching schoolbook legend. The little boy has become a hero and the victory over rabies the greatest of all scientific exploits.

Fig. 70. Mechanical money box "Mag Dog," from the period when Pasteur undertook his experiments in fighting hydrophobia. If one pulls the button the dog snatches the coin from the stooping boy

The truth is that the cure of the Meister boy by fourteen injections of vaccine in no sense marked a turning point in the history of mankind, nor yet even in Pasteur's career. Actually the great Frenchman accomplished things of far greater consequence. In point of fact, anti-rabies inoculation was not a real cure, but a prophylaxis, in principle no different from vaccination against smallpox, which had been a common medical technique for nearly a century. As for contributing to the general health of mankind, Pasteur's anti-rabies vaccine was much less significant than the prophylactic treatment for blennorrhea of the eyes among the newly born, introduced at about this same time by Credé. Credé's prophylaxis brought about a marked reduction in infant blindness.

Moreover, inoculation was a much less decisive factor in the decline of rabies than the Pasteur legend makes it appear. The disease, actually, was never too common. In Pasteur's day rabies was rapidly declining in all civilized countries. Indeed, when he launched his research Pasteur had a great deal of difficulty in obtaining enough experimental material to work with until he bred his own supply of rabid dogs and rabbits. In Prussia, between 1800 and 1810, over a hundred persons died annually of rabies. From 1864 to 1867, in the same country, only seventeen died annually from the same cause and from 1877 to 1881 only thirteen. In later decades this decline levelled off at an average of only three deaths from rabies annually. It is obvious that this diminution cannot be attributed solely to the introduction of anti-rabies inoculation. In France, where inoculation was assiduously practised, but where the dog laws were not strictly enforced, the number of rabid dogs and deaths from rabies continued to be much higher than in Prussia.

MARTYRS OF SERUM THERAPY

The voyages of discovery into the underworld of micro-organism brought rich yields. After the techniques of microscopy had been developed dozens of virulent bacilli and cocci were revealed, in the course of only a few years, each of which caused a specific disease. Of the fifty bacteria known today, the great majority was discovered in the 1880s and 1890s. These findings were of the greatest importance in diagnosis, but bacteriotherapy, that is, the use of bacteria or their products in curing disease, advanced more slowly. Most vaccines proved to be either useless or undependable. Yet an attempt had to be made to get the maximum good for humanity out of the new knowledge.

Animals had to bear the brunt of experiment. Probably never have so many animals been killed in the interests of science as during the last decades of the nineteenth century. In the early stages of microbiology experimenters had to economize with their animal material, but when the new science was accorded general recognition and rich grants flowed in from private patrons and the state, they could afford to destroy whole menageries of animals and their zeal knew no bounds. The two most important experimental centres—the Pasteur Institute, located first on the rue d'Ulm, later on the rue Dutot, in Paris, and Robert Koch's more modest laboratory on Schumannstrasse, in Berlin—became the scene of mass murders. In Paris Pasteur's impetuous lieutenant, Roux, held sway. In Berlin, under Koch's supervision, two Prussian military surgeons, Friedrich Loeffler and Emil Behring, were in command. It is hard to say where more animals were massacred, but certain it is that in both institutes thousands of rabbits, guinea pigs and much larger animals as well died a martyr's death for the advancement of mankind's health.

The usual attitude towards animal experiment was that if the end did not justify the means, success surely did. Since successes were numerous, the death of a few hundred animals more or less did not matter. Most significant progress was made in the field of diphtheria control. The mysterious feature of this disease was the fact that the bacteria did not act in large masses, as in the case of anthrax or tuberculosis. In diphtheria patients only a relatively small concentration of pathogens could be found, nevertheless their effect was frightfully virulent. Loeffler, the discoverer of diphtheria microbes, suspected that they produced an extraordinarily toxic substance and Roux proved this to be true. It was indeed a terrible poison. A cubic centimetre of it was enough to kill twenty thousand guinea pigs.

For the confirmed bacteriologist this discovery was a disappointment. Bacteriology in conflict with chemistry had developed into an independent science. Its basic idea was that living organisms, not chemical substances, caused infectious diseases, but just how micro-organisms carried on their sinister work no one could say with any certainty. Some investigators offered rather mysterious vitalistic explanations. Bacteria, they said, had a vital force in them which spelt death for the animals and humans in which they worked their mischief. They were parasitic, they ate up the lungs, intestines and skin of their hosts. On the whole the tendency was towards mechanical, physical explanations. Now science wavered and returned to the chemical theory. Bacteria caused disease by means of chemical influences. The bacteria themselves did the animal or human being no harm. It was their poisons that had the lethal effect, even when not a trace of the living microbe could be detected.

According to the general scheme of the older school of bacteriology, it was to be expected that small doses of microbial toxins would immunize animals and humans against stronger doses, but nature did not completely agree with this logic. It appeared that in the blood of animals which, with or without medical help, had withstood the disease, nature produced a counter-poison, or antitoxin. This antitoxin immunized other animals which had never been infected. It was Behring who made the discovery and evolved the technique; Roux followed after some hesitation.

All the world's mothers breathed more easily now that their children's lives seemed more secure. Behring was hailed as mankind's greatest benefactor; he became the first recipient of the Nobel Prize for medicine. Then came the reverses. To this very day the statistics on diphtheria are not conclusive. Mortality among sufferers from this disease fluctuates, being now great, now small. Yet Behring's therapeutic successes were so spectacular that his blood serum techniques came to be ubiquitously used in tetanus, snakebite and a whole series of other ailments as well as in diphtheria. One horse yielded enough serum—the watery part of the blood containing the antibodies—to protect eight hundred other horses, and many more human beings, against diphtheria. Today the demand for serums useful in therapy or in prophylaxis to prevent epidemics has become so great that whole herds of horses, as well as flocks of sheep and goats, must be kept to serve the sole purpose of yielding blood made impure by man. These animals are carefully tended not only during their artificially induced sickness but later on as well. They have good quarters and eat the best of fodder. Nevertheless, they are certain candidates for death. Most of them are gone after a year or a year and a half. The serum factories are grim death traps for the animals.

Hundreds of Millions with Malaria

After Koch had shown that anthrax bacilli propagate outside their animal victims through spores, somewhat in the manner of ferns, it was held to be confirmed fact that pathogenic microbes were plants rather than animals. It was nature's revenge—plants both give and take animal life—wonderful material for the moral-biologic views so fashionable during the second half of the nineteenth century. However, the belief that microscopically small plants were man's and the higher animals' worst enemies was soon upset by new discoveries. Plant-like microbes were certainly the worst mischief-makers but they had no monopoly. Other microbes, unquestionably belonging to the animal world, were found to be responsible for some of the most horrible plagues.

In 1875 Loesch found amoebae in the stools of patients suffering from intestinal disease. These unicellular organisms were awkward in their movements and constantly changing shape as they propelled themselves about. Loesch called this new species *Amoeba coli,* but did not dare come right out and name it a new pathogen. Robert Koch so often found these minuscular animals present in the intestines and stools of dysenteric patients in Egypt that he boldly identified them as the basic pathogen in dysentery. Koch's surmise seemed to have been proved after other investigators succeeded in infecting cats with these same amoebae, thus speeding them to their death. Then the situation became doubtful. So many different amoebae, some harmless, some not, were discovered in the intestinal tracts, both of the well and the sick, that some of the bacteriologists let off the protozoa with a clean bill of health. Not until the beginning of the twentieth century was the question finally settled, in tragic fashion, by F. Schaudinn, discoverer of the pathogen of syphilis.

He inoculated himself with the most dangerous of the amoebae, *Entamoeba histolytica,* and died from the effects.

Meanwhile still another species of amoeba had kindled an even more violent argument among the bacteriologists. At the beginning of the 1880s, when Pasteur's miracle cures were astonishing the whole world, a French military doctor, Alphonse Laveran, reported to the Parisian Academy of Medicine that he had repeatedly found an amoeboid parasite in the blood of malarial patients, which was very likely the source of this most widespread of tropical diseases. The report was not taken very seriously at first, for Laveran was an unknown colonial doctor. He did not belong to Pasteur's circle and, besides, a whole series of alleged malarial pathogens had been reported for years past, every one of which had proved wrong in its turn.

For fifteen long years Laveran's report was classed among the pseudo-discoveries, until Sir Ronald Ross and MacCallum showed experimentally, using the blood of birds, that malaria protozoa were carried by mosquitoes, and Grassi proved that human beings were infected by the bite of the anopheles mosquito. This, however, did not mean that any remedy had been found to improve on the old quinine treatment. All efforts to work out an absolutely dependable prophylaxis have failed to this day. However, there now exists one effective preventive measure—the extermination of the carrying mosquitoes. Wherever this has been successful, malaria has virtually disappeared. According to a 1950 report from the health organization of the United Nations, there are still hundreds of millions of malaria sufferers throughout the world. As a direct or indirect cause of death malaria is the chief menace in all tropical and subtropical lowlands.

MOSQUITOES, FLIES AND FLEAS

The conquest of yellow fever, which had not only made wide areas of the tropics practically uninhabitable but periodically claimed thousands of victims in the United States, had lasting results. Yellow fever blocked the way of men seeking to open up and conquer new areas. It was because of this disease that the first attempt to build the Panama Canal had failed. The financial losses resulting from this spoke a more eloquent language than the only too familiar mortality lists. Something just had to be done.

The pathogenic agent in yellow fever continued to elude discovery: probably it was too small to be seen under a microscope. They did find out, however, that in yellow fever, as in malaria, a certain species of mosquito carried the germ. So there was a possibility of overcoming the disease. Doctors from the United States applied sanitation methods in Cuba; in Brazil it was Oswaldo Cruz who led the fight.

War was now declared on the carriers of infectious diseases. Death to all noxious insects became the watchword. Body lice were found to be the carriers of spotted fever, seemingly harmless creatures were added to the black list. The housefly was suspected of spreading typhoid microbes. Experiments with monkeys showed that the tsetse fly of the African tropics carried the trypanosomes which caused sleeping sickness. On a research trip through East Africa, Robert Koch, the elderly microbe hunter, made the amazing discovery of crocodile blood in the intestines of tsetse flies. This led him to conclude that crocodiles are the great reservoirs for trypanosomes, though themselves immune to sleeping sickness.

That ships' rats carried the bubonic plague from country to country and were themselves subject to the disease had long been known. Heaps of dead rats were always found in plague-stricken areas, but exactly how the plague was transmitted from rats to human beings was not discovered until much later, when fleas, which are common to both rats and humans, fell under suspicion. Yersin had previously discovered the plague bacillus; now the French investigator, Simond, found the same microorganism in the digestive tract of the rat-flea. Galli-Valerio, however, claimed that rat-fleas did not bite human beings. An English research commission finally decided the savants' war of the fleas. The common human flea, *Pulex irritans,* was cleared of blame for the plague. At the same time it was established that human beings could be bitten and infected by other kinds of fleas that did transmit the plague.

War was waged on the rats as well as on the insect carriers of bubonic plague, but with less success. Rats are relative new-comers to Europe. The black house rat, for instance, apparently arrived in Europe on the ships that brought the Crusaders home from the middle east, for it was at about this time that the great cholera epidemics broke out, after which they continued to erupt at frequent intervals. Little is known about the epidemiology of these early waves of the plague, except that they first hit the port cities. There can be no doubt, however, that rats contributed a great deal to the spread of the disease.

The black rat, prime evil-doer and at the same time a victim in these early epidemics, has actually all but disappeared from the western world, with the exception of South America, where he is still plentiful. However, the black rat was not exterminated by human effort. He has simply been supplanted by a stronger and more active rodent species, the brown, or Norway, rat. The zoologists named the species *Mus norvegicus,* though in fact this rat comes from the Orient and not from Scandinavia.

The brown rat's migratory route through Europe in the eighteenth century is pretty well known. In 1727 an enormous host of these hitherto unknown animals gathered near Astrakhan on the east bank of the Volga. After an earthquake, they attempted to cross the river and, according to the naturalist Pallas, millions of them drowned; but the survivors continued their westward march, and multiplied so rapidly that it was not long before they had become a scourge throughout Europe. They moved swiftly through the Ukraine, southern Poland and Bohemia. In 1740 another army of rats was reported as having arrived in East Prussia. In 1753 they celebrated their triumphal entry into Paris. Buffon obtained his first specimens from a botanical garden inspector and wrote a short description of them. He proposed the name *"surmulot"* for the new species, a term which got into the dictionaries but which never became popular in France. In the nineteenth century the brown rat arrived in force in North America, crossed the continent and by 1851 had reached the Pacific coast.

Everywhere rats have come to be regarded as the worst kind of criminals. They do more damage to agriculture than any other rodents. Their depredations in England alone are estimated to amount to £15 million annually. The brown rat has supplanted the black rat, too, as principal disease carrier. The plague, typhus, foot-and-mouth disease and various other human and animal maladies are charged, with more or less justification, to their account.

All the animals involved in human contagious diseases certainly could not be exterminated, but by means of quarantine and such pest control measures as using petroleum and other disinfectants on watery breeding places a large number of the disease carriers has been done away with. It was not the least achievement of the nineteenth century, which began with murderous wars and shameless exploitation, only later to win for itself so many scientific laurels, that it will go down in history as one of the most peaceful and humanitarian of epochs.

回 XXIV 回

The Intelligent Animal

MICROBIOLOGICAL discovery had weakened the feeling of affinity between men and animals. The Darwinists might marshal all rational arguments for the claim that the animals are man's relatives but the fact remains that they are man's vicious cousins of whom he must beware. Indeed, precisely because biologically they had so much in common with human beings they were so much the more dangerous.

Not since prehistoric days had man been more afraid of animals than in the period when the bacteriologists and hygienists were opening his eyes. Even animals which had always been considered to be man's friends—horses, cattle, sheep, etc.—were now suspected of spreading horrible diseases. Whoever tried to defend them himself fell under dire suspicion. When Robert Koch brought forward the theory that bovine tuberculosis was caused by a special bacillus that did not affect human beings, it was rumoured that he was giving the cattle a clean bill of health in order to promote the South African meat export business. In any case the domestic cattle of a country were not dangerous. Those from outside were definitely infected. Economic interests exploited this fear. Strict veterinary and border controls were an easy means of advancing protection. They were a substitute for tariffs.

FELINE AESTHETIC

Fear of being infected by animals even spread to the realm of the aesthetic. People began to worry about the cleanliness of pets kept in the house or animals touched out of curiosity while on a trip in the country. People had come to think it was better not to pat dogs and horses indiscriminately. At least, the doctors warned against it and cautious folk behaved accordingly.

The new movement towards cleanliness was all to the good for one animal which, up to this time, had never stood very high on the social scale: the cat, obviously the cleanest of all animals, began to win man's sympathy. The feline habit of cleaning the fur a hundred times a day until every speck of dirt had been licked off seemed to accord with the rules of modern hygiene, though the hygienists themselves might have a different idea on the subject. In any case, cats had stood up pretty well under bacteriological tests. They were not immune to contagious diseases but as disease carriers were less dangerous than most other animals. None of the severe infectious diseases could be ascribed to them. Indeed, cats deserved a lot of credit for their assistance to the public health authorities in the war on rats and mice.

On these general premises was based the new feline aesthetic which spread out from Paris towards the end of the nineteenth century and became an international fad. Since their heyday in ancient Egypt, cats had not been getting too many compliments from mankind. They had come into Europe from North Africa, apparently at about the time of the Arab invasion. Following Mohammed's example, the Arabs were very fond of cats, but this Infidel sentiment hardly recommended the little animals to Europeans. For several centuries cats led a rather obscure life. It was not until after the Crusades, when such traditional rodent-hunters as the weasel, the genet and the ferret could not cope with the invading masses of rats, that cats were made regular servant members of the household. By the thirteenth century they were known as "hearth cats" in France, to distinguish them from "wild cats," which were of interest only to the tanner or to the tax collector who collected a tax on their skins.

Some particularly beautiful specimens of the cat species had long since been highly prized, however, first in England and later in Italy, where the Angora cat, so-called, a breed actually originating in Persia, was introduced in the sixteenth century. But this handful of aristocrats did not improve the common cat's living standard, which continued to be a modest one as befitted a loyal but lowly member of the petit-bourgeois household. Since the cat was not as submissive as the dog and could not be trained for racing or other sports, he was regarded as unsociable and relegated to the kitchen. In humble taverns he guarded the larder; from the salon he was barred.

Suddenly all this changed. The cat, like the dog six hundred years before, became eligible for polite society. Sculptors and poets took him up and discovered the grace of his movements. Cat sculptures became numerous on mantelpieces and even got into the museums. The cat became the symbol of Montmartre night life. The French-Swiss artist, Théophile-Alexandre Steinlen, created a new feline type with long, slim legs. Steinlen's first album of drawings was called *Des Chats*. The cat cult may have originated as a literary joke, for Steinlen had got to know the song-writer, Aristide Bruant, in a little café known as the Chat Noir. Anyway, the symbol caught on and the Chat Noir became the model for the modern literary cabaret, providing a name for a magazine which attracted a whole generation of young Parisian draughtsmen.

The Montmartre cat of 1900 was very different from any of its literary or artistic ancestors. In Germany certain tom cats had achieved some degree of fame, such as Puss-in-Boots, as taken from Perrault, and E. T. A. Hoffman's Kater Murr or, in loose translation, Old Tom Growler. But these toms were hardly likable chaps. In German the word for "hangover" is *"Kater"* or, literally, "tom cat." Of course, the philologists assure us that *"Kater"* is only a mutilated form of *"Katarrh."* Yet the assimilation shows what a low reputation tom cats had.

Even in France not much good had been said of the cat; but now cats became feminized. The cat was thought of as a tender female thing and infinitely coquettish. Even when she slipped out into the moonlight for romantic adventures she was still a most charming creature. Kitty found her Homer in Colette. Her clever animal books—*Sept dialogues de bêtes* and *Paix chez les bêtes*—are related to the old French tradition of fable. However, her *Kiki-la-Douceste* is not a fabulous animal, that is a human in disguise, but a real cat, observed closely and with much sensitivity.

INSTINCT AND INTELLIGENCE

Colette's cat books have become a part of world literature. Their only competitor is Maeterlinck's *Life of the Bees*, a book which, the profundity of its philosophy notwithstanding, has become universally popular. Although Maeterlinck approached his subject with scientific seriousness and attempts to make his description of the life of the bees as true to nature as possible, his bees are actually more caught up in anthropomorphic metaphor than the cats of Colette's novels. Nor is Maeterlinck really a fabulist. If animals seem to have a close resemblance to human beings, it is because human beings are so like animals. Animals think and feel even as we do, Maeterlinck suggests, and even plants have "mind," a conscious and subconscious, like anything else organic.

Making distinctions in the Cartesian manner in order to secure a privileged position for man is a distortion of nature. Such was the philosophy of the new animal symbolism which went far beyond Darwinism. Not only does the evolutionary succession demonstrate the unity of nature. It also stands revealed, wherever one may care to look, in the sameness of desires, of joys and sufferings, of disposition. This similarity is not, as in the old animal fables, a merely literary device. It conforms to reality itself, which the writer sees more clearly than the zoologist.

The boundary between instinct and reflective intelligence is not so sharply drawn as the doctrinaires of *Homo sapiens* claim. Many qualities which man regards as intellectual in himself are likewise developed in animals to such high degree that it would be ridiculous to consider them as entirely different and com-

Fig. 71. Dogs' heads from Lavater's *Physiognomische Fragmente zur Beförderung der Menschenkenntnis und Menschenliebe*

pletely unintellectual. These qualities are commonly bound up with the thought organ, yet go far beyond what can be physiologically deduced from the properties of this nerve apparatus. Outstanding in this connection is the sense of orientation. This has nothing to do with keen scent and superior olfactory nerves nor a larger visual field and sharper eyesight nor a superior auditory equipment. A man who can orient himself in a featureless landscape by making use of seemingly trivial signs is considered to be intelligent. Why, therefore, should this same ability in animals, whose sense of orientation is incomparably superior to man's, be ascribed to instinct alone? Even if it is only instinct, man can, so to speak, profit by it, for human intelligence and animal instinct are complementary and if the two are linked new abilities can arise. The principle had been known a long time, but now it was more systematically applied in association with mechanical techniques.

Whereas the animal's purely physical accomplishments were becoming devaluated, since machines could do more work than animals, on the other hand the animal's mental capacities gained in respect. The Red Cross pressed dogs into service and gave them the Red Cross badge which protects their human officials. The police, too, have learned how to make use of the dog's intelligence, although the police dog as criminal investigator who, singlehanded, solves serious crimes and outshines the most experienced detectives in criminological resource is more effective in literature than in the real world. While in police work the dog's ability to track is exploited and perfected by training, by virtue of his function the police dog has acquired moral status. He has now become a supporter of law and order.

THE FIRST AIR MAIL

Still higher intelligence, or an instinct so closely resembling it as to pass for it, belongs to a bird. During the nineteenth century many means of communication were completely revolutionized, with the result that draught and riding animals were pushed into the background. In one area of communications man had to rely on a creature whose cleverness and endurance no nineteenth-century machine could match. Since dependable, steerable flying machines had not as yet been built, the first practical air mail was a carrier pigeon service. The name is still widely current to this day.

Putting the birds to this use was nothing new. The fact that certain birds always tend to fly back to the same place had been discovered in antiquity and gave rise to ingenious postal systems. Pliny reports that sailors on Egyptian and Greek vessels used to take pigeons along with them, and on the return trip release them as they were nearing home so that their relatives might know that the biggest part of the voyage was safely over and that the voyagers themselves would soon be home. These birds were merely harbingers, identified by a badge, and carried no messages. Yet it appears that even at this time carrier pigeons were used for carrying messages over great distances on land as well as over the sea. It is believed that Caesar maintained an information service of this sort, and Diocletian is also said to have set up a regular pigeon post.

Like so many other ingenious achievements of ancient times, the use of carrier pigeons in Europe ceased after the fall of western Rome. In the Orient, however, the custom persisted. The caliphs of Baghdad kept in touch with their territories by using birds. During the Crusades the men of the west lifted this technique from the Infidels, and brought it home as part of their intellectual plunder. Henceforth carrier pigeons were mainly used for military purposes. When Henry IV besieged Paris in 1590, the Parisians used carrier pigeons to keep in touch with the outside world. The besiegers are said to have sent up falcons to try to intercept the pigeons, but the pigeons, it appears, were quicker and more dependable than the hawks.

At the beginning of the nineteenth century business people also got the idea of exploiting the pigeon's sense of orientation. The London banker Nathan Rothschild had news on the military situation brought to him by pigeon from the Continent during the Napoleonic wars, and the Stock Exchange operations which he engineered on the basis of these on-the-spot bulletins richly repaid the outlay. A whole body of legend arose about the fabulous profits which Rothschild is supposed to have made with the help of his carrier pigeons. Other financiers imitated Rothschild's example. In the 1840s the German newspaperman Reuter—founder of the English news service that bears his name—organized a regular carrier pigeon run between Aachen and Verviers to bridge the gap between the German and the Franco-Belgian telegraph networks.

The "exchange pigeons," as the birds serving the Stock Exchange were called, did not go out of fashion until land and submarine telegraph lines had connected all the large cities. For a time these peaceful creatures performed no military services but they resumed their erstwhile martial career during the Franco-Prussian War in 1870.

THE CARRIER PIGEONS' WAR MEMORIAL

When Paris was under German siege during the Franco-Prussian War, the authorities remembered the air mail system that had saved the city from complete isolation during the days of Henry IV. Rampont, the director of posts, collected a few hundred trained birds whose homing instinct was focused on Paris in sufficient degree to ensure their return. Unlike the good old days, they were dispatched on their mission with all the comforts of modernity.

The pigeons were stowed in the basket of a balloon and in it successfully crossed the enemy lines without as much as stirring a wing. Once safely outside, they were divided up in such a way as to keep the capital in contact with all the various regions of France. Actually only a hundred of these pigeons ever returned and even so were desultory about delivering their tidings, good or bad. Later it was claimed that these hundred feathered heroes, who had withstood the winter's cold and escaped the besiegers' bullet, brought in 150,000 official dispatches and a million private messages in addition. These figures are scarcely credible, for a pigeon flying long distances can carry only one gramme, and at the time micro-photography was still in its infancy. Nevertheless there can be no doubt that the pigeons at least gave Paris a psychological lift. Subsequently a well-earned memorial in their honour was placed at one of the gates of Paris.

However, the pigeons were unable to avert the city's military fate, as had been the case three hundred years before at the time when Paris was beleaguered by good King Henry. After the war had been over for some time Frenchmen troubled their heads no more about the strategic value of an aerial mail service, and pigeon racing again became an innocent amateur sport; but in Germany, Russia and several other countries the experience gained in the siege of Paris was put to military use. Carrier pigeons became a permanent branch of the army. There were regular pigeon barracks, to which were attached specialists in training birds and in sending messages by them. The general staff devoted serious attention to the problems of war by dove and racked their brains over technical improvements.

The distressing thing about this system was the one-way limitation of pigeon flight. Nature seemed to have endowed pigeons with a sense of orientation for only one spot. If they were asked to achieve a second goal, they became confused and lost their way. If they were sent up from their own station, they showed no particular place sense. Often they flew far away but apparently completely at random.

Malagoli, an Italian, succeeded in surmounting this obstacle. He improved on nature after the precept laid down by Schiller. "Until philosophy holds together the structure of the world," Schiller wrote, "the machine is kept going by hunger and by love." Malagoli so arranged the pigeons' training programme that their sexual needs, as well as their feeding, were amply satisfied. Having accustomed the birds to these requirements, Malagoli, as it were, spatially divided the Schillerian principle

into two parts. On arrival at their home station the birds were
richly fed but at the same time strictly prohibited from engaging
in sexual activity. They were then taken to another site where
they could mate at will. The birds soon got the idea. This simple
trick had them frantically flying back and forth between two
stations.

On the eve of the First World War both military and civil
authorities expected great deeds of the pigeons in event of conflict. As yet no flying machine could equal them in speed or
endurance. The pigeons could fly at a rate of 54 m.p.h. and in
fifteen or twenty hours could cover about six hundred miles. No
express train or racing car could match such a record. In France
swallows flying at 90 m.p.h. had been trained for army use. The
dependability of the avian post had also been improved. As war
was about to break out, the birds in most countries were inspected, just like soldiers and horses, and given their mobiliza-
tion orders. The thousands of pigeon-breeding associations—in
Germany alone there were 1,300 of them—by this time had
become little more than preparatory schools for the military
communications service.

Then came the great let-down. Not that the pigeons were
defeatists or shirkers of their military duty; it was simply that
the machine put an end to their martial career. Neither pigeons
nor swallows could hold their end up with wireless telegraphy.
Marconi had gone one better than his countryman Malagoli.

ARITHMETICAL HORSES

All stories, true or fictional, about animal intelligence are
thrown into the shade by the exploits of certain horses reported
at the turn of the last century. The world was truly amazed by
these equine accomplishments. First of all, Wilhelm von Osten,
an elderly German of independent means living in Berlin, whose
hobby was breeding horses, taught a Russian stallion how to
calculate. The horse, named Kluge Hans or "Clever Jack," by
pawing the ground with his hoof could count off numbers shown

to him on a blackboard. That was not all. Clever Jack could add, subtract, multiply and divide as well as any fourteen-year-old who had been to a grammar school.

At first, naturally, people suspected some trick; but the experts —veterinaries, circus managers, cavalry officers, university professors and others—who studied Clever Jack's performance could detect nothing suspicious. A second scientific commission was more sceptical, however. Oscar Pfungst, a German psychologist, turned in a long report in which he declared that Clever Jack had not the least idea of the arts of reading and reckoning. He was prompted to give the right answers, Pfungst said, by means of barely perceptible signs given by Herr von Osten. Of course that did not make Clever Jack less deserving of his name but, after all, the performance was only a new kind of circus act, of no interest to science.

The case was closed and man's arithmetical prerogative had been saved. Herr von Osten, meanwhile, had found a student of the art of teaching horses who proved to be more persistent and even more successful than his master. Karl Krall, a rich jewellery manufacturer from Elberfeld, inherited the discredited Clever Jack, together with several other horses of divers origin. Krall set to work teaching these horses. His stable became a regular cramming school for calculators. In a few days he had taught his horses the rudiments of arithmetic. A few months later they were able to work out square and cube roots. They struck off the unit numbers with the left foot and the tens with the right and seldom did a mistake creep into their reckoning.

This was not all. The Elberfeld Master taught his pupils the alphabet. Presently they were breaking up complicated words into letters and reading and writing like scholars. Pawing with their hoofs was their way of writing, and they were good enough at it to give highly intelligent answers to tricky questions. They obviously understood not only what their teacher was saying but what everybody else was saying as well. In their master's absence they carried on conversations with guests who had come to Elberfeld to view the miracle of the talking horses.

The best pupil was Mohammed, an Arab stallion. Mohammed solved the most difficult arithmetical problems with playful ease. At the same time he was a brilliant conversationalist, never at a loss for a pithy answer. Since Mohammed had gone to school in Germany, he spoke German, yet his mode of expression had something in common with written Arabic, for he used only con-

Fig. 72. "Three Little Wolves" by Walt Disney

sonants, leaving out the vowels. With his feet he "talked" a phonetically unobjectionable, if somewhat abbreviated, language. With him "horse"—"*Pferd*" in German—became "Frt"; and "sugar"—"*Zucker*" in German—became "Zkr." And so on. Yet he was well aware of polite usage: in giving proper names he carefully spelt out the vowels. Probably the most intuitively penetrating description of the Elberfeld wonder horses was written by Maurice Maeterlinck, the Belgian author. Others who critically inspected the horses were more sceptical but no one went so far as to dismiss the performance as mere humbug. Unfortunately none of the savants who published fat volumes on Mohammed and his stablemates thought to continue the experiment. Krall, somewhat discouraged, finally broke up his school,

after having presented his teaching method in an excellent monograph without the least trace of bluff or affectation of mystery.

When world war had intervened these remarkable educational
experiments were forgotten. Since no one cared any more, the
animals apparently lost their ability to read, write and reckon.
It was like the Greek myth in which the goddess Hera gave
Xanthos, Achilles's horse, the power of speech, but the Furies
took it from him.

THE RUBICON OF SPEECH

The decadence of intellectual phenomena among animals or,
more correctly, public indifference towards these phenomena,
did not come about by mere chance. This changed attitude was
the sign of a new age. The enormous interest in animals shown
by the first generations of Darwinians had now vanished.
Lengthy works on animals such as Brehm's *Tierleben* (*Animal
Life*), which came out in ten massive volumes, or the equally
comprehensive *Souvenirs entomologiques* of Jean-Henri Fabre,
an inexhaustible source for zoologists, were no longer read as
avidly as the most thrilling novels. No longer was the informed
reading public delighted by such works as the studies of mental
evolution among animals by the Canadian biologist, George John
Romanes.

The philosophy of the twentieth century is out of touch with
the animal world, it is neither for nor against, but—which is
worse—completely neutral. Modern trends such as psychoanaly-
sis, phenomenonology and its most recent offshoot, existentialism,
derive from introspection, a method obviously not applicable to
the animal kingdom. The zoologists themselves have become
more cautious and more critical, even more sceptical, in respect
of everything relating to animal psychology. A brand-new method
of investigation has arisen under the influence of work done by
the Englishman C. Lloyd Morgan, that is, the method of the
behaviourist school of thought. Behaviourist psychology is a
sober science, one that excludes all anthropocentric interpreta-

tion and all speculation on the animal's inner life, especially on questions relating to consciousness. "What animal psychology studies," one of the masters of the behaviourist school has written, "is not more or less than the actions and behaviour of animals, in relation to conditions, past and present, that surround and condition them—it is their conduct."

In behaviourist practice animals are more apt to be studied under laboratory conditions than freely moving about out in the open. Even so, laboratory experiments have yielded a great many interesting observations. Experiment has demonstrated, for example, that animal instinct is not an innate and unchangeable thing but, within limits, can be developed by training. Manifestly acquired psychic attributes leave their mark on the offspring, for, if they are exposed to the same dangers and alternatives to which the parents have been exposed, they react much more intelligently.

Regular intelligence contests have been arranged among animals of different species, families, sexes and age levels, patterned on psychotechnical tests for estimating human intelligence. These experiments have led to a revision of opinions, favourable and unfavourable, concerning certain groups. Long-tailed and capuchin monkeys were the winners in one of these remarkable intelligence experiments, with rats a close second. The rats, however, did better in the tests than many monkeys and lemurs, with females superior to males. The capuchin, a lower species of monkey, especially astonished the scientists with his intelligence. In some respects he was superior to the anthropoid apes.

The critical question as to the dividing line between human and animal intelligence had yet to be answered. Shortly after the First World War, Wolfgang Koehler, a German psychologist, carried out experiments in Teneriffe with chimpanzees. These experiments attracted widespread attention because they demonstrated amazing similarities between human and simian actions and reactions. The chimpanzees, Koehler found, were able to manipulate relatively complicated apparatus as well as and perhaps even better than a four-year-old child.

Is it possible to conclude from such experiments that the anthropoid apes have an intelligence potentially as active and highly ordered as that of a human, a man able to talk and form opinions on many subjects? Countless psychologists have denied

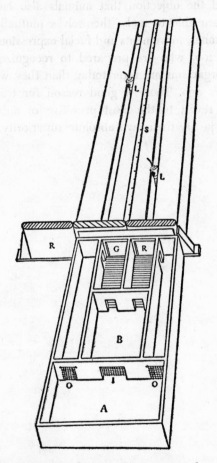

Fig. 73. Apparatus for experimenting on the colour sensitivity of animals (R—red; G—green; the animal in B is meant to find its way to A)

this. For lack of a better argument they fall back on Descartes's old theory. Speech bound up with the power of forming ideas, they say, is the final criterion. The children of *Homo sapiens* learn this art in eighteen months. "That is the rubicon which no animal will ever cross!"

Those who consider that humans have a monopoly on intelligence discard the objection that animals also have their languages and are able to make themselves mutually understood by means of tones, movements and facial expressions. Specialists, and laymen, too, who are prepared to recognize the psychic unity of all organisms are rarer today than they were fifty or a hundred years ago. There is good reason for this. In warlike periods men revert to the most primitive of animal instincts; they need to justify their own absolute superiority.

THE AGE OF CHEMISTRY

Village street as seen by man

The same street seen through the eye of a fly (after Uexküll and Brock)

Carrier pigeon as cameraman . . . and the picture which the
camera took between the wing tips

The animal in philately

American poster advertising a remedy for hog cholera

French courting card

🔲 XXV 🔲

Natural Propagation and Eugenics

THE twentieth century, in the scientific field, began as an age of revolution. It was ushered in by two great discoveries or, more precisely, by a discovery and a rediscovery. From his observations on thermal radiation, Max Planck, the Berlin physicist, derived the principle that energy is radiated or absorbed in multiples of a unit quantum, a "quantum" representing a very small, yet measurable, quantity. Planck was able to determine the value of this elemental quantum and describe the radiation process in a relatively simple mathematical formula.

At first this quantum theory, formulated in 1900, was familiar only to the specialists. With the passage of time it became not only the foundation stone of modern physics but was expanded, quite contrary to Planck's intention, into a *Weltanschauung*, a philosophical attitude towards life as a whole. The basic tenet of this philosophy is that nature makes saltations. This does not mean, however, that the flow of natural events is completely haphazard, determined by mere chance. The new concept, like the old, sees nature as characterized by lawfulness, a lawfulness which, up to a certain point, can be apprehended and interpreted by the human mind. At the same time, the quantum theory and its derivative points of view are absolutely opposed to the idea that had previously governed the approach to biological investigation and which had reached its high point in the

Darwinian theory—namely, that all change is a continuous, unbroken evolutionary process.

MATHEMATICS AND HEREDITY

At about the same time that this new orientation had become established in physics, similar ideas concerning organic nature appeared. The Dutch botanist Hugo de Vries, a confirmed Darwinist, while experimenting with the evening primrose had observed that varieties with transmissible, permanent characteristics sometimes evolved out of thin air. This phenomenon could not be explained simply in terms of the rules of natural selection. De Vries called this sudden kind of change "mutation." Since it occurred most frequently in hybrids, it seemed that hereditary factors must be involved but as yet little was known about these matters. Despite all the advances in embryology, the theory of heredity remained a closed book.

While searching for material evidence to support his conjecture, de Vries chanced upon the work of a completely unknown Austrian botanist. In the 1860s Gregor Johann Mendel, an Augustinian monk, had made a series of experiments with peas in the cloister garden at Bruenn, then the provincial capital of Moravia. He had crossed tall and short, and red and white, peas, repeating the same experiment thousands of times and always getting the same results. In the first generation the crosses from longs and shorts were mostly long, and those from reds and whites mostly red. In the second, self-fertilized, generation, the count was nearly always three longs and one short or three reds and one white.

Mendel noted, however, that this three-to-one proportion was due to an optical illusion. More closely observed, the crosses from reds and whites consisted always of two rose, one red, and one white flower. But since red is "dominant" and white "recessive" among these colours, superficially there seemed to be three reds and but one white. The same was true of size.

De Vries and other investigators repeated the experiments

using various kinds of plants and some animals as well. Complicated crossings of hybrids and pure-breds confirmed the rule. Always the proportion discovered by Mendel was revealed.

It seemed as if a great secret had been disclosed. Overnight the name of Gregor Mendel became one of the most popular in the natural sciences. His modest work on hybridization was justly ranked among the classics. The "Mendelian laws" were incorporated into textbooks as irrefragable truths. Biologists began to use the verb "Mendelize." The slogan "Mendelism" became almost as widely current as Darwinism.

The author of the new theory himself became a legendary figure. In Gregor Mendel the best of the Middle Ages seemed to have been reborn. It was extraordinary, to say the least of it, that a monk, in modern times, should devote himself to such studies and achieve such unique results. Yet basically Mendel's career was not so different from that of many another neglected genius. The real Mendel was never the kind of monk who is turned completely away from the world; nor was he a scientific amateur. While a member of the Augustinian order, he spent two years studying biology in Vienna before carrying out his experiments. Although he had probably never read Darwin's *Origin of Species*, undoubtedly he had heard of the theory of evolution. When he was finished with his experiments, he was not content to limit the news of his discovery to the Bruenn Natural History Society, the organization which first published his monograph, but also got into touch with foreign experts. He submitted his experimental results to Naegeli the Swiss, one of the greatest botanists of his time, for critical examination, but never received any acknowledgment from that quarter. After a second publication had failed to elicit any response Mendel became discouraged, abandoned his biological studies, and devoted himself entirely to spiritual duties. Later he became abbot of the Koenigkloster at Bruenn and in this capacity led a bitter fight against the Austrian tax administration.

Mendel's special gift lay not so much in the art of scientific observation as in the art of formulating mathematical-statistical relationships. A hundred years earlier a chaplain, Suessmilch, had seen evidence of the "divine order" of the world in population statistics. Mendel, in turn, saw signs of an irrefutable and ubiquitous world order in the statistics of heredity. The discovery of such simple numerical relationships might well be as far as man could advance in the knowledge of nature. Mendel apparently felt that to probe below this level in search of final causes was so much speculation.

The mathematical approach to the problems of genetics, which Mendel was the first to use in a strictly methodical fashion, has continued to dominate the field to this very day. Books on the science of genetics superficially resemble those on mathematics. They are filled with formulae and numerical paradigms which seem to be uncommonly involved, until the reader discovers that each animal and plant genus has a characteristic and fixed number of chromosomes in the nucleus of the germ cell. These chromosomes, as their name suggests, are easily stained miniature bodies. In the germ cells the chromosomes act differently from those in other kinds of cells and it would seem as if they contained the genetic material determining the various species. The number of chromosomes in the germ cells of the different species does not correspond at all with the hierarchy that zoologists have set up for the animal kingdom, however. The ovum of a mare contains 18 chromosomes; of a cow, 19; of a sow, 20; of a frog, 26; and of a hen, 40. Man, with 48 chromosomes, is one of the most highly endowed organisms in respect of genetics and fulfils hierarchic expectations.

LABORATORY-PRODUCED CREATURES

The concept of heredity assumes that like does not literally follow from like but rather that a common line of descent gives rise either to similarities or grades of differentiation. The aim of genetic science is to ascertain and explain these gradated differences.

In the preliminary stages of this enterprise the Mendelian laws served as a *point d'appui,* but the formulations made possible on this basis were, after all, rather crude and macroscopic. An attempt had to be made to trace out the genetic process on the microscopic and ultra-microscopic levels, so in hundreds of biological institutes investigators set up their microscopes and began to track down mutations in the germ cell itself. The most successful line of research developed in the United States. Thomas Hunt Morgan, a zoologist working at Columbia University, hit on the idea of experimenting with a very short-lived species of insect, the fruit fly. These flies propagate so rapidly that in the course of a few months the developmental process can be observed through several generations. Moreover, the germ cells of the fruit fly contain only four pairs of chromosomes, which facilitates observation and reckoning.

The experiments carried out by Morgan and his pupils since 1910 have been of epochal significance. First, they have shown that mutations are much more frequent in the animal world than had ever been supposed. Second, and of even more importance, they have shown that new varieties can be produced with remarkable ease—and this discovery, of course, has opened up entirely new vistas to breeders. By carefully selecting from his experimental subjects, Morgan was able to produce, for example, a strain of flies with ever smaller eyes, until at last he got a generation with no eyes at all. Then, for a time, nature seemed to fight back against her new masters. After a few generations the eyeless flies recovered their sight, indeed were born with especially large eyes. In still later generations these residual characters of the "wild" race of fruit flies disappeared and the artificial strain produced in the laboratory kept the upper hand.

Even deeper mutations could be brought about by irradiation of the chromosomes. By the use of x-rays changes were produced in the shape of the head and body which became hereditary in the offspring. Cosmic rays also seemed to produce similar effects. Fruit flies sent up into the stratosphere in a balloon later showed five times as many mutations as flies kept at sea level. From this experiment it was inferred that natural mutations are, partly at least, conditioned by radiation from radioactive substances, by ultra-violet light and by other cosmic influences. Much simpler chemical measures also served to stimulate mutations. It seemed possible that radioactive potassium could induce mutations even

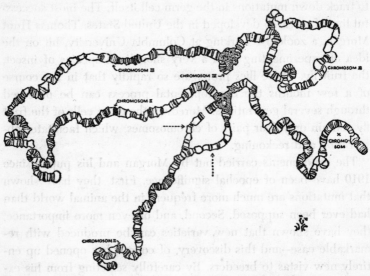

Fig. 74. Chromosomes of the Fruit fly (*Drosophila melanogaster*), on which innumerable modern experiments in heredity have been made

in the protoplasm of the germ cell. In any case, many facts were gradually revealed on which ingenious theories as to the origin of mutations could be built. All these theories, in one way or another, indicated that the genesis of new varieties, even of new species, could be traced back to chemical processes occurring in the germ cells.

GENETIC CHARACTERS AT WILL

The geneticists had excellent reasons for taking refuge in radiation chemistry. Their hope that heredity could be explained, to some degree, by microscopic investigation, had not been fulfilled. Strong lenses permitted the experimenter to observe changes of form in the chromosomes but were powerless to detect what was going on inside them. The chromosomes were relatively large physical bodies, whereas the hereditary process seemingly took place on a much more subtle level. Even in the genus *Drosophila* over four hundred specific, hereditary characters had been established, none of them clearly evidenced under the microscope. The only thing, and this could be seen under the microscope, was that in some mutations certain parts of the chromosomes were found to be changed.

Anatomy, in the genetic context, lagged behind physiology. To explain physiological effects an anatomical working hypothesis was necessary. For the time being the geneticists unanimously agreed that the real bearers of the specific hereditary characters— that is, the type of visual apparatus or of pigmentation or the tendency to have nose bleeds and the like—were not the chromosomes themselves, but infinitely smaller and, at this stage of microscopy, invisible bodies, located at certain places within the chromosomes. These entities the geneticists called "genes." They were thought of as complex protein molecules, though nothing was actually known about their chemical composition or physical shape. Caution decreed that, for the time being, they should be used as pure hypotheses helpful in interpreting certain symptoms.

This gene theory was obviously an organic counterpart of the recently developed atom theory. Genes, though assumed to be hundreds of times larger than atoms, are still invisible to the human eye. In Bohr's model of the atom, the electrons whirl about the nucleus in definite orbits and radiation occurs when, and only when, electrons jump from one orbit to another. Genes likewise are effective only under certain definite conditions. They are strung together like pearls on or in the chromosomes. Each gene has its fixed place and form. No chromosome ever has more than one of the same kind of gene. Genes which produce related effects —e.g., the black and white pigmentation in mottled cows—are bound together. Yet these same genes can function in other and larger groupings.

There are good, bad and lethal genes. Some of them are indispensable in producing normal offspring and when they are missing anomalies such as albinism occur. Others may engender sickness, still others early death. A mortality table has been worked out for the *Drosophila* similar to the tables used by the insurance companies. Experiments with salamanders showed that genes are functionally hierarchized. The high command among amphibian genes has a definite location in the chromosome and, if artificially transposed elsewhere, monster forms will result. Spemann, who discovered this "organizer" among the genes, also succeeded in splitting the ovum by irritant stimuli and thus produced artificial twins.

Great hopes were raised by these sensational discoveries in the field of genetics. When male and female chromosomes were distinguished it was assumed that soon the sex of the offspring would easily be regulated at will. The X-shaped female chromosomes seemed to be subject to stimulation by acids and the Y-shaped male chromosomes by potassium. The observation having been made that among birds and, under certain conditions, among frogs, the X-chromosomes could take over the functions of the Y-chromosomes, the experimenters came to the conclusion that the female germinal arrangement could be transformed into a male arrangement. In both scientific and popular circles it was suggested that a knowledge of genes would soon give rise to a real science of eugenics, making it possible to eliminate unfavourable characteristics from human posterity while retaining the favourable ones.

Practically none of these vaulting hopes has actually been fulfilled. In spite of the amazing laboratory experiments carried out during several decades, the practical application of genetic findings to mammals has remained extremely limited. The geneticists have certainly provided superior insight into the origin of mixed races and the inheritance of colour, hair, horns and the like, yet there is still no microscopic proof that such entities as genes actually exist. As for the animal breeders, they have always had an elementary knowledge and made practical use of these relationships without benefit of the gene theory. Nor have the animal breeders needed any scientific persuasion to be convinced that degeneration and sterility do not necessarily follow from inbreeding, a popular misconception which, of course, has been invali-

Fig. 75. The eternal stork legend. Illustration by Theodor Hosemann of Hans Andersen's fairy tale "The Storks" (1851)

dated by genetics. Valuable horses are always produced by inbreeding and incest and are no more adversely affected by it than were Cleopatra's spiritual and physical qualities by three hundred years of Ptolemaic inbreeding.

The mutation and gene theories, as based on Mendel's and Morgan's experiments, have not achieved anticipated results in the purely theoretical field either. The thesis that evolution is a discontinuous process, rather than a continuous one as Darwin believed, is no more demonstrable than the opposite opinion. The mutationists, of course, can flatter themselves that their theory is based on experiment, whereas Darwin's is supported only by palaeontological findings. Still, neither natural nor artificial mutations by themselves are sufficiently convincing to serve as the foundation of an entirely new biological rationale.

Strangely enough, mutationism suffers from a glut of evidence. Mutations are amazingly numerous in nature. If anomalies and malformations are taken into account, there is one mutation in every ten thousand—or even in every thousand—living beings. Indeed, in many species the proportion increases to one out of every hundred. The reason for this frequency of mutation is unknown. If only a small number of these mutations turns out to be permanent, it would certainly seem as if deep-reaching changes in the animal and plant kingdoms should become observable within one human generation. Actually nothing of the sort occurs. The great majority of mutations lead to degeneration, to impairments of organic function, to sterility, and very often to early death. Even in those relatively rare cases where new characters persist through several generations, they tend to weaken progressively, and in the end the residual change is so slight that it is hardly possible to speak in terms of a new, more or less stable, variety. All in all the life process seems to be more evolutionary than revolutionary, moving slowly and with very limited consequences. Mutation cannot, therefore, be regarded, as it was by some for a time after Morgan's sensational experiments, as the great balance wheel of evolution. Indeed, Morgan himself, unlike so many of his school, recognized this fact.

The die-hard mutationist, confronted by the only too modest results of his own experiments, must fall back on definitive changes brought about in the past by mutation. For example, yellow canaries, first known to exist at the end of the seventeenth century, were produced by the mutation of green canaries. Among the mammals, such long-haired strains as the Angora cat originated through mutation. The anthropoid apes and man himself have mutation to thank for their not having tails like their simian ancestors. However, even if due consideration is given to all this evidence, one is still a long way from proving the fantastic notions current on the eve of Darwinism: that a snake was born one fine day from a fish egg or a mammal from the egg of an ostrich.

In order that they should not get lost among highly improbable hypotheses, prudent mutationists have reverted to Lamarck and Darwin. Although they argue against the influence of environment and function in the evolution of organs, they admit that new characters originating by mutation can persist only under favourable environmental conditions, otherwise they will be lost in the struggle for existence. They admit, too, that the prospects for the survival of living organisms which have only recently come into being through mutation are not as good as the prospects of those which have already withstood the rigorous tests of natural selection and found the climate, food supply and other conditions essential to their existence.

HEREDITY IN EAST AND WEST

The return to Lamarck was even more decisive in the young Russian school of genetics. Lysenko and his colleagues particularly dispute Weismann's dualistic concept, the point of view generally accepted by Morgan and his followers. Weismann makes a categorical distinction between "germ" and "soma," that is between sexual cells and the other cells of the body. Only germ cells, and within these cells only the chromosomes, have the ability to transmit hereditary substance to the next generation. This theory, which is neither logically invulnerable nor fruitful of practical results, has unquestionably led to an undervaluation of other factors at work in the reproductive process, especially of the cytoplasm, an indispensable germ-cell element in protecting and nourishing the chromosomes. Older experiments have shown that the cytoplasm can adjust itself to environmental conditions. This fact alone makes heredity a less rigid and autochthonous process than Weismann's adherents claim it to be. Moreover, the hormones exercise an important influence on cellular division. Thus, in order to create types useful to mankind, proper influences must be brought to bear on the cytoplasm and hormonal secretions, not on the chromosomes alone.

Up to this point many western critics of Weismann's and of the chromosome theories agree, but Russian scientists want to do away entirely with the interpretations linked with the names of Mendel, Weismann and Morgan. "T. D. Lysenko has the honour," we are informed in an official account of his teachings, "of having purified the Darwinian theory of selection of its Weismannian distortions." While the Russians think of themselves as orthodox Darwinians, they try to give Darwinism a more activist form, to reshape it as "creative Darwinism." They place less emphasis on natural selection and more on artificial selection, this presumably in the interest of improving the resources of mankind.

Ivan Vladimirovitch Mitshurin, a clever horticulturist from the government of Tambov, is considered to be the real founder of this school. Under both the Tsarist and later, with state help, the Soviet régime, Mitshurin was very successful in creating new kinds of fruit by crossbreeding and changing the plant's environment. Like many Russians of peasant stock, Mitshurin was fond of philosophizing. He read and wrote a great deal, speculated on the laws of evolution, and pondered means of improving nature for the benefit of suffering humanity. In common with most breeders, he firmly believed in the transmission of acquired characteristics and considered the Mendelian experiments to be so much idle trifling, leading to nowhere but error.

The master himself having died, an octogenarian, in 1935, Mitshurin's disciples on the whole held fast to their teacher's views. Being better equipped scientifically, however, they were more cautious about the way they expressed their ideas on the "laws of improvement." "The hereditary tendencies," Lysenko explained, "result from the concentration of the effects of environmental conditions which have been assimilated by the organism throughout a number of precedent generations." According to this assumption, heredity can be controlled. By changing environmental conditions it is possible, Lysenko claims, to alter inherited tendencies.

The most important means of bringing about a "lability of heredity tendencies" is through hybridization. Mitshurin had already made some daring experiments along this line, crossing apple trees with pear trees, mulberry trees with cherry trees, etc. But his followers went much farther. To the amazement of western biologists, they asserted that by the simple grafting of different varieties and species of plants they had created brand-new types with fixed characters. Since it would be quite impossible for the sexual chromosomes of the scion to form a union with those of the parent stock, it must be assumed that all parts of the living material, including that material which, in Weismann's terminology, belongs to the "soma," must possess hereditary capabilities. The change in the hereditary tendency is occasioned by "exchange of sap between scion and stock." The basic experiments were carried out on plants but the same principle is theoretically applicable to the animal world.

Although similar experiments had been made at an earlier date in other countries, giving rise to similar explanations, the Russian claims were greeted with extreme scepticism in the west. None of Lysenko's results has ever been scientifically corroborated outside the Soviet countries.

Despite their apparent irreconcilability it is by no means impossible theoretically to reconcile the Russian and western attitudes towards heredity, yet this purely scientific question has been forcibly diverted into political channels. As during the early days of Darwinism, champions from both sides have attacked each other hammer and tongs with rude exchanges of insult. The Russians accuse the adherents of Mendel and Morgan of clinging to an utterly sterile and fossilized theory through sheer political reaction and racial arrogance. They declare that western genetics at its best is a waste of time. For forty years, they say, western geneticists have been doing nothing but play about with fruit flies. In America, on the other hand, the Russian biologists are accused of using pseudo-scientific methods. The Russians, Americans declare, not only tailor their theories to fit their politics but distort facts as well. In western Europe the polemics were couched in milder language, but all in all it must be said that the quarrels over a question so important both in theory and in practice does little honour to our times.

ARTIFICIAL INSEMINATION

The process known in animal breeding as artificial insemination has hardly anything to do with the science of heredity. It is a crude technique aimed at avoiding the necessity of the sexual act. Semen is collected from the male and injected into the female. In this manner more frequent conceptions are assured. In Denmark this method was used systematically over a period of two years and semen was introduced into 2,677 cows. On the average there were 100 impregnations for every 163 inseminations, as compared with 100 for every 208 by the natural method. Human ingenuity has proved more potent than bullish passion.

The artificial insemination of fowl has been even more spectacularly successful. The natural crossbreeding of poultry of different sizes yielded but scant results; only 4 per cent of the eggs proved fertile. Artificial insemination increased the proportion of fertile eggs to 97 per cent.

Breeders praise artificial insemination especially for its economy. A whole series of females can be impregnated with one charge of semen, making it possible for the best sires to produce far more offspring. Moreover, the sperm of some animals, e.g., that of bulls and he-goats, is easily preserved, though it is somewhat harder to keep stallion or boar sperm. The seed of superior studs has even been flown by plane from one country to another, obviating the purchase of expensive sires.

Artificial insemination is not quite as new a method as it might seem. Many centuries ago the Arabs were artificially impregnating their mares. Thanks to his improved technique and sanitary precautions, the modern breeder is unquestionably doing a better job than his predecessors, both in a quantitative and a qualitative sense. In the case of pigs and sheep, which periodically maturate several ova, it is quite possible that eventually twins and triplets will be produced with moderate frequency by the use of artificial insemination. Cattle breeders in the United States have been pretty successful, too, in transplanting the ova of valuable cows into the uteri of less valuable ordinary females. The possibilities of rationalized breeding methods and animal eugenics are unlimited.

The only question that remains is whether the maternal animal's disposition is adversely affected. Animal psychologists who have gone into this matter are unanimously agreed that artificial insemination does not harm the female's health. In any case, they need not be completely deprived of a normal love life before the veterinary applies his seminal syringe. All the same, artificial insemination portends a drastic change in animal life. Since time immemorial man has castrated the great majority of useful male beasts. Now he is interfering in the female's sexual life. If the experiments now being carried out in many places should meet expectations, in the not too distant future a strict system of birth control will be decreed for domestic animals.

Synthetics and Substitutes

ONCE animals had lost their ancient monopoly in the field of transport, other ways were sought to make use of them, but elsewhere, too, competition had increased. Animal products, whether of food or clothing, have suffered a decline.

Actually animals have never had a complete monopoly in the matter of supplying food and clothing, except among primitive hunter folk. Yet on the whole animal products have traditionally always been ranked higher than plant products. The rich have always preferred animal food and clothing. Vegetables have always been the food of the poor; clothes from plant fibres have always been the poor man's clothes.

The first breach in this ancient order of precedence occurred when cane sugar was introduced into Europe. This forced bee culture to become a minor branch of animal husbandry. The bees, however, still retained a special place in the economic scheme because of their seoond product—wax. Many apiaries were kept going by the great demand for candle wax. The largest user of wax was the Church, but candles, the only means of illumination without unpleasant odour, were also in daily use in the homes of the well-to-do. The bees lost their monopoly after the middle of the nineteenth century, when petroleum production increased and gas lighting spread in homes and streets.

THE ORIGIN OF MARGARINE

Not long after this revolution in lighting a serious competitor to animal fats as food came into the picture. In the course of oversea military expeditions into subtropical lands, undertaken by the French during the Second Empire, it came to light that the soldiers had no fat to spread on their bread that would keep in a warm climate. Napoleon III, a great promoter in the technical and economic fields, offered a big reward to anyone who could make a fat that would stand up to hot climates. After long experimentation a French chemist, Hyppolite Mège-Mouriés, found a solution. The margarine he first proposed was made of a mixture of animal substances, the most important one of which was mutton fat, but further research showed that plant oils were better suited for the job, and cheaper, too. The modern margarine industry, first built up in Holland—land of milk and butter—prefers to use tropical vegetable oils, although some animal substances, notably whale oil, are also occasionally employed.

Margarine was the first out-and-out substitute for animal food. Though not equal to animal fat in quality, it was perfectly edible. This substitute, originally made for the use of seafarers, has today become the principal fat in the diet of millions of people in northern countries, an indispensable feature of the poor man's kitchen everywhere.

On the production side the manufacture of margarine has become a branch of the chemical industry, allied to the manufacture of soap, another product in which vegetable oils have largely supplanted animal fats. Both soap and margarine use the same basic raw material, mostly cotton seed or palm oil. The palm plantations in French West Africa, Nigeria and the Congo are a great reservoir of vegetable oil.

Apparently chemistry has not said its final word on fat substitutes, though attempts to replace animal and vegetable fats with mineral products have not got very far as yet. German efforts to make a kind of butter substitute from coal before the Second World War elicited a great deal of mockery but achieved small practical result. Yet there is no reason why such an enterprise should be laughed down. In Europe, Asia and Africa at least two-thirds of the population are inadequately provided with fatty foods and in the near future neither animal nor vegetable fats are likely to be available in adequate quantity to meet this dietary need.

Numerous attempts have been made in related fields to substitute vegetable for animal food products, not because they are better but because they cost less. Sugar preparations with some sort of fruit juice added have been brought out under the name of "artificial honey." Beet sugar has replaced cane sugar in northern countries ever since the Napoleonic wars, but here, too, chemistry has opened up new prospects. Saccharine, first extracted from coal tar in 1879, is five hundred times as sweet as sugar, but has no nutritive value.

Since 1912 sugar has been made in the laboratory from wood. This sugar is not *ersatz* but chemically and physiologically the equivalent of regular plant sugar. Only the high cost of manufacture has prevented the industrialization of the process before now. Animals, however, are already being fed on a chemical product which contains a wood sugar solution and nitrogen, magnesium and phosphorus. The mixture serves as a substitute for oil cake.

It is only proteinous meat food for which no substitute has yet been found, since at this point animal proteins cannot be synthesized. Thus, animals reared for meat are assured of a continued existence—though they must pay for their right to live by a premature death.

ARTIFICIAL SILK AND WOOL

The great domain of *ersatz* in the last few decades has been the clothing field. All the four great natural textile products—wool, cotton, silk and flax—have been affected. Of these four the two animal products have been more seriously threatened than the plant stuffs.

The model for textile chemistry is the silkworm. Ever since the seventeenth century the chemists have been working on the problem of manufacturing artificial fibre. Robert Hooke, the English chemist, one of the most versatile minds and skilful experimenters of his age, was the first, in 1665, clearly to recognize the principle involved. He saw it would be necessary first to make a solution of some plant substance, force the solution through pinpoint apertures, then harden the resulting filament. Two generations after Hooke, Réaumur, who had had experience in thermal measurement, animal psychology and other scientific fields, also tried to find a practical solution to the artificial fibre problem, but in the end he was frustrated, like so many other physicists and chemists who tackled the same question. Then, in about the middle of the seventeenth century, a suitable raw material was finally discovered. The chemists succeeded in nitrating cotton, which chemically is pure cellulose, also in bringing wood cellulose into solution.

A definitive technique was formulated a century later in France by Count Hilaire de Chardonnet, who staked a fortune on the process and lost. His apparatus forced a wood cellulose solution through fine glass tubes, producing shiny, silk-like fibres. When he exhibited it at the Paris exposition in 1889 it immediately attracted interest. Two German industrialists wanted to buy his patent but Chardonnet conscientiously explained that his invention was not ready for large-scale mechanical application. Seven years passed before Chardonnet himself established the first rayon factory in Besançon, which turned out to be a complete commercial failure.

However, after some technical improvements had been introduced and the material made less inflammable, rayon gained rapid acceptance among women. Within two decades a great industry had sprung up in England, Germany and Italy, and merged into international trusts.

The silkworm was now in a serious plight. Silkworm breeders and silk manufacturers fought heroically against the ignoble competition of wood and cotton cellulose, from which materials true silk could never be spun. They turned to the courts for help and the judges declared for *Bombyx*, banning the use of the trade name "artificial silk" in advertising. Whether the new textile was called artificial silk, rayon or art silk, there was no longer any doubt as to its success. Even the old silk countries had to capitulate. Japan, greatest exporter of natural silk, built up a huge artificial silk industry. In Lyons, home of the finest silk textiles, erstwhile silk manufacturers shifted over to rayon to save themselves from ruin. Animal silk soon took second place behind plant silk.

The only advantage to *Bombyx* silk seemed to be its superior durability; but this monopoly, too, was broken when the Americans made a fibre from coal that was close to natural silk in fineness and appearance and almost indestructible. This time the manufacturers did not even try to profane the honourable name of silk. They gave their product a Greek-sounding fantasy name, "nylon," which has become more popular than the now virtually forgotten one of the *Bombyx* material ever was.

So long as chemically produced fibres were light in weight, they competed only with silk, cotton and flax. But it was only a question of time before cellulose textiles made from wood spelt a threat to wool. Technically, the manufacture of artificial wool set an entirely new problem. The manufacturers of silk substitutes prided themselves on making the finest and lightest of fibres, equal to the best efforts of *Bombyx*. In Germany fibres were produced so fine that a filament 11¼ miles long weighed only 15½ grains. Yet even this record was surpassed in the United States, where a filament is claimed that will make a thread long enough to span the Atlantic Ocean. Now, however, the chemists wanted to produce a heavy, warm type of fibre.

Using a process previously suggested by Girard in 1912, many short, fine filaments were pressed together under steam and the product was a felt-like fibre very much like wool. Mixed with sheep's wool it was woven into a fairly elastic and durable textile. The manufacture of artificial wool was launched in Germany during the First World War, at a time when it was impossible to import natural wool fibre and the public had to put up with all manner of *ersatz* materials, good and bad. However, the manufacture of cellulose wool did not grow into an important industry until two decades later. Japan followed the German example and engaged in a trade war with Australia, leading exporter of sheep's wool. The textile armament of the totalitarian states was carried out under the sign of artificial wool.

As usual the new product was at first greeted with derision. Artificial wool was condemned as a piece of fascist folly, a material for plebeians, miserable trash that would dissolve in snow or rain. Gradually the process was refined. England, and even the United States, went in for making wool substitutes. Today, though the new *ersatz* material has yet to compare either in quality or quantity with the artificial silks, artificial wool has undoubtedly become a serious and permanent competitor of the natural article. Its future will depend a great deal on whether the supply of wood is sufficient to clothe mankind.

TEXTILES FROM MILK

Strangely enough, the cow became involved in this war against the sheep. The cow, too, the chemists thought, should contribute something towards making wool superfluous. Naturally they were not thinking in terms of primitive man's luxurious custom of using cowhide for clothing; but casein could be extracted from milk, and from casein it was possible to make fibres which even chemically are very similar to natural wool.

Experiments along this line had already been under way in various countries. Keen interest was aroused in November, 1935, during the Abyssinian conflict, when there was talk of imposing an economic blockade on Italy, by Mussolini's announcement that from now on Italy would make wool from milk by the Feretti process. Although the Italians are far richer in children than in milk, for some years the new product, "lanital," actually was manufactured in large quantity. However, this product has never become a significant factor in the international market.

The chemists had long been interested in the use of casein for other than nutritive purposes. The Egyptians used casein as a mastic in pigments. Casein is a veteran, too, among modern chemical products. A Hanover printer by the name of Krische became interested in the material at the end of the last century and soon casein plastic was a favourite material for making table clock-frames, dominoes, Indian heads and other commodities of greater or lesser indispensability.

The plastic specialists assure us that the manufacture of casein will not deprive infants of their nourishment, since casein is made from skim milk but casein is actually a highly proteinous and valuable food. Nineteen million hektolitres of milk, or nearly the total production of Switzerland, were used to yield the seventy thousand tons of casein produced annually at the beginning of the Second World War. These figures show to what senseless extremes we have been led by the *ersatz* techniques.

Fortunately milk is the only animal product used as a raw material in the synthetics industry. Urea, though it has a physiological name, is today synthesized for industrial use entirely from inorganic material. On the other hand industrial chemistry has appropriated quite a few of the uses of animal products. One of the oldest and most successful materials is artificial horn, a mixture of nitrocellulose, camphor and alcohol invented in the 1860s by Alexander Parkes of Birmingham.

It would be grossly unjust, however, to represent chemistry as nothing but a rude competitor of the animal world. The chemists, for instance, have contributed a great deal towards improving the animals' food supply. Of course, the fertilizer industry, which performed this service, has at the same time taken over one of the animals' oldest agricultural functions. Today animal manures are of small consequence compared with vegetable or chemical fertilizers, particularly the latter. In old agricultural countries the farmers, out of sheer habit, still pile up manure into smoking mounds. Even if they did not, the fertility of the soil would not be drastically affected. Even South American guano has lost much of its former importance in agriculture, although the Peruvian government exploits the guano deposits according to the monopolistic rules of the mining industry. Only a very small part of the guano is still exported abroad. The phosphate and potassium mines and the nitrate factories have become the dispensers of fertility.

Breeding Rare Animals

Man has seldom troubled his head about animal welfare for purely altruistic reasons, but one of the infrequent exceptions to the rule is his interest in species threatened by extinction. It may be that Darwinism sharpened the human conscience in this regard and awakened, if not a pronounced feeling of relationship with animals, at least a better understanding of the universal process of growth and decay. Of course this should not be taken to mean that man has come to protect all harmless animals from extinction. In the last three hundred years thirteen species of mammals and birds have vanished from as small an area as Silesia, leaving out of account all the lower animals whose disappearance would be noticed only by a handful of specialists.

At the same time it can be said that during the last half-century more measures have been taken to preserve and restore animals grown rare than in any previous epoch. In several countries huge animal preserves have been created and special legislation passed to protect animals from hunters and thoughtless miscreants. Today conservation is not limited to animals of possible future use to man, such as the elk, but goes even beyond the bounds of purely scientific interest.

Naturally man likes to flatter himself that his conservation programmes are of a social kind, prompted by the goodness of his heart, by pity for lesser creatures menaced by death. Such noble motives may play a part in this particular kind of animal protection. The early advocates of the conservation movement were no doubt honestly convinced that they were carrying out a mission, that it was seemly for man, highest, wisest and fittest of all creatures in the struggle for survival, to assume the obligation of saving the lesser orders from decline, especially since man in times past had contributed so much to their diminution. In the struggle

Fig. 76. Dance of the Mock Turtle and the Gryphon.
From Lewis Carroll's *Alice in Wonderland*

for existence man feels no compassion for the animals, any more than he does for his own kind; but in the case of organisms which, because they are so few in number, cannot be harmful to man, he feels kindly towards them and treats them as a conqueror treats a wounded enemy. He will make them captive, but as a rule will not do away with them.

Yet it would be misleading and contrary to the truth to view this conservation process solely from a moral standpoint. One of the chief motives involved in the artificial preservation of moribund animal species is very definitely man's pleasure in rare things. Rarity in itself increases value in human estimation. It is one of the determining factors in fixing the price of any object. There are economic theories based on the rarity concept. To a certain degree rarity value is everywhere a definite psychological factor, even when it is in no way linked to utility value.

Man loves rare animals, and those grown so rare that they are on the verge of extinction profit by the sentiment. They enjoy man's special dispensation precisely because they are so scarce. If these animals happen to be prized on aesthetic grounds as well, protection and restoration through breeding become a highly remunerative business besides a matter of honour. This mixture of humanitarian and economic motives has led, during the last decades, to the growth of a number of animal-rearing industries which, in point of ambition and skill expended, surpass anything of a similar nature ever accomplished in Roman times.

OUTFOXING THE FOXES

The breeding of fur-bearing animals heads these industries though animals bred for their pelts have not been domesticated in the real sense of the word. At any rate, none of the martens or foxes kept in captivity have up to now shown any signs of losing their natural wildness. All northern fur-bearing animals have remained wild in captivity and will remain so for a long time to come, but wildness has not hindered man from making them an investment yielding far better profits than trapping.

We have already described the adventurous development and historical consequences of the trapping industry, an activity which, until very recent times, continued to be both romantic and profitable. Not since the eighteenth century have countries gone to war to get control of the trapping grounds but trapping and the fur trade, far beyond their actual economic importance, continued to serve as an excuse for political expansion. Following the trail of fur-bearing animals, enterprising men have tried again and again to conquer the world. After the struggle between the English and the French over the fur trade had been composed, fresh conflicts with Russia broke out.

The first imperialistic dream ever dreamed by an American was linked with the idea of establishing a global fur trade that would break the English hegemony in North America and Asia. This American was John Jacob Astor, later to have better luck with other plans. His adventurous fur-trading enterprise is not only famous in world economic history but has been given a place of honour in literature by Washington Irving. Beyond this he also deserves at least a word of mention in a history of animals.

In the year 1810, in order to extend the American fur trade to the far east and establish a regular shipping connection with China, then the greatest market for furs, Astor founded the city of Astoria in the extreme northwest corner of the United States. This name "Astoria" on cigarettes and hotel signs to this day proclaims Astor's fame throughout the world. A few years after its settlement, the fur town of Astoria was occupied by the English and turned into a fort. After the settlement had been restored to American hands, the English fur traders stayed on and for another half-century were the masters. Eventually Astoria became a salmon cannery town instead of a fur depot. The great trade route was still the north Atlantic, and the English Hudson's Bay Company the leading power in the world fur market.

Traffic in furs did not change much until 1910, when an amazing development rocked the trade. In that year twenty-five Canadian farm-bred silver foxes were sent to the London fur auction. The breeders, Charles Dalton and R. T. Oulton, had experimented for fifteen years in crossing black foxes and, though apparently knowing nothing about Mendel's law, finally succeeded in "Mendelizing" them. By repeatedly hybridizing ever darker black foxes, they finally produced a secondary strain, as it were, of silver foxes. By inbreeding this strain they created choice specimens of pure-blooded silver fox.

Silver was the colour most in demand in the world market, but there was the danger, too, that over-production of fox-farm pelts would result in a price collapse. The first effect was something quite different. The fur people were less interested in the pelts than in the living animals. Hundreds were eager to follow Dalton's and Oulton's example. Higher prices were paid for a mated pair of silver foxes—these animals mate for life—than for the finest breeding bulls or stud horses. In 1912 a silver fox and his vixen were sold at auction for over £7,000. Since the supply of breeding animals was not great enough to fill the demand, speculators took options on animals as yet unborn. Speculation in silver foxes became as extravagant as it had been in gold mines a few years before. Two hundred companies suddenly sprang up, into which profit-hungry financiers poured some £6 million.

The war in 1914 put an end to this frenzy, but breeding animals for their fur survived the war years and became big business. In 1938 there were more than ten thousand fur farms in Canada. Practically all silver fox and more than half the mink in the trade are farm-bred. At first the breeders believed that it was best for the animals to live under conditions as closely approximating to the wild state as possible. The farms were large establishments with enough acreage to permit the foxes to move about freely. Their monogamous inclinations were likewise favoured by keeping them in pairs; but these sentimentalities added greatly to the overheads.

Today more money is spent on sanitary arrangements—every large farm has its own animal hospital—but otherwise the animals are packed tightly together in narrow pens like regular prisoners. Their masters have also forced them to adjust their sexual life to a different régime. The foxes have been thrust, so to speak, into polygamy, for now each male animal must serve four females. It would seem that from the sexual aspect the foxes are only too easily outfoxed. Not only have the males quickly accustomed themselves to their pasha existence, but the vixens, too, have accepted the life of the harem.

Artificial breeding, as is always the rule, led to cosmopolitism. Peruvian chinchillas and Persian caracul sheep are now bred in Canada. The Persian sheep are no better off in North America than they were at home. The mother is either aborted according to Asiatic custom or the lambs killed immediately after birth to get the fine skin used in making astrakhan coats.

OSTRICH AND ALLIGATOR FARMS

Protection against the cold at least serves as an excuse for breeding rare animals, but the African ostrich survives, thanks to the human need for ornament. The African ostrich would probably have been exterminated long ago, like his even larger New Zealand cousin, had not civilized people found the same pleasure as the aborigines in decking themselves out with waving plumes. Under the Second Empire, when ostrich feathers were high

Fig. 77. Pen drawing by an unknown artist of the nineteenth century
(Courtesy of the Metropolitan Museum of Art)

fashion in Paris and not enough birds could be captured to satisfy the demand, French breeders established the first ostrich
farms in Algiers. Shortly after, Englishmen followed suit in South
Africa, also to supply the European market.

Since that time ostrich-breeding has been carried on with
greater or lesser success in many parts of the tropical and temperate zones. Some attempts to breed ostriches have even been
made in the South of France, yet the great domain of the ostrich
continues to be the Union of South Africa, where some 300,000
birds lead a rather contemplative life under the watchful eyes of
their warders. Once or twice a year their feathers are plucked out,
and the rest of the time they give the breeders little to do. They
eat anything that comes along. Even in captivity the ostrich
stomach lives up to its traditional robustness.

In order to get as many offspring as possible from the ostriches,
their love life has to be corrected to some degree but in a sense
opposite to that applied in the case of the foxes. Out in the wild,
ostriches usually live together in polygamous groups, one cock
to every four or five hens. Under these conditions the ostrich hens
very often do not lay enough eggs. On this account the ostrich
farmers prescribe a *ménage à trois*—one cock has to manage with
only two hens. Under these conditions an ostrich hen brings several dozen young into the world annually. Many trios have over
a hundred chicks in one year which within six months' time have
become as big and amply feathered as their parents.

Ostrich-breeding, as can be seen from the dividends paid by
the farming companies, is excellent business—providing that fashion does not upset the apple cart by banning, for an interval,
feathery decoration for hats, clothes, fans and shoes. When this
occurs, the birds are plucked only once a year and the cocks enjoy a close season until the mode changes once again.

One of the most curious products of fashion is alligator-breeding in the United States. Since crocodiles ceased to be sacred to
the Egyptians, men have been on a war footing with these beasts
for several thousand years. After handbags and shoes made of

crocodile leather had captured the ladies' fancy, crocodiles and their relatives, the alligators, became included in the ranks of animals bred in captivity. In California and Florida they are kept by the hundreds in small reservoirs, where they are permitted to live a prison life for years before being delivered up to higher purposes. At the same time crocodiles, genuine and otherwise, are steadily hunted in the rivers of Africa, China and South America, in consequence of which the breeders must still reckon with an irregular competition. As yet no international crocodile cartel has been formed.

JAPANESE PEARL CULTURE

The animals longest bred for luxury purposes are oysters, not only because they have been served on the tables of the rich since the days of Lucullus, but also because they have furnished pearls and mother-of-pearl. For thousands of years divers have been searching the sea bottom for oysters, with only one chance in a thousand of finding a pearl the size of a grain of sand; but for at least seven hundred years the Japanese and Chinese have known that pearls can be artificially produced by planting a foreign body in the oyster shell.

The invention of pearl culture is credited to Ye Yin Yang, a Chinese from the city of Hu-tsen. In the thirteenth century Ye Yin Yang was so successful in artificially stimulating oysters to form pearls that his efforts gave rise to a flourishing industry. Ye Yin Yang's method of pearl culture is still used in the region round the Chinese city of Tehsien. The oyster is prised open with a spatula. With a little bamboo rod objects are placed in the bared shell—particles of mud, splinters of bone or wood, metal pellets, etc.—and then the animal is flopped over and the other side subjected to the same treatment. Heavily laden, the oyster is returned to the water. The animal inside the shell tries to protect itself against the foreign bodies by encrusting them with calcium containing albumen. These pathological encasements of nacre are the pearls which the breeders seek. Many months after the operation they are removed and the oysters themselves eaten.

Chinese cultured pearls are seldom perfectly round, but Ye Yin Yang knew how to make up for this deficiency. He put into the shells little lead figures representing a sitting Buddha and the pearls were formed accordingly. Shells have been found containing eight such miniature Buddhas. The Buddha-shaped pearls were, of course, highly prized among the faithful, and even the shell showing the negative impress drew a high price as an amulet.

In the west, pearl culture was long regarded as a curious sort of trifling. Only a few collectors took any interest in it. However, cultured pearls began to give the natural pearls—concretions caused by parasites, chance injuries or some other kind of non-human intervention—stiffer competition when the Japanese set about producing them on a scientific basis. Professor Mitsukuri, a zoologist at the University of Tokyo, after a series of experiments carried out in 1889, came to the conclusion that by artificial stimulation pearls could be produced equal to the finest natural pearls found in the Persian Gulf. A trader in nacre, Kokichi Mikimoto, carried Mitsukuri's experiments along on a broader basis and after twenty years of effort Japan had a new and important industry unlike any other in the world.

Japanese pearl culture is based on the same general principle as the old Chinese method, but in technical detail is so different that it may be thought of as a brand-new invention. The critical difference is that the Japanese use tiny round particles of nacre from living oysters, rather than foreign bodies to stimulate the pearly deposit. These nacreous particles are implanted in the oyster with infinite care. The process involves a double vivisection requiring more skill and patience than most laboratory experiments carried out for medical purposes. The oysters used to form the pearls are carefully cultured specimens that have been kept under water for three years in cages. The oyster is allowed seven years for the nacreous concentration to accumulate, so that the whole pearl-culturing process takes ten years.

The bulk of the treated oysters form pearls but only one in twenty produces a marketable pearl. Mikimoto, who became the richest man in Japan from pearl culture, found a method of utilizing the less valuable pearls, an outlet similar to the one used by the old master of the craft, Ye Yin Yang. He ground them into a powder, which he sold as an elixir ensuring strength and longevity. The miracle elixir is especially in demand among Japanese seamen.

Mikimoto's pearls completely revolutionized the pearl market. They broadened the sales base, but at the same time did the business mortal injury. The old pearl dealers insist that no cultured pearl has ever attained the perfection of the natural product. And in fact natural pearls can be easily distinguished from artificial ones by means of x-rays, electromagnets and specially constructed lamps. Specialists with long experience can even do it with the naked eye. Chemically there is no difference, except perhaps that the cultured pearls are purer. To most people, however, both types look so much alike that natural pearls have lost much of their old glamour, with a consequent drop in price. There is little likelihood that the theft of a pearl necklace would raise the hue and cry it did in the days of Marie Antoinette.

▣ XXVIII ▣

The Political Economists' Reckoning

UNTIL nearly the end of the nineteenth century there were only two kinds of measuring units to apply to food products, one being money, the other quantitative measures for number, weight or size. These measuring units were adequate for producer and merchant but not for the consumer, since they did not enable him to know how much nourishment he was getting for his money. The consumer's stomach, of course, gave him an answer of sorts when he overloaded it with food or let it go hungry, but there was a wide range between these two extremes. The cleverest physiologist and the most experienced steward had no exact idea of the minimum amount of nourishment needed by a working man or how various foods compared in nutritive value.

It was an epochal innovation when, in 1885, the physiologist Max Rubner provided a quantitative explanation of the matter. Rubner found that one gramme of carbohydrate and one gramme of protein gave the body about the same amount of thermal energy—4.1 calories. One gramme of fat, however, supplied double this amount. These findings, of course, did not settle all nutritional questions. They merely showed that fats and carbohydrates could be widely interchanged but that a certain minimum of protein was always necessary to keep the body functioning properly. They also showed that a proper diet had to contain certain other elements, which were given the name of "vitamins." In any case, calorie measurement was a great step forward. Henceforth it was possible to calculate not only the individual's nutritive needs with ease but a whole country's needs as well. The resulting figures could be compared with the country's potential food production and thus determine how much, if any, food would have to be imported to feed the inhabitants adequately.

Such socio-economic calculations are not universally practised even today. At the beginning of the Second World War very few countries had food supply plans based on calorific reckoning. Once the worst food shortages are past, nearly everything in this field is given over to experience and chance. None the less, the basic scheme stands fast and offers a sounder footing for the food economy.

BREAD OR MEAT

Measurement by calorie provided above all a means of comparing the nutritive value of plant and animal foods. Since the animal's dietary needs could also be measured in calories, still another question arose. How much of the human food supply is consumed by livestock? To ensure a country's food supply is it more advantageous to plant more fields of cereal grains, vegetable gardens and orchards, or to devote more land to raising fodder or supplying pasturage, so that there may be bigger meat and dairy yields?

It is a life-and-death question for animals, since there is no prospect that cattle and pigs, goats and sheep should continue to exist anywhere on earth against man's will. Even if there were tracts of uncultivated land to provide pasturage for countless herds, man would never allow his animals to go free. He would much rather slaughter his breeding stock than permit them to revert to the wild. If the question is seriously pondered, the nature of the choice between a grain or a meat economy becomes clear. The choice revolves about a "struggle for existence" between man and animal, a struggle for food-producing space in a literal sense. The outcome is foreordained. The animals cannot win. All that remains is to decide whether the defeated shall be decimated or spared.

If the agronomist's opinion were strictly followed, domestic animals in thickly settled countries would have a very poor outlook indeed. Calorific estimates clearly indicate that in countries with limited agricultural areas the animals use up more nourishment than they give back. Beef cattle return only half the calories they consume. With pigs, the loss mounts to 75 per cent, with hens to 90 per cent. This means that pigs need four calories and hens ten for every calorie man gets from eating their flesh.

The nature of the land itself, of course, determines whether these formulae have any practical application. Where the land is too damp or stony for cultivation, yet grows enough grass to feed cattle, goats or the like, raising livestock, even figured on a calorie basis, is obviously more profitable than raising grain. Moreover, good combination fodder coupled with a proper selection of meat-producing animals reduces the discrepancy between expenditure and yield. Yet, on the whole, where people live on level land, a greater number of people can be adequately fed by raising grain and other plant products for direct consumption than by the indirect consumption of livestock in the form of meat, eggs and dairy products.

Quantitatively the direct road to the human stomach is more efficient than the roundabout way through the animal stomach.

WARTIME SLAUGHTERING

In times of stress this principle asserts itself without recourse to calorie tables. The livestock of western and central Europe declined 10 to 20 per cent during the First World War. In round numbers this meant 6 million fewer beef cattle, 16 million fewer pigs and 22 million fewer sheep. Bread also became short but not so quickly as meat. In order to have more bread there were mass slaughterings.

During the Second World War, when the Nazi armies were in control of the European continent, the results were even more obvious. From 1939 to 1942 the number of Danish pigs declined from 3 to 1 million. Two-thirds of the pigs in the Netherlands vanished. The number of fowls in Denmark dropped from 29 to 11 million and in Holland from 33 million to less than 4 million. France got out of it comparatively well, since nearly 4 of her 7 million pigs survived. The beef cattle population of European countries west of the Soviet Union sank from 96 to 80 million, with an additional decline in weight. In Russia the number of beef cattle and calves dropped by a third and out of every hundred pigs only twenty-two were left.

These statistics must not be regarded as reflecting rational decisions deliberately taken. As a rule the people who slaughtered their livestock were not thinking at all in terms of production costs or of what they would do later on about rearing new stock. Hunger and predatory instinct simply drove them to take the easiest and quickest way to get provisions for flight or to prevent their livestock from being seized by their own country's authorities. Forced deliveries of grain and potatoes also made the farmers cut down on their livestock. Under stress life's hierarchic arrangement stood out stark and clear. First, man had to get along. Only then would he grant other members of the animal kingdom the right to live.

In more peaceful times this principle is not so effective. The adherents of calorific reckoning may preach as much as they like that there would not be so much hunger in the world if people bred fewer cattle and tilled more land. Up to the present this humanitarian teaching has attracted but few followers, not because man loves animals, but because it leaves the psychological hierarchy of individual tendencies out of account.

If the struggle for existence drives man to the brink of hunger, he is satisfied with mere quantity of food. But if he is as much as a hairbreadth away from the dividing line, say if he enjoys a 10 per cent safety factor of two or three hundred calories beyond his minimum daily requirements, then the desire for quality comes into play and supplants mere quantity. The choice between quality and quantity is mostly decided in favor of quality. Even in those instances where almost all foods had been rationed, the authorities did not dare to eliminate meat entirely, thus giving calorific quantity absolute precedence. Whenever the meat- and animal-fat supply has been drastically curtailed, this has come about involuntarily, usually as the result of difficulties in securing imports, rather than through the imposition of a 100 per cent rational plan for making a compromise between agronomic potential and physiological need.

The fact that meat is more highly prized than plant food can be clearly seen in the great cattle-rearing countries where meat is very cheap, as for example in southern Brazil. Among the well-to-do of this region plant foods are quite as much a secondary choice as in those agricultural countries where meat is scarce and therefore desirable.

GANDHI AND THE SACRED COW

To this day the religious codes in eastern countries have a strong influence on animal husbandry. The Islamic ban on pork has greatly limited pig-breeding in extensive Mohammedan regions of Asia and Africa. In India contempt for the pig as an unclean animal is found in conjunction with veneration for the cow as a sacred animal.

Both these evaluations, working from opposite directions, on one occasion combined to generate a significant historical event. The immediate cause of the Indian Mutiny in 1857, one of the worst threats ever experienced by the British Empire, was the use of pig fat and tallow in greasing soldiers' rifles. This practice seemed sinful to both the Hindu and the Moslem devout. When Indian soldiers were punished for refusing to load such weapons this became the signal for mutiny which grew into a widespread revolt. Though the uprising was finally suppressed, it put an end to the two-hundred-year-old rule of the East India Company.

The sacredness of the cow has also played a part in the modern

Indian movement for independence. Gandhi made veneration of the cow part of his creed. Indeed, he saw it as the real distinguishing mark separating Hinduism from all other religions. At the same time he warned against carrying cow worship too far. For example, he pointed out that killing a man to save a cow meant flouting the precepts of Hinduism. Gandhi was not much interested in the external manifestations of cow adoration which foreigners find so absurd (which, incidentally, led some wag to name the plane used by the president of the United States the "Sacred Cow"), but to the Hindu the cow is symbolic of all creatures and specifically of motherhood. To injure this symbol meant in effect committing an act against God.

Although many millions of Hindus even surpass Gandhi in reverence for the cow, India is not a bovine paradise. Cows are very numerous in India. The cattle population is estimated at 150 million, twice as many as in the United States and Russia, the runners up, and far, far more, even in proportion to the population, than in most European countries. But these unfortunate animals are as scrawny, famished and diseased as the people themselves. They may escape the slaughterer's knife but they still die an early death from undernourishment and the rinderpest. The Hindus keep cows mainly for their milk, from which they make ghee, a kind of watery butter. When cattle die the Hindus, though they do not eat the meat, skin the beasts and make use of the hides. Sacredness, even in India, has its limits. Gandhi himself admonished his countrymen to make as good use as they could of the dead livestock.

THE LATIFUNDIAN ECONOMY

A remarkable dietary line of division runs north and south through the middle of Asia. Whereas in western and central Asiatic countries milk production has always been the chief purpose of animal husbandry, dairy products have never had much significance in the far east. Milk was also held in low esteem among the aborigines of the Americas on the far side of the

Pacific. If the Indians seemingly brought their aversion to milk with them from Asia, they took up the raising of livestock for meat quickly enough, while attempts along this line in east Asia have come to naught. There are fewer beef cattle in Japan than in Denmark. Fish is virtually the only animal food eaten by 500 million Asiatics in China and Japan. The proponents of diet by calorific reckoning like to cite this fact in support of their thesis. They claim that east Asiatic countries could not feed so many people had they not traditionally turned from animal-breeding to subsistence on a plant food diet.

The fact that Australia and the Americas are thinly populated also indirectly supports this conclusion. Where livestock are numerous, there are few people. At least this applies where animals are bred for meat, not milk. Raising animals for slaughter requires a lot of land but relatively little human labour. On the great South American estancias half a dozen Gauchos can tend several thousand steers. There are no cowbarns and no dairying operations. In the mornings the animals are watered and occasionally they are driven through a narrow trough filled with disinfectant. Other than this nature is allowed to take its course. For the big ranches this is all much more convenient than farming operations requiring hundreds of field hands, capital outlay on farm machinery and the risk of bad crops.

In central and eastern Europe the situation is reversed. The latifundia, or large estates, in this part of the world are associated with the tradition of tilling the soil, whereas cattle belong on the small mixed farms. This has generally resulted in the depopulation of lands where grain is grown on a large scale, whereas animal husbandry has been a means of binding the peasant to the land and of keeping him from migrating to the towns. Whether a latifundian or a small freehold agriculture is preferable is a question that has been argued for decades, both in socialistic domestic programmes for the future and in colonial settlement policy. A whole school of agrarian politicians, in opposition to calorific reckoning, maintain that the only solution to the socio-economic problem of food supply is an agriculture based on small-scale animal farming.

The situation in Holland and Denmark seems to prove that even where the available land area is small people and livestock can co-exist providing natural conditions are favourable and farm practice intelligent. Yet in fact this solution has worked only in one small corner of Europe, along the English Channel and the shores of the North Sea. The agricultural economy of the world as a whole is obviously developing in another direction. The broad tendency is towards specialization, a separation of tillage and animal husbandry and an even greater separation of dairy farming and the raising of livestock for meat.

THE BIG FOUR OF CHICAGO

After the refrigeration process had been perfected, it was possible to supply a whole country with meat from one base point, where slaughter and cooling houses, and perhaps packing-plants as well, had been set up. The meat industry is most highly centralized in the United States where, in the Chicago slaughter houses, over 2 million steers and calves, 4 million pigs and 2½ million sheep lose their lives annually. Some of these animals are brought to Chicago from great distances but transportation costs are cancelled out by extremely efficient mass slaughtering methods and, more than anything, by the profits from the sale of by-products. Bone meal and soap, fertilizer and glue, glycerine and stearin, wool and hair are all produced by the meat industry. The most important "waste product," one on which another large industry is based, is leather for shoe soles, drive belts and footballs. Nothing edible, needless to say, is lost. Hearts and kidneys, livers and lights are processed and sent all over the world.

Cincinnati was the great meat-processing centre of the United States before Chicago became the most famous—and notorious—stockyard metropolis in the world. As early as the 1840s Cincinnati had been named "Porkopolis" for obvious reasons, and it was not until the Civil War that Chicago forged ahead and stepped into first place. The real founders of the great Chicago packing industry were Philip D. Armour, who had previously won his spurs as a gold miner, and Gustavus F. Swift, a village butcher from Massachusetts. Later two more powerful competitors and allies, Wilson and Cudahy, came into the picture. The companies built up by the "big four" are today still the main pillars of the American meat industry. Their empire extends far beyond Chicago. They have slaughter houses and packing plants in a number of other cities inside and outside the United States, and their products roll in refrigerated cars all over the world. In North America, before the war, they supplied four-fifths of all the meat consumed in urban centres.

Whereas the meat industry has overcome distance and meat has become an international commodity, milk continues to be tied down to a limited market, since it cannot be carried long distances without drastic transformation. At about the middle of the nineteenth century a milk-condensing process was worked out and after improvements introduced by the Swiss in the 1880s the condensed milk industry became big business on an international scale. Even so, condensed and powdered milk have never become as important a factor in nutrition as frozen and processed meat.

It is interesting to note that milk has kept another peculiarity through the years. Milk is one of the few raw products not classified in the trade according to quality. The fat content and chemical properties of milk can, of course, be measured easily enough, and even without technical means the consumer can judge pretty well how good the milk is; but in the dairy business milk is just milk and in most countries the price is entirely based on quantity rather than quality. Milk is one of the few really democratic foods, with no distinction made—at least in point of quality—between rich and poor.

Quantitatively, on the other hand, the difference between the rich man's and the poor man's consumption of milk is enormous. Milk, not to mention butter, is still a luxury which the poor can afford only in limited amounts. In the United States four times as much milk is consumed *per capita* as in Italy, and six times as much as in Brazil, though in these last two countries there are relatively more children. This fact, of course, did not keep the Italian fascists from making artificial wool from milk.

⟐ XXIX ⟐

The Animal's Future

ALL historical writing, though many of the writers themselves contend otherwise, plays with the idea of foretelling a little of the future from the past. The writer of animal history is particularly subject to this temptation, since all evolutionary theories aim, essentially, at discovering general laws that hold good for the future as well as for the past. That which exists today is the product of yesterday and bears in itself the seed of tomorrow. Anyone who believes this must have the courage to speculate on the future.

It is true that the evolutionary idea which dominated the eighteenth and nineteenth centuries and which seemed to have developed into a powerful biological tool in the Darwinian theory has experienced severe setbacks in the last fifty years. The concept of discontinuity has gained ground both in physics and in physiology and from the philosophical side Bergson's "creative evolution" has shaken the traditional idea of continuous evolution.

Yet the fact of descent remains. Even though contemporary biologists today are interested more in sudden changes, revolutionary innovations of form and the diversities of generations than in slow, imperceptible transitions, they cannot abandon the concept of an ancestral line. Even a succession of revolutions must reveal a tendency, otherwise scientific observation would become mere senseless inventory, against which the human mind rebels. There may be some doubt as to whether evolutionary theory in a wider sense corresponds objectively to natural law. It is a postulate in knowledge of nature and this justifies its existence.

It may be Darwinism's greatest weakness that in this regard it offers so few salient points. Even after a century of experimental research and theoretical speculation the most convinced evolutionist is quite unable to say how a species or family will look ten thousand or a hundred thousand or a million years from now. He does not know whether mammals will have more or fewer feet or toes, or whether the sight of birds will have sharpened or dimmed. He has no idea which species among the lower animals will develop most rapidly. Most important of all, he is unable to say whether man will undergo essential morphological change.

The geologists, who believe we are living in an interglacial period, like to theorize on when and where the next Ice Age will occur. Using these hypotheses the zoologists can speculate about which animal species are doomed to extinction or destined to migrate. Yet even in pre-historical times amazing phenomena have occurred. The mammoth, after having retreated into the far north without apparent reason, perished from the cold, whereas animals much more poorly equipped were somehow able to adapt themselves to the rigours of the northern climate.

The few and quite unconfirmed laws relating to the growth and duration of the species still offer no clear indication of the future. On the face of things it would seem reasonable to make a poor prognosis for the reptiles, these impoverished remnants of a once ruling dynasty; but no one would dare prophesy whether they will simply perish or whether they have enough life force left in them to develop into higher forms, as did some of their ancestors when they became birds. It is very daring even to say that certain groups of molluscs and crustacea have come to the end of their evolution, because for long epochs they have not shown any further signs of essential change.

ECOLOGY

Morphology having left us in a complete quandary as to the shape of the future, a number of zoologists have attacked the problem from a different angle. If we accept the validity of the Malthus-Darwin "struggle for existence" formula, the next step, in this new approach, would be to explore the present nature of the struggle and from this perhaps deduce some idea of the future. In order to study nature in the raw it is not necessary to go into the rain forest of Brazil or voyage to the islands of the South Seas, as did the biologists of Darwin's time. Every tree, every patch of arable land affords opportunity for such observations.

The branch of modern zoology given over to such studies was first called "ecology" by Haeckel in 1869. Actually the term "ecology," which is akin to the word "economy"—literally, "household management"—of Aristotelian origin, was not a very happy choice, for ecology aims to do more than investigate economic or domestic relationships in the plant and animal kingdoms. Although its field of operations is still poorly defined—one of its zoological opponents dismissed ecologists as an "obscure sect of Lamarckians"—this new, though basically ancient, science might be better defined as the sociology of plants and animals.

As in so many other fields of research, it was the botanists who did the pioneer work in this field, with the zoologists rather hesitantly following. Since the beginning of the twentieth century, thanks largely to the work of Americans, so much authenticated and systematized material has been accumulated that animal ecology—or sociology—has become an independent and respectable science.

Ecology is concerned not only with the social structure of such highly organized animal communities as those of the bees or the ants, but also attempts to investigate the voluntary or involuntary (parasitic) symbiosis and co-operation of individuals of different species, especially in regard to how these animals live from one another, that is, which feed on or with each other. Animals living on the same tree, for example, constitute a life community in the sense that some are the hunters, some the hunted. Despite the fact that for thousands of years man has been aware of these relationships—as shown by animal fables— up to this time he had known only a very few *"Nahrungskreise,"* "alimentary spheres," among animals living together in a limited space and all competing with each other to exist.

Many lower animals are extremely selective in their diet, which leads to the assumption that here not only physiological need but taste as well plays an important part. If one species lives exclusively on another, and this other exclusively on a third, it becomes possible to construct a "food chain." This having been done, it is reasonable to conclude that if one species in the chain dies out or is drastically reduced, this will give rise to the diminution of a whole series of species. For the time being, however, this is only a theory, for very little is known about just how much animals will change their customary diet under stress and turn definitively to other forms of nourishment. Shifts from a meat to a plant food diet and the reverse seem to have occurred quite often in the past, and it may be assumed that the adaptability of the animal's digestive organs to external conditions will make for survival.

One of the ecologist's good points is that he is interested not only in the being or not-being, the continuance or the extinction, of the species, but also in determining the number of individuals in a species or an animal community. Counting the protozoa, worms, beetles and—above all—the birds living in a certain area has developed into a special study and, although at times this strikes the layman as rather ridiculous, a very useful one. Only by so doing is it possible to throw light on the mystery of these great and in part periodically recurrent variations in animal populations which not only account for vastly increased crop damage and infectious animal diseases but human epidemics as well. Moreover, census-taking provides a means of finding out about the prospects of survival for certain species. Here again the scientific methods and the international organization necessary for census-taking are still in their infancy. There are no regular world-counts of the animal populations and even the ones carried out on a national scale are limited in most countries to domestic animals, while ignoring the equally important task of counting the organisms injurious to man.

The Most Numerous Large Animal

Great as other environmental influences may be, the factor which today mainly decides whether animals shall live or die is the will of man. This is the end-conclusion reached from the arguments in this book, which we will briefly recapitulate.

It can be argued, certainly, that there are far too many animals in far too great diversity for man ever to subject all of them to his will, that great areas of the animal kingdom, like the depths of the sea, still lie outside man's control. He does not exert any influence at all on the animal life of the higher levels of the atmosphere. Also there are extensive land areas in which the animals live out their lives unmolested by man. Still, these as yet unconquered preserves seem trivial in the face of the violent transformation wrought by man among the animals in the last few thousand, even in the last few hundred, years.

The crucial aspect of this process of subjection is not the extinction of whole genera and species. This has happened intentionally only in rare cases in recent times where systematic attempts have been made to exterminate injurious protozoa and insects. In any event, the pathogens and disease-carriers which have been eliminated from most countries by sanitation measures have by no means completely vanished from the earth. This holds true, for example, for the mosquito, *Stegomyia fasciata*, which spreads yellow fever. These pests have only been driven out of their accustomed haunts and reduced to a point where the danger of great epidemics may be regarded as more or less removed.

Gaucho on the Argentine Pampas

The holy ram, early Ptolemaic period

The sheep as a domestic animal; merino ram

Wonderfully trained animals shown on an English variety stage

The Elephant of Notre-Dame, Paris

In spite of its incompleteness, man's victory over the animals has had incisive consequences. It has affected the animals in three ways: by increasing some species; by diminishing others; and by transplanting still others.

Homo sapiens' mastery over the animal kingdom is first manifested by an increase in the number of his own kind. Physiologically, man has no advantage over the rest of the large mammals. His embryonic development is almost as slow as that of the

Fig. 78. Baluchitherium, the largest extinct mammal, giants of the present day and man (drawing by H. Ziska)

horse or cow. Multiple births are infrequent. Even after being born, man grows slowly and is late in achieving sexual maturity. These genetic disadvantages tend to cancel out the advantages of a relatively long life span.

Despite these handicaps, man is by far the most numerous species among the large animals. We have to go down the scale of size as far as the cats and rabbits to find other species numbered by thousands of millions. The last figures published before the Second World War by the International Agricultural Institute at Rome, listed for the whole world approximately 700 million cattle, 600 million sheep and 300 million swine. The num-

ber of horses had dropped under the 100 million mark. The
human population of 2,000 million was as large as that of all the
large animals taken together.

Since then, man's numerical superiority has increased even
more. The great butchery called the Second World War inflicted
far greater losses on the animals than on man, though this time
animals were not used on the battlefield. Whereas from 1938 to
1948 the human population of the world increased by nearly 10
per cent, the number of domestic animals declined considerably.
Only beef cattle were able to hold their own, thanks to a marked
increase in North and South America. The total number of pigs
dropped by 18 million, of sheep by 26 million and of horses by
11 million. Fowls, bred in great quantity in the United States
during the war, in China were the chief victims of the civil war,
dropping from 200 to 100 million. Even in North America the
number of fowls has been reduced by 70 million since the end of
the war because there was no market for their eggs.

Although all these numerical changes need not necessarily be
regarded as expressing a deliberate "population policy" on the
part of *Homo sapiens*, man is still unquestionably responsible
for them. He is the one who decides how many of the animals
with whom he shares the fruits of the soil, and the breeding of
which makes work for him, shall be permitted to live. He is the
absolute master over 2,000 million land animals whose primary
function is to provide him with food. If tomorrow he should find
a more convenient source of protein food-energy tasting as good
as meat to him, he would decimate his livestock without a moment's hesitation.

Man's present more or less benevolent attitude towards the
animals subjected to his will represents the second phase of the
population policy which he has followed since his appearance
on this earth. During the first and far more violent phase, man
was mainly bent on subduing the large animals capable of doing
him injury. Even in prehistoric times we can plainly see that he
was killing them off in large numbers and since the invention of

gunpowder the process, of course, has been accelerated. During the settlement of the New World by Europeans, a few genera-tions sufficed to reduce the number of large wild animals to a point where many of them became rarities. The last episode of this kind was the near-extermination of the North American buffalo. During the Civil War there were estimated to be 60 mil-lion buffalo or twice the number of the human population of the United States. A considerable portion of these gigantic herds perished in the great prairie and forest fires which lighted the way for the settlers flowing westward in triumphal procession.

With the exception of the forests of India and of the Amazon region, and the uninhabitable deserts of Africa and Asia, this crude form of population-control over the animal kingdom may be considered ended. It is very unlikely, however, that lions, tigers, hyenas, bears, wolves and the like will ever again be numbered in millions, or even in hundreds of thousands. Their future will be determined by the needs of the zoological gardens and, in some cases, by the vagaries of fashion.

THE BIRDS' SPECIAL PRIVILEGE

Among the smaller wild creatures of no immediate use to man, birds have the most favourable outlook. Curiously enough, *Homo sapiens*, most acquisitive of all the predators, has created a moral-aesthetic zone of tabu within the animal kingdom which all civilized people have more or less respected. This tabu covers more than the canaries and parrots and other such birds held captive because of their voice or plumage, and more, too, than the relatively few songbirds living in the wild. The songbirds' attraction for man is more legendary than real. The great ma-jority of city-dwellers has never sacrificed a moment of sleep to hear a bird concert.

Quite apart from their singing art, the splendours of their plumage and the gracefulness of their flight, birds have held man's sympathy. Even the invention of the aeroplane, which deprived the birds of much of their glamour, has not changed

this attitude. With the exception of domestic fowl and some wild
fowl, the whole avian branch of the animal kingdom seems—the
only one so favoured—to be safe for the time being from human
attack. Obviously the increased industrialization and "chimney-
fication" of level regions, and the use of chemicals instead of the
harmless scarecrow to protect the grainfields, have made life
somewhat more difficult for the birds, yet their food-gathering
space is still large enough to permit an increase in the bird population, even in such thickly settled industrial countries as England.

Much more important than this well-meaning policy of *laissez-
faire* in man's relationship with the animal world is his attitude
towards animals whose increase he encourages for his own practical ends. It is a fateful question for these animals whether, in
the future, they will offer man enough advantages for him to
keep on rearing them and let them live for at least a few more
years.

Horses out of Work

There is no doubt that the list of advantages offered by animals of utility has grown even shorter. Only on the most primitive levels of civilization have animals ever supplied man with
material for housing, such as hides—unless animals are credited
with the limestones made of fossil shells used in the manufacture
of cement or petroleum. In any case, no animals on earth will be
used in filling man's housing needs in the foreseeable future.

For thousands of years the three great functions performed
by useful animals have been to furnish man with food, clothing
and transport. Of these three categories, the last, transport, has
declined most. Riding, draught and pack animals, to be sure,
have not been eliminated so rapidly by the machine as was anticipated a hundred years ago. First the railway put the horse
out of business as a means of transport over long distances. It
was an ominous sign, too, that despite improved living standards
and increased commerce, the horse population did not keep pace

with the human population. For still another fifty years, however, the horse continued to monopolize city transport until at
last he was supplanted by the electric tram and finished off by
the car. Even in technologically backward countries the horse as
as means of transport has completely vanished from the big cities
and there is no reason to believe that he will ever reconquer his
former domain.

Fig. 79. Prairie horses. Copper engraving from Catlin, *North American
Indians* (London, 1845)

The horse is out of work and he is not covered by unemploy-
ment insurance. In recent years no one has thought of establishing "retirement farms" for worn-out cab horses as was done a
century earlier in England and the United States. Actually, of
course, whole states would be needed to provide surplus animals
with a peaceful existence. The problem has been pitilessly
solved in Malthusian fashion, that is, by breeding fewer horses.
In the short span between the two world wars the horse population of the world dropped from 150 million to only 80 million.

This decline, to all appearances, will continue at an accelerated rate.

Horses have suffered another setback, too, in the military sphere, a loss of face both material and moral. No longer are they used as chargers on the battlefield, a role that for thousands of years cost them rivers of blood but which also earned them great honour. In the First World War some attempts were made to send them out under fire in dashing cavalry attacks, but in the Second World War, when used at all, they served as draught animals performing behind-the-lines duties. Very apparently they will be relieved even of these duties in future wars and end their lives quietly amid stable straw. True animal lovers will not much regret this change, and the horses themselves will certainly manage nicely in their unheroic role, for they have never been as combative as the bards would have us believe. This loss of prestige, however, can have material consequences, for the use of horses for military purposes has been one of the most important motives in breeding them.

The humble cousins of the horse, the mule, the hinny and the ass, thanks to the technological backwardness and poverty of southern peoples are better protected against the hegemony of the machine, and it is quite possible that they may outlast the horse as a means of transport. Yet we must not paint too tragic a picture of the horse's future. To supplant the horse family entirely not only will many railways have to be built but five times as many cars as there are in the world today. And—what is even less likely in any immediate future—the people who now have to get along with a horse-drawn vehicle or a pack donkey, must become economically capable of buying and running a car if horses are to disappear. We come to the conclusion that poverty is the best protector of the progeny of Eohippus.

WOOL WITHOUT SHEEP

The reasons underlying transformations in the second great category of animal-breeding—animals bred for textile fibres—are exactly the opposite. The future of these animals is threatened in this case because cheaper and easily manufactured synthetic substitutes have been found. It is very unlikely that the silkworm will ever regain his ancient importance, nor do sheep seem to have a very bright outlook. Even if, because of inferior quality or a shortage of wood, plant-derivative substitute materials do not advance beyond their present position, it is possible that in the future fewer animals will be required to provide the necessary quantities of wool.

Experiments have shown that skin tissue from sheep can be kept alive for a long time and even made to grow by putting it in nutrient solutions, after the method first used by Carrel with chick embryos. Chemical stimulants can be used to make the cells hypertrophy. Laboratory-grown sheep skin has been made to yield six times as much wool per square inch as the sheep. Moreover, by modifying the nutrient medium, fine or thick fibres can be created at will and the quality of the wool otherwise determined.

Although these experiments, first carried out in England, have not got very far beyond the laboratory stage, they may well have far-reaching effects on sheep-rearing. Why should sheep be bred in South Africa and Australia when wool can be produced biochemically in any convenient large manufacturing centre? It boils down to a question of cost. When and if the process is perfected, this question will probably be decided in favour of the chemical method.

Here it is neither a question of a substitute material nor, really, a synthetic process but rather a new form of organic life, a simple combination of cells able to take in food and reproduce without any nervous system or blood supply. These artificially propagated tissues are "comparable to ideal laboratory animals," except that they have no individuality. Although they derive from highly developed animals they are more helpless and rudimentary than protozoa. None the less, since they serve man's needs, they have a good chance of attaining a firm position in the organic world. Tissue-breeding instead of animal-breeding, even though as yet the formula has a magical air, seems to be among the ways of the future.

DECLINE IN MEAT CONSUMPTION

Should the development of textile animals progress in this direction, animals would be even more thrown back on their most painful function, serving human beings as food. Cattle, goats and hens even then would have a good chance of a longer life; for the other animals it would mean a shortening of their life span by a fourth, a sixth or a tenth of the years allotted to them by nature.

In any case, the future of animals reared for meat seems secure, at least as far as we can see ahead. Whether man will allow this category of animals to increase very much in numbers is another question. The agronomic reasons militating against this possibility have been discussed in the previous chapter. Though these reasons are very impressive theoretically, we still do not believe they will be decisive in practice, at least in times of peace. The decisive factor will be the direction in which human taste develops. This will determine whether man is on the road to becoming a meat-eater or a plant-food eater. Physiology provides no clear answer to this question and related statistical data also are equivocal.

About the middle of the last century the idea became popular that man is naturally carnivorous and eats plant-food only when he must. Ernst Engel, a statistician who made a name for himself as discoverer of the "laws" of food consumption, concluded, on the strength of having analyzed a few hundred household accounts kept by Belgian and Saxon working families, that human beings, as soon as their income permits, turn to a meat diet. Yet the general validity of this proposition seems very dubious, especially when applied to the Hindus and the Chinese. To think of this tendency as a physiological law is out of the question. Even in the western world it is only a partial truth.

It is a fact, however, that city people eat a great deal more meat—in many countries ten times as much—as rural people, yet within two generations urban meat consumption has declined. In Paris, from 1889 to 1928, the *per capita* meat consumption sank from 154 to 110 pounds a year. This decrease cannot be accounted for by progressive impoverishment, since during the same period the consumption of wine, for example, increased by half. In the United States the annual meat consumption from 1900 to 1938, notwithstanding a steady rise in urban population and improvement in living standards, dropped from 150 to 125 pounds *per capita*. Not until the war years did mass consumption by the military and the defence workers reverse the downward trend.

The same phenomenon can be observed in many other countries. If the workers earn more, they do indeed buy more meat, but a meat-rich diet soon loses its attraction in competition with other values—radio, car, better clothing, etc. In the United States, which in this connection can be regarded as pointing the way for the western world, the population doubled between 1900 and 1950, but the number of cattle increased by barely one-third. Should there be no drastic changes in income distribution or in popular custom, it is not very likely that the number of livestock raised for meat will keep pace with the increase in human population.

THE LAW OF DEVITALIZATION

These facts and developmental tendencies permit a general inference, which we shall designate as the "law of devitalization." This law asserts that human beings are steadily turning from animal to plant food and from organic to inorganic raw materials. In lieu of a lengthy exposition we have collected some of the facts on which this law is based into a table. This table might easily be elaborated, and for the future even greater transformations are forshadowed, say, if proteins are ever produced synthetically, a consummation now well within the realm of possibility.

	Sweetening	Fats	Fabrics	Containers	Light Heat	Manuring	Transport
ANIMAL	honey	butter lard bacon	silk wool	hides sausage-skins, etc.	wax tallow	dung of domestic animals, guano	oxen donkeys horses camels
VEGETABLE	cane- and beet-sugar	oil margarine	artificial silk and wool made from wood	wood rubber	wood	hops, green manure	carts and wooden boats
MINERAL	saccharin	butter-substitute from coal, lubricating oil	nylon from coal	metal plastics	coal petroleum	potash nitrates phosphates	railway motor car aeroplane

Fig. 80. Transition from animal to vegetable and mineral matter

The fact that animal materials are being used less than plant materials, and still less than inorganic ones, is partly due to man's failure to transform animals substantially according to his will. He has tamed them, but without bringing about any marked qualitative changes. The expectation arising from Morgan's experiments, that soon man would be creating new species as he desired, has not been fulfilled. Crossbreeding methods have been perfected but not basically altered. No new creatures have been successfully produced in the animal, as in the plant world. New races of horses and cattle produced by crossing merely represent an emphasis of certain characteristics regarded as desirable by man. The most economically important product of hybridization continues to be the mule, who already existed even before man coupled donkeys and mares to get an inexpensive draught animal.

INDEPENDENCE OF MAN

Breeding, however, has had a great significance in the geographical spread of animals, certainly in the sense of making them cosmopolitan. Tested strains have been exported all over the world, often by smuggling them out, and though not all of them have become acclimatized, the fact remains that domestic animals everywhere are much more alike than in earlier times. By distributing the sperm of breeding stock, particularly that of bulls and stallions, the internationalization of the so-called thoroughbred races will be carried to even greater lengths, even as has occurred on the human level through the interbreeding of the high nobility.

Breeding animals or their seed, as exported under man's aegis, are only one small part of all animal migration. In some exceptional cases the animals have even availed themselves of the most modern means of transport without human intervention, as in the case of *Anopheles gambiae*, the African malarial mosquito. These insects came on the first transatlantic plane flights from Dakar to Brazil and were driven out of South America only after a stubborn battle. More often, however, the lower animals make their long journeys on more modest conveyances. Floating tree trunks are the most common means of getting about. In spite of his sedentary habits, the common earthworm has become a cosmopolite found all over the world by travelling in this fashion. Plants carefully packed away in ships' holds for transport across the sea also facilitate animal migration. Flora not only draw fauna in their wake but take them along as well.

Through such involuntary effects of civilization man widens his influence over the animal kingdom. On the other hand man has deliberately extended his influence to only a few hundred species. To the zoologist, who is interested in the small animals just as much as in the big ones, it may well seem a matter of little consequence that man should exterminate a few species while developing others by artificial means and forcing still others to accommodate themselves, according to Malthusian principles, to his own needs. At present there are some million and a half known species, with ten thousand new ones being registered annually.

What does the sum total of human activity in respect of the animal kingdom mean compared with all this multiplicity of form and number? What can man accomplish, even with all his technical skills and instruments of destruction, against the creatures of nature? Did not the goats of Bikini, whom man exposed to the blast and poisonous vapours of the atom bomb, stand the test as well as the sheep, the cock and the duck who made the first balloon ascent?

These Solomonic observations do not alter the fact that man is subjecting the animal kingdom to his will in ever wider measure. First he imposed his will on the large animals. Some he exterminated, some he decimated and, this accomplished, he brought the more submissive ones so completely under this thumb that he must be regarded as absolute master of their continued existence. By slaughtering and breeding them man determines how many of them shall exist, and by selection he strives to modify their characteristics. He has been less successful in dealing with the smaller organisms, but even here in the last hundred years he has been able to effect deep-reaching changes. He has destroyed whole races and driven others back into restricted areas of the earth's surface. In Darwinian language, man's struggle for existence has entailed both qualitative and quantitative selection, not only among his own species but among many others as well.

Certainly this Herculean labour of selection is not yet finished. Over wide areas man is still ceaselessly battling against creatures that endanger his life, above all against insects which carry deadly diseases or destroy the crops in the fields. In some parts of the earth man has been forced into retreat. But on the whole he has won greater victories, in what, geologically, is a very short span, than any other animal before him. Everything that man has done leads to the conclusion that in the future the continued existence or the extermination of animals is going to depend even more on the human will than it has in the past.

Bibliographic Note

The following are the chief direct reference sources used in the preparation of this book. They are listed in the order in which they occur in the text.

PART ONE

E. S. Goodrich, *Living Organisms* (Oxford, 1924)

Leon Moret, *Manuel de paléontologie animale* (Paris, 1940)

Maurice Gignoux, *Géologie stratigraphique* (Paris, 1936)

Charles Darwin, *The Origin of Species* (1859)

Ernst Haeckel, *Natürliche Schöpfungsgeschichte* (Berlin, 1870)

H. Jeffreys, *The Earth* (Cambridge, 1924)

Fred Hoyle, *The Nature of the Universe* (New York, 1950)

F. A. Lange, *Geschichte des Materialismus* (Leipzig, 1866)

A. Spencer Jones, *Life on Other Worlds* (New York, 1949)

Immanuel Velikovsky, *Worlds in Collision* (New York, 1950)

Georges Lakhovsky, *La Matière* (Paris, 1934)

Aristotle, *Parts of Animals*

Sir William Cecil Dampier, *A History of Science* (New York, 1942)

Charles Lyell, *The Principles of Geology* (1830–33)

Ernest William Barnes, *Scientific Theory and Religion* (New York, 1933)

Neues Jahrbuch für Mineralogie, Geographie und Paläontologie, 1861

Sir Richard Owen, *On the Archaeopteryx von Meyer* (Philosophical Transactions of the Royal Society of London, 1863)

B. W. Tucker, *Functional Evolutionary Morphology: The Origin of Birds in Evolution* (Oxford, 1938)

W. G. Matthew, "The Evolution of the Horse," *Quarterly Review of Biology*, vol. 1 (1926)

A. Cabrera, *El Origen del caballo domestico* (Buenos Aires, 1938)

William King Gregory, "Mammaliae," *Encyclopaedia Britannica* (1941)

Archaeologia, vol. XVIII (1800)

Principes de Philosophie zoologique (1830–32), Goethes sämtliche Werke (Stuttgart, 1868)

Georges Cuvier, *Recherches sur les ossements fossiles des quadrupèdes* (Paris, 1812)

P. C. Schmerling, *Recherches sur les ossements fossiles découverts dans les cavernes de la province de Liége* (Luttich, 1833–34)

Victor Meunier, *Les Ancêtres d'Adam, Histoire de l'homme fossile* (Paris, 1900)

J. C. Fuhlrott, "Menschliche Überreste aus einer Felsengrotte des Düsseltales," Verhandlungen des Naturwissenschaftlichen Vereins der preussischen Rheinlande und Westfalens (1859)

T. H. Huxley, *Man's Place in Nature* (1863)

E. Dubois, *Pithecanthropus erectus. Eine menschliche Übergangsform aus Java* (Batavia, 1894)

G. H. R. Koenigswald, *A Review of the Stratigraphy of Java and Its Relations to Early Man* (London, 1937)

G. Montandon, *L'homme et les préhumains* (Paris, 1943)

F. M. Bergounioux et A. Glory, *Les premiers hommes* (Toulouse, Paris, 1943)

Anibal Mattos, *Monumentos historicos, artisticos e religiosos de Minas Gerais* (Belo-Horizonte, 1935)

F. Wood Jones, *The Problem of Man's Ancestry* (1918)

L. Bolk, *Das Problem der Menschwerdung* (Jena, 1926)

Jean Rostand, *Les grands courants de la biologie* (Paris, 1951)

L. Cuénot, *L'Homme, ce néoténique.* Bulletin de l'Académie Royale de Belgique, Classe des Sciences, 31 (Brussels, 1945)

PART TWO

Padre Fernão Cardim, *Tratados da terra e gente do Brasil* (1585; São Paulo, 1939)

W. B. Wright, *The Quatenary Age* (London, 1937)

James Fisher, *Watching Birds* (London, 1940)

Marcelino Sautuola, *Breves apuntes sobre algunos objetos prehistoricos de la provincia de Santander* (1880)

Miles C. Burkett, *The Old Stone Age. A Study of Palaeolithic Times* (Cambridge, 1933)

H. Breuil and H. Obermayer, *The Cave of Altamira* (Madrid, 1935)

August Weismann, *Die Kontinuität des Keimplasmas als Grundlage einer Theorie der Vererbung* (1885)

Hugo de Vries, *Die Mutationstheorie* (1901)

T. H. Morgan, *The Theory of Gene* (Newhaven, 1926)

R. A. Fisher, *The Genetical Theory of Natural Selection* (Oxford, 1930)

Richard Semon, *Die Mneme als erhaltendes Prinzip im Wechsel des organischen Lebens* (1904)

Edmund Whittaker, *A History of Economic Ideas* (New York, 1943)

"Domestication," *Encyclopedia of the Social Sciences*, vol. III (New York, 1935)

L. Cuénot, *La Genèse des espèces animales* (Paris, 1932)

Die Reden Gotamo Buddhos, vol. III (Munich, 1922)

N. W. Thomas, "Animals," *Encyclopaedia of Religion and Ethics* (Edinburgh, 1908)

A. C. Bouquet, *Comparative Religion* (London, 1941)

E. Cones, *Journals of A. Henry and D. Thompson* (London, 1897)

Sir James Frazer, *The Golden Bough* (New York, 1922)

Adolphe Lods, *La Religión de Israel* (Buenos Aires, 1939)

Adolf Erman, "Die ägyptische Religion," *Religionen des Orients* (Leipzig, Berlin, 1923)

Sir W. Ridgeway, *Origin and Influence of the Thoroughbred Horse* (Cambridge, 1905)

Hermann Kees, "Kulturgeschichte des alten Orients. Erster Abschnitt: Ägypten," *Handbuch der Altertumswissenschaft* (Munich, 1933)

P. Decharme, *Mythologie de la Grèce antique* (Paris, 1884)

Wilhelm Schmid und Otto Stählin, *Geschichte der griechischen Literatur*, vol. I (Munich, 1929)

Sémonide d'Amorgos, "Poème sur les femmes" in *Hésiode et les poètes élégiaques et moralistes de la Grèce* (Paris, 1940)

Rudolf Eucken, *Die Methode der aristotelischen Forschung* (Berlin, 1872)

Juvenal, *Satires*, X, 81

J. Toutain, *L'Economie antique. Spanish translation: La Economia en la Edad Antigua* (Barcelona, 1929)

Hugo Blümner, *Römische Privat-Altertümer* (Munich, 1911)

Cicero, *De natura deorum*, II, 63, 159

Varro, *De re rustica*, II, 5, 12

Eduard O. von Lippmann, *Geschichte des Zuckers*, vol. I. Portuguese translation: *Historia do Açucar* (Rio de Janeiro, 1941)

Georg Wissowa, *Religion und Kultus der Römer* (Munich, 1911)

Albert Grenier, *The Roman Spirit in Religion, Thought and Art* (London, 1926)

"Cirque," *Dictionnaire des antiquités grecques et romaines*, vol. I, 2 (Paris, 1887)

Johannes Kromayer and Georg Veith, *Heerwesen und Kriegführung der Griechen und Römer* (Munich, 1928)

E. Hunnington, *The Pulse of Asia* (London, 1907)

Ammianus Marcellinus, *Historia Romana*, XXXI

T. Peisker, "The Asiatic Background," *The Cambridge Medieval History*, vol. I, chap. XII (Cambridge, 1936)

"Koran," *Encyclopédie de l'Islam*, vol. I (Leyden, Paris, 1913)

Harold Lamb, *Genghis Khan* (Philadelphia, 1944)

Guillaume de Tyr, *Histoire des croisades*

A. Schultze, *Das höfische Leben zur Zeit der Minnesänger*, vol. II (Leipzig, 1889)

Foichtinger, *Geschichte der Falkenjagd* (Leipzig, 1879)

PART THREE

Enrique de Gandia, "Descobrimento da América," *Historia das Américas*, vol. III (Rio de Janeiro, 1945)

Elaine Sanceau, *D. Henrique, o Navegador* (Oporto, 1942)

Richard Hertwig, *Die Abstammungslehre* (Leipzig, Berlin, 1914)

Salvador de Madariaga, *Vida del muy manifico Señor Don Cristóbal Colón* (Buenos Aires, 1944)

Martin Fernandez de Navarrete, *Colección de los viajes y descubrimientos que hicieron por mar los Españoles*, vol. I (Madrid, 1825)

Bartolomé de las Casas, *Historia de las Indias* (1559; Madrid, 1927)

William H. Prescott, *History of the Conquest of Mexico* (1843)

William H. Prescott, *History of the Conquest of Peru* (1847)

Bernal Diaz del Castillo, *Historia Verdadera de la Conquista de la Nueva España* (1632)

David R. Moore, *A History of Latin America* (New York, 1945)

A. R. Wallace, *Geographical Distribution of Animals* (1876)

Charles de la Roncière, *Jacques Cartier et la découverte de la Nouvelle-France* (Paris, 1931)

E. W. Kemmerer, *Money* (New York, 1938)

Huntley M. Sinclair, *The Principles of International Trade* (New York, 1932)

Adam Smith, *The Wealth of Nations* (1776)

Leland Dewitt Baldwin, *The Story of the Americas. The Discovery, Settlement and Development of the New World* (New York, 1943)

O. Bryce, *Remarkable History of the Hudson's Bay Company* (London, 1900)

J. Klein, *Der sibirische Pelzhandel und seine Bedeutung für die Eroberung Sibiriens* (Bonn, 1906)

Charles Edward Chapman, *Hispanic America* (New York, 1942)

Julio Rey Pastor, *La Ciencia y la técnica en el descubrimiento de América* (Buenos Aires, Mexico, 1942)

Charles Gould, *Mythical Monsters* (London, 1886)

Gibson, *Monsters of the Sea* (London, 1887)

Oudemans, *The Great Sea-Serpent* (Leyden, London, 1892)

Olga Obry, *Catarina do Brasil—A India que descobriu a Europe* (Rio de Janeiro, 1935)

Gabriel Soares de Sousa, *Tratado descriptivo do Brasil em 1587* (São Paulo, 1938)

The Autobiography of Benvenuto Cellini (1558–62)

Victor Robinson, *The Story of Medicine* (New York, 1943)

Jacob Burckhardt, *Die Kultur der Renaissance in Italien* (1860; Bern, 1943)

Herodotus, *History*, XI, 10

Bernard Palissy, *Discours admirables de la nature des eaux et fontaines* (1580)

Summary of the Principal Chinese Treatises upon the Culture of the Mulberry and the Rearing of Silk-worms (Washington, 1836)

Sacred Books of the East, vol. XXVIII, book XXI, 8 (Oxford, 1879–1910)

Perry Walton, *The Story of Textiles* (New York, 1937)

Georges-G. Toudouze, *La Costume français* (Paris, 1945)

The Cambridge Economic History, vol. I (Cambridge, 1944)

J. Klein, *The Mesta* (Cambridge, Mass., 1920)

E. Lipson, *The Economic History of England* (London, 1945)

Virginia de Castro e Almeida, *Itinéraire historique du Portugal* (Lisbon, 1940)

Federico Grisone, *Gli Ordini di cavalcare* (Naples, 1550)

G. A. G. Bogeng, *Geschichte des Sports aller Völker und Zeiten* (Leipzig, 1926)

Rafael Sabatini, *César Borgia* (Paris, 1937)

José Maria de Cossio, *Los Toros. Tratado técnico historico* (Madrid, 1945)

PART FOUR

Titus Maccius Plautus, *Asinaria*, II, 4, 88

Michel de Montaigne, *Essais* (1580), Book II, Chap. XII

Hieronymus Rorarius, *Quod animalia bruta saepe ratione utantur melius homine* (Paris, 1648)

René Descartes, *Discours de la méthode* (1637)

René Descartes, *Méditations métaphysiques—cinquièmes objections faites par Monsieur Gassendi contre les six Méditations*

Baruch Spinoza, *Ethics* (1677)

G. F. Meier, *Versuch eines Lehrgebäudes von der Seele der Tiere* (1749)

Immanuel Kant, *Anthropologie*

Le livre des lumières ou la conduite des rois, composé par le sage Pilpay, indien (Paris, 1664)

La Fontaine, *Fables,* II, 18

Bernard Mandeville, *Esop dressed, or collection of fables in familiar verse* (1704)

William Shakespeare, *King Henry V*

John Maynard Keynes, *The General Theory of Employment, Interest and Money* (New York, 1936)

Marcgraf, *Historia rerum naturalium Brasiliae* (Leyden, 1648)

Emile Guyénot, *Les Sciences de la vie aux XVII° et XVIII° siècles* (Paris, 1941)

Cornelius de Jode, *Speculum orbis terrae* (Antwerp, 1593)

James Cook, *Account of a Voyage Round the World* (1773)

H. Burrell, *The Platypus* (Sydney, 1927)

William Harvey, *Exercitatio anatomica de motu cordis et sanguinis in animalibus* (1628)

Arthur Schopenhauer, *Animalischer Magnetismus und Magie. Über den Willen in der Natur* (1854)

A. Trembley, *Mémoire pour servir à l'histoire d'un genre de Polypes d'eau douce à bras en forme de cornes* (Leyden, 1744)

Edward Jenner, *An Inquiry into the Causes and Effects of the Variolae Vaccinae* (London, 1798)

J.-J. Rousseau, *Emilie ou de l'éducation* (1762)

PART FIVE

Johan Peter Sussmilch, *Die Göttliche Ordnung in den Verhältnissen des menschlichen Geschlechts* (1761)

Thomas R. Malthus, *An Essay on the Principle of Population; or a View on its Past and Present Effects on Human Happiness* (London, 1803)

William Godwin, *Of Population. An Enquiry concerning the Power of Increase of the Number of Mankind, being an Answer to Mr. Malthus's Essay on that Subject* (London, 1820)

José Ingenieros, *Sociologia Argentina* (Buenos Aires, 1939)

Pierre Rousseau, *Histoire de la vitesse* (Paris, 1948)

Ruth Karpf, "John Bull 'Goes to the Dogs,'" *New York Times Magazine*, May 11, 1947

M. Willson Disher, *Fairs, Circuses and Music Halls* (London, 1942)

G. W. F. Hegel, *Vorlesungen über die Philosophie der Geschichte* (1882–31), Einleitung, III: *Der Gang der Weltgeschichte* (Ausg. F. Brunstädt, Leipzig)

Robert Chambers (ed.), *Vestiges of the Natural History of Creation* (6th edition, 1847)

Arthur Schopenhauer, *Zur Philosophie und Wissenschaft der Natur—Parerga und Paralipomena* (1851)

Jean-Baptiste Lamarck, *Philosophie zoologique* (1809)

Erasmus Darwin, *Zoonomia; or the Laws of Organic Life* (1794)

Henshaw Ward, *Charles Darwin and the Theory of Evolution* (New York, 1943)

Leo Markun, *A Short History of the Civil War* (Kansas, 1927)

Claude Bernard, *Introduction à l'étude de la médecine expérimentale* (1865)

Schüder, *Über Tollwut* (Jena, 1909)

A. Grotjahn, *Soziale Pathologie* (Berlin, 1923)

Kenneth L. Burdon, *Medical Microbiology* (New York, 1940)

H. Salanoue-Ipin, *Précis de pathologie tropicale* (Paris, 1910)

Organisation Mondiale de la Santé, *Série des Rapports Techniques No. 8* (Geneva, 1950)

Peter Simon Pallas, *Zoographia Russiae asiaticae* (St. Petersburg, 1811)

René Thévenin, *Les Migrations des animaux* (Paris, 1948)

Hans Zinsser, *Rats, Lice and History* (New York, 1945)

Du Puy de Podio, *Die Brieftaube in der Kriegskunst* (Leipzig, 1872)

Maurice Maeterlinck, *Les Chevaux d'Elberfeld—l'hôte inconnu* (Paris, 1917)

Karl Krall, *Denkende Tiere* (Leipzig, 1912)

Homer, *Iliad*, XIX, 418

George John Romanes, *Animal Intelligence* (1881), *Mental Evolution in Animals* (1883)

C. Lloyd Morgan, *Animal Behavior* (London, 1900)

Henri Piéron, *Psychologia zoologique* (Paris, 1941)

J. A. Bierens de Haan, "Du degré de l'intelligence chez les animaux et leur place dans le système zoologique," *Journal de Psychologie*, XXXIV (1937)

Wolfgang Köhler, *Intelligenzprüfungen an Menschenaffen* (1921)

André Rey, *L'intelligence pratique chez les enfants* (Paris, 1935)

Albert Barloud, *Psychologie* (Paris, 1948)

PART SIX

G. J. Mendel, *Versuche über Pflanzenhybriden* (1865)

Emile Borel, *Les Probabilités et la vie* (Paris, 1946)

T. H. Morgan, *The Mechanism of Mendelian Heredity* (New York, 1915)

H. J. Muller, "Radiation and Genetics," *American Naturalist*, vol. LXIV (May, June, 1930)

Julian Huxley, *Evolution, the Modern Synthesis* (New York, 1942)

T. H. Morgan, *The Scientific Basis of Evolution* (New York, 1932)

Emile Guyénot, *L'Origine des espèces* (Paris, 1947)

T. D. Lyssenko, *Heredity and Its Variability* (New York, 1946)

August Weismann, *Das Keimplasma. Eine Theorie der Vererbung* (1892). *Vorträge über Descendenztheorie* (Jena, 1902)

R. Moricard, *Facteurs hormoneux et cytoplasmique de la division nucléaire* (Paris, 1940)

A. N. Studitski, *Die Entwicklungslehre von Lamarck bis Lyssenko* (Berlin, 1951)

La Situation dans la science biologique. Session de l'Académie Lénine des Sciences agricoles de l'U.R.S.S. (July 31–August 7) (Moscow, 1949)

"Union of Soviet Socialist Republics" in 1949 *Britannica Book of the Year* (Encyclopaedia Britannica, Chicago, 1949)

Julian Huxley, *Heredity East and West* (New York, 1950)

Jean Brachet, "L'Hérédité." *Revue de l'Université de Bruxelles.* (January, February, 1950)

Chapman Pincher, *The Breeding of Farm Animals* (New York, 1946)

Anton Zischka, *Wissenschaft bricht Monopole* (Pôrto-Alegre, 1942)

V. E. Yarsley and E. G. Couzens, *Plastics* (New York, 1941)

Washington Irving, *Astoria, or Anecdotes of an Enterprise beyond the Rocky Mountains* (1836)

Dominion Bureau of Statistics, Department of Trade and Commerce, *Canada* (Ottawa, 1942)

Louis Kornitzer, *Pearls and Men* (New York, 1946)

Karl Brandt, *The Reconstruction of World Agriculture* (New York, 1945)

Gandhi, *La Independencia de la India* (Buenos Aires, 1942)

L. F. Rushbrook Williams, *What about India?* (New York, 1938)

Deane W. Malott and Boyce F. Martin, *The Agriculture Industries* (New York, 1939)

F. M. Bergounioux, *Esquisse d'une historie de la vie* (Paris, 1945)

R. N. Chapman, *Animal Ecology; with Especial Reference to Insects* (Minneapolis, 1926)

Charles S. Elton, *Animal Ecology* (New York, 1927)

F. B. Kirkman, *Bird Behavior* (New York, 1937)

Food and Agriculture Organization of the United Nations, *Yearbook of Food and Agriculture Statistics 1949* (Washington, 1950)

M. S. Garretson, *Les Bisons d'Amérique* (Paris, 1939)

Arthur Vernon, *The History and Romance of the Horse* (New York, 1946)

Lecomte de Noüy, *Le Temps et la vie* (Paris, 1936)

Carle C. Zimmermann, *Consumption and Standards of Living* (New York, 1936)

Maurice Halbwachs, *L'Evolution des besoins dans les classes ouvrières* (Paris, 1933)

🔲 INDEX 🔲

Academy of Medicine, Paris, 313
Academy of Moral and Political Science, French, 263
Academy of Sciences, Prussian, 263
Achilles, 85, 86, 329
Acquired characteristics, 293; *see also* Mutations
Adonis, 87
Aesop, 92–93, 122, 208, 212, 213
Aesthetic element, 18th century materialism and, 199
Africanthropus, 44
Agrarian revolution, 173–74
Agriculture
    Agrarian revolution, 173–74
    Malthusianism and the food supply, 261–72
    natural propagation and eugenics, 335–49
    political economy and the food supply, 368–77
    prehistoric, 57–61, 67–70
Albert of Saxony, 161
Albertus Magnus, 161
Alborak, horse of Mohammed, 111–12
d'Alembert, 229
Alexander the Great, 85, 94, 101, 107
Alexandria, cult of Adonis and Aphrodite at, 81
Alfonso VII, of Castile, 181
Algae, 6, 16
Alligator-breeding, 364–65
Alpaca, 133
Altamira, cave paintings of, 63
America, *see* North America; South America; United States
American Civil War, 385
Ammian, 109
Ammonites, 8
Amoeba dysentry, 312–13
Amphibians, 10–11
Amphitheatrum Flavium (Colosseum), 105–06

Amsterdam, 140
Andalusian bull, 185
Angora cat, 318–19, 344
Animal cults, in ancient Egypt, 79–82
Animal psychology, 191–203, 320–22, 329–32
Anopheles mosquito, 313
Ant-eater, 237
Anthrax, 302–07
Anthropologie (Kant), 201
Anthropology, *see* Man
Anthropomorphism, in ancient Greece, 87–89
Anti-toxins, 311
Antonius, Marcus, 111
Ape, anthropoid, 38
Ape Men, 41–44
Aphrodite, 81
Apis, 80
Apperception, 195–97
Arabs
    Andalusian bull introduced into Spain by, 185
    artificial insemination and, 348
    camel-meat and, 79
    fondness for cats, 318
    gazelle hunts, 117–18
    horse in England and, 278
    horses of, 111–12
    merino sheep, introduction, 171
    tabu on pork, 78
Archaeopteryx, 17–22
Archaeornis, 20
Arctogaea, 241
Argentina, sheep and cattle of, 270–72
Arion, 85
Aristophanes, 89, 214
Aristotle, 93–95, 120, 163–64, 191, 195–96, 217, 222, 224, 380
Arithmetical horses, 326–29
d'Arlande, Marquis, 253
Armadillo, 135

Armour, Philip D., 376
Army transport, decline in use of horse for, 388
Art
  animals depicted in, 205–07
  cave, of Stone Age, 61–65
Art of Hunting with Birds (Frederick II), 118
Artaxerxes Mnemon, 117
Artemisia, Queen, 88
Artificial clothing materials, 352–57
Artificial insemination, 348–49
Asepsis, 305
Asoka, King, 256
Ass, 388
Astley, Sergeant Philip, 284
Astor, John Jacob, 361
Astoria, fur trade in, 361
Athena, 88
Augury, *see* Prophecy
Aurelian, Emperor, 164
Aurelius, Marcus, 243
Auricle, 222
Aurochs, 185
Australia
  discovery, 231–32
  fauna, 232–41
  isolation, in Eocene period, 25–26
  Spanish origin of sheep in, 269
Avicenna of Cordoba, 156–57
Azores, 126, 128
Aztecs, 131–33

Babylonians, mastery of the horse and, 83
Bach, Johann Sebastian, 204
Bacon, Francis, 191
Bacteria, bacteriology, 302–16
Badger, 142
Bagford, Mr., 32
Balios, 85
Balloons, early experiments with, 251–53, 274
Baluchitherium, 26
Bandilleros, 183
Banks, Joseph, 235
Basilisk, 154, 155
Batrachomyachy, 87, 88
Beagle, ship, 297
Bears, 141, 147

Beaver, hunted in Canada, 142–45
Beef-cattle, 186, 269, 370, 371, 384
Bees
  eggs of, 266
  in Greece and Rome, 100–01
  Mandeville's fable of, 214–15
Beet sugar, 352
Behaviorist psychology, 329–30
Behring, Emil, 310, 311
Belon, Pierre, 158
Bentinck, Count, 247
Bergson, Henri, 378
Bernard, Claude, 305
Bestiaries, medieval, 121
Betting, 281–83
Bezoar, 157
Bichat, François Xavier, 230
Bikini atom bomb, 394
Biogenetic principle, of J. F. Meckel, 291
Biology, in the Renaissance, 157–58
Birds
  carrier pigeons, 322–26
  cure of leprosy and, 79
  man's affection for, 385–86
  reptilian, 17–22
Birds, The (Aristophanes), 89
Birth-control, 348–49
Bit, invention of, 180
Black rat, 315, 316
Blackwell, Robert, 268
Blood
  animals with and without, Aristotelian classification, 94, 217–18, 222
  circulation, 198–99, 242
Blumenbach, Johann Friedrich, 235, 254
Boar, wild, 116
Bohr, Niels, 341
Bolk, 46–47
Bombyx, 166, 167, 354
Bombyx mori, 164
Bonaparte, Lucien, 280
Bonnet, Charles, 248–49
Borgia, Cesare, 181
Bos primigenius, 68
Bos taurus ibericus, 185
Botanical Philosophy (Linnaeus), 224

Botany
  classification of plants on sexual basis, 221
  transmutation theory, 226
  work of Ray and Linnaeus, 217–20
Boucher de Perthes, 36, 38
Bourgelat, Claude, 256
Boyar pelts, 145–47
Brain
  dinosaur, 16
  early man, 49–50
  factor of, in taming of animals, 67
  human and animal, 199
Brazil
  cannibalism, 136
  etymology, 126
  fauna, 134–35
Bread, for the masses, 96–97
Breeding of animals
  ancient Rome, 100
  cattle for sport, 184–88
  crossbreeding, 267–69
  Henry the Navigator's experiments, 127–28
  horses for racing, 277–79
  rare animals, 358–67
  Stone Age, 68–70
Brehm, zoologist, 329
Breton fishermen, 139, 140
Breuil, Abbé, 48, 62
Bronx Zoo, in New York, 285
Brown rat, 315–16
Browne, Sir Thomas, 155
Bruant, Aristide, 319
Bruenn Natural History Society, 337
Bubonic plague, 314–15
Bucephalus, 85
Buddha, Gautama, 74–75
Buffalo, 385
Buffon, 224, 226, 227–30, 232, 235, 237, 254, 315
Bullfighting, 181–88
Burrell, biologist, 237
Butter, prohibited in ancient Rome, 100
Butterflies, 135
Byerly, stallion, 279

Cabot, John and Sebastian, 138, 139

Caesar, Julius, 97, 164, 323
Caldwell, zoologist, 237
Callisthenes, 94
Calorific value of food, 368–70, 371
Cambrian Age, 6
Camel
  Arabian and Jewish attitudes to, 79
  Egypt, in, 84
  evolution, 29–30
Canada, 137
  fur trade, 142–45, 361, 362
Canaries, 344
Canary Islands, 126
Cane sugar, 101, 352
Cannibalism, in Brazil, 136
Capek, Joseph and Karel, 89
Capital, origin, 68–70
Capons, 100
Capuchin monkeys, 330
Carajou, 142
Caramuru, 136
Carboniferous Age, 10–11
Cardim, Padre Fernão, 58, 153
Carnivores, 26
Carrel, biologist, 389
Carrier pigeons, 323–26
Cartier, Jacques, 141–42
Casein, 355–56
Castration, of animals, 69, 100
Cat
  aesthetic appeal, 317–20
  literature, in, 210, 319–20
Cataclysms, see Creationist theory
Catastrophe theory, see Creationist theory
Catherine de' Medici, 156, 157, 162
Cattle
  bred for bull-ring, 184–88
  English, Australian and Argentine, 268–70
  heavy slaughter in war-time, 370–72
  sacred cow of India, 372–73
  shorthorned, 68, 269
  statistics, 383–84
  wool from cows' milk, 355
Cavalry, see Horse
Cave art, 61–65
Cell division, 4–5

Cellini, Benvenuto, 154–55
Cellular pathology, of Virchow, 230
Cellulose textiles, 353–54
Celsius, Olaf, 219
Cerasus, 98
Ceres, 101
Cervantes, 175
Chambers, Robert, 291
Champlain, 144
Chancelade race, 63
Chantecler (Rostand), 89
Chardonnet, Count Hilaire de, 353
Chariot races, Roman, 103–04
Charlemagne, 114
Charles II, 144
Charles V, Emperor, 181
Charles IX, of France, 157
Charles the Bad, 119
Chat Noir cafe, 319
Cheese, in ancient Rome, 100
Chemical industry, 351
Cherry, introduced into Europe, 98
Chester, origin of horse-racing and, 277
Chicago
  meat processing center, 375–76
  World's Fair at, 287
Chimpanzee, 330–31
China
  pearl culture, 365
  silk culture, 165
Chromosomes, 338–49
Cicero, 99
Cincinnati, meat-processing center, 375
Circulation of the blood, 198–99, 242
Circus, Roman, 103–06
  eastern origin, 105
  modern times, in, 284
Claudius, Emperor, 32
Clement VI, Pope, 261
Clement VII, Pope, 156
Clever Jack, horse, 326–27
Climate, animal migration and, 60–61
Clothing, artificial, 352–57
Coal, formation, 10
Cockfighting, 186
Cod, 141
Coke, horse-breeder, 279

Coke, Thomas, Earl of Leicester, 268
Colbert, 170
Colette, 320
Colosseum, Roman, 105
Color sensitivity, of animals, 331
Columbus, Christopher, 128–30, 133, 148–49, 154, 175, 231, 264
Condensed milk, 376
Conservation and protection of animals, 253–58, 358–60
Constantinople, circuses in, 104–05
Conyers, 32
Cook, Captain James, 231–34, 235, 239
Corals, 6, 159
Corpuscles, red blood, 242
Cortés, Hernando, 131, 132, 167
Cos, pseudo-silk from, 164
Cosmography (Sebastian Muenster), 150
Cossacks, 147
Cotton, 352
Cotton seed, 351
Cotylosaurians, 11
Court-taster, office of, 255
Cow, sacred, of India, 372–73
Cowpox, 254
Cranial index, 50
Creationist theory, of Cuvier, 12, 13, 34–36, 300
Creative evolution, Bergson's, 378
Credé, bacteriologist, 308
Criminal investigation, dogs used in, 322
Critique of Pure Reason (Kant), 204
Crocodile, 81, 364–65
  reservoir of trypanosomes, 314
Croesus, 92
Cro-Magnon man, 49, 63
Crossbreeding, 267–69, 336, 346, 348, 361, 392
Crusades, the, 114, 315, 318, 323
Crust, of the earth, 24–25
Cruz, Oswaldo, 314
Ctesias, 117
Cudahy, meat-packing firm, 376
Cuénot, Lucien, 46–47
Cugnot, physicist, 273–74

Curb bit, invention of, 180
Cuvier, Georges, 12, 13, 27, 34–35, 36, 94, 300

Daedalus, 251
Da Gama, Vasco, 175
Dalton, Charles, 361
Darley, stallion, 278, 279
Darwin, Charles Robert, 13, 17, 20–21, 41, 289–301, 337, 343, 345, 380
Darwin, Erasmus, 296
Daubenton, zoologist, 285
Davaine, bacteriologist, 303
de Blainville, zoologist, 237
de Jussieu, Bernard, 220
de la Tour, Cagniard, 305
de Vroies, Hugo, 66, 336
Decomposition, 304
Demeter, 85
Derby, 12th Earl of, 280, 282
Derby, the, 282
Des Chats (Steinlen), 319
Descartes, René, 193–95, 197, 199, 211, 263, 299, 332
Descent of man, see Man
Descent of Man (Darwin), 41, 300
Devitalization, law of, 391–92
Devonian period, 10
Didelphia, 237
Diderot, Denis, 230
Dingo, 239–40
Dinocyon dog, 65
Dinosaurs, 15, 22
Diocletian, Emperor, 323
Diodorus, 85
Diogenes of Apollonia, 93
Diomed, stallion, 279
Diomedes, 86
Diphtheria, 310–11
Diplodocus, 16
Direction, sense of, 322, 325
Discours à Madame de la Sablière (La Fontaine), 211
Discours de la Méthode (Descartes), 193, 204
Disease
  microbes and, 302–16
  prehistoric, theory, 30
Dishley cattle, 268

Divination, in ancient Greece, 102–03
Dog
  combat with elephant, organized by Romans, 106
  first domesticated animal, 65
  Greek contempt for, 91
  imaginative power, 192
  medieval times, in, 118–19
  rabies and, 307–08
  Red Cross and police work in, 322
  used as food, 132
  used for racing, 282–83
Domestication of animals, 59–61, 65–70
Dominants, 336
Donkey
  ancient Egypt, in, 84
  descendant of wild ass, 68
Drosophila, 340, 341, 342
Dryopithecus, 41
Du Bois-Reymond, physiologist, 247, 253
Dubois, Eugene, 42–43
Duckbilled platypus, 235–38
Dürer, Albrecht, 158, 206
Dutch animal paintings, 206–07

East India Company, 372
Eclipse, stallion, 278
Ecology, 380–82
Education, evolution and, 201
Egg-laying mammals (monotremes), 235–37
Egypt, ancient
  animal cults, 79–82
  belief in transmigration of souls, 73–74
  horse, donkey and camel in, 84
Electric rays, 245–46
Electricity, animal, 246–47
Elephantine, 81
Elephants
  combat with dogs, organized by Romans, 106
  fossil remains, discovered in Thames, 32–33
  migrations, in Tertiary and Quaternary periods, 26
  used in war, 107

Elizabeth I, Queen, 167–68
Embryology, 95, 221, 291
Empedocles, 4–5, 93
Encyclopedias, 217, 229
Engel, Ernst, 390
England
    animal satire and, 213–16
    Canadian fur trade and, 144
    cattle, quality, 267–68
    depredations of rats in, 316
    dog-racing in, 282–83
    fur trade in Russia, 145
    horse-racing in, 277–82
    population increase in 18th cen-
        tury, 262
    silk culture, 168
    wool and the agrarian revolution,
        172–74
Enriques de Gandia, 126
Environment, evolution and, 293
Eocene period, 25, 28
Eohippus, 28, 388
Epidemics, 256, 261–62
Epigenetic theory, 222
Epsom, horse-racing at, 280, 282
Equidae, 28
Equus prjevalsky, 287
Eric the Red, 125
Ericsson, Leif, 125
Ersatz foods and materials, 350–57
Essay on Population (Malthus), 294
Ethics (Spinoza), 195
Eugenics, 342–49
Evolution
    education and, 201
    mammals, 22–23
    man, 38–53
    metempsychosis and, 73–74
    migration periods, 24–31
    reptiles, 14–17
    reptiles and flight, 17–22
    teeth, 9–11
Evolution, theory:
    acceptance of Darwinism, 300–01
    contributions of Alfred Russel
        Wallace, 293–95
    Cuvier's, Lyell's and Darwinian
        concepts, 12–14
    Darwin's work and background,
        294–298

Evolution, theory—Cont'd
    Hegel, Schopenhauer and La-
        marck's theories, 289–93
    Huxley-Wilberforce controversy,
        298–300
    ideas of Empedocles, 4–5
    mutations and, 343–45
    Russian theory, 346–48
Existentialism, 329

Fable of the Bees (Mandeville),
    213, 216
Fables, animal, see also Satire
    Greek, 87–93
    Indian, 208
    La Fontaine, 207–12
    medieval, 121–22
Fables choisies (La Fontaine), 208
Fabre, Jean-Henri, 329
Fabulous animals, of the Renais-
    sance, 149–57
Fagara-silkworm, 169
Falconry, 116–18
Fats, animal and vegetable, 350–
    52
Fear of animals, in primitive man,
    72–73
Feretti process, 356
Fermentation, 304
Ferret, 318
Fertility, potency and, 264–67
Fiber, artificial, 352–55
Fisheries, deep sea, of Europe, 139–
    41
Fishes
    amphibian descent from, 10–11
    electric, 245–46
    main animal food of China and
        Japan, 374
    ostracoderms, 9
    Renaissance interest in, 157–62
Fish-lizards, 17
FitzRoy, Captain, 297
Flax, 225
Fleas, 314–15
Flies, 314
Flora, 101
Fola, 180
Folk-migrations, of 4th century A.D.,
    108

Food, *see also* Meat
  calorific measurement, 368–70, 371–72
  gourmandism in ancient Rome, 97–101
  Malthusianism and the food supply, 261–72
  prehistoric man, 57–61, 67–70
  supply, in modern world, 372–77
  synthetic, 350–52
Forest-prison, 99
Fossils, *see* Palaeontology
Fowl, wild, 384
Fox, 142
  crossbreeding, in modern fur trade, 361–62
Fox fur, 147
Fracastoro, Girolamo, 161, 303
France
  exploration of Canada, and the fur trade, 141–45
  horse-racing in, 281–82
  medieval cuisine, 117
  silk culture in, 169–70
Francis I, of France, 141, 156, 167–69
Franco-Prussian War, 324
Franklin, Benjamin, 245
Franks, 117
Frazer, Sir J. G., 78
Frederick II, Emperor, 118, 176
French Revolution, 264
Frere, John, 33
Freud, Sigmund, 221
Frogs
  Galvani's experiment with legs of, 245–46
  spawn of, 266
  war with mice and, in Greek batrachomyachy, 87–88
Frogs, The (Aristophanes), 89
Frozen meat, 270–72
Fruit-fly, 339
Fuhlrott, Johann Carl, 39
Fur trade
  Canadian, 142–45
  modern developments, 360–63
  Russian, 145–47
Fur-seal, 147

Galen, 243
Galli-Valerio, bacteriologist, 314
Galvani, Luigi, 245–46
Gandhi, 373
Gassendi, 193, 194, 196, 299
Gauchos, 269–70, 374
Genera, 226
General Morphology (Haeckel), 41, 293
Genet, 318
Genetics, 67, 127, 338–49
Genghis Khan, 112, 113, 270, 287
Geoffroi de Preuilly, 115
Geological periods, chart, 51
Germany
  arithmetical horses of, 326–29
  artificial silk production, 354
  mediaeval cuisine, 117
Gesner, Konrad, 151, 158
Ghee, 373
Gigantism, 15, 23
Gilbert, William, 243
Giraffe, 176, 288
Girard, 354
Gluecksritter, 113
Godolphin horse, 279
Gods, animals as, in ancient Egypt, 79–82
Godwin, William, 267
Gondwana Land, 24, 25
Gonneville, Binot Paulmier de, 231
Gordon, Colonel, 269
Gracchi, the, 97
Grand Prix, 282
Grassi, bacteriologist, 313
Greece, ancient
  Alexander the Great's use of elephants in war, 107
  anthropomorphism in terms of frogs and mice, 87–89
  anthropomorphism of Simonides, Phocylides and Aesop, 90–93
  Aristotle's *Natural History*, 93–95
  horse and, 84–86
  sacrifice of animals, 101
Greenland, 125, 137
Gregory, W. K., 30
Grisone, Federico, 180
Grosseilliers, Sieur de, 144
Gryphon, 154

Gryphosaurus, 19
Guano, 356
Guillotin, physician, 251
Gulliver's Travels (Swift), 215
Gunnbjörn, 125

Haeckel, Ernst, 41–42, 46, 291, 293, 300, 380
Hagenbeck, Karl, 287, 288
Haiti, 130
Haller, Albrecht von, 246
Ham, van, 198
Hammurabi, 83
Hannibal, 107
Hanseatic League, 139–40
Harvey, William, 242, 291
Hathor, 81
Hawaii, 240
Healsville, animal sanctuary at, 238
Hegel, G. W. F., 289–90
Heliogabalus, Emperor, 106
Henle, Jacob, 303
Henry II, King of England, 277
Henry II, King of France, 116
Henry IV, of France, 168, 169, 324, 325
Henry the Navigator, of Portugal, 127–28
Henslow, schoolmaster, 298
Herakles, 86
Herbivores, 25
Herd instinct, 27–28, 71–72
Heredity, 66, 67, 336–49
Herod, stallion, 279
Herodotus, 81, 155, 160, 161
Herrera, Cristóbal Perez, 181
Herring spawn, 266
Herring trade, controlled by Hanseatic League, 139–40
Hesiod, 85
High school, Italian, riding and, 180
Hinduism, 373
Hinny, 388
Hippodamia, 85–86
Histoire naturelle (Buffon), 229
Histoire naturelle de l'âme (La Mettrie), 200
Historia animalium (Gesner), 158
Historia plantarum (Ray), 218

History of the Crusades (William of Tyre), 114
History of Fishes (Belon), 158
Hobbes, Thomas, 191
Hochelaga, 142
Hoffman, E. T. A., 319
Holland, see also Netherlands
    origin of margarine in, 351
Holoarctic zone, 138
Home, zoologist, 235
Homer, 85, 86, 88
Homme machine, L' (La Mettrie), 200, 201, 202
Homo primogenius, 40
Homo sapiens, see Man
Honey
    decline in use, 149
    only sweetening agent used in antiquity, 100–01
Hooke, Robert, 352
Hormones, 345
Horn
    artificial, 356
    unicorn, 156
Horse
    ancestors of, 28, 138
    Arabian, 111–12, 114
    arithmetical, 326–29
    decline of, 386–88
    feudal Europe, in, 113–16
    Greek attitude to, 84–86
    Huns, 110
    imaginative power, 192
    Italian technique of manège, 178–80
    Mongolian, 112–13
    Prjevalsky's wild horse, 287
    racing, 277–83
    Roman cavalry, 110–11
    Spanish cavalry and the Aztecs and Incas, 130–32
    statistics, 384
    Swift's satirical use of, 215
    takes man longest to tame, 83–84
    tamed by Babylonians, 83
    threatened by steam power, 273
    used for supply of serum, 311–12
Huang-Ti, Emperor, 165
Hudson, Henry, 145
Hudson's Bay Company, 144, 361

Humanists, Renaissance, and wonder beasts, 154–57
Humboldt, Alexander von, 94
Hume, David, 228
Hundred Years' War, 116, 261
Huns, 109–10
Hunting by Stone Age men, 57–59
Huxley, T. H., 41, 299, 300
Hybridization, see Crossbreeding
Hyksos kings of Egypt, 84
Hypnotism, 243–45

Ice Age, 29, 30, 52, 60, 137
Ichthyornis, 21
Ichthyosaurians, 17
Ichthyostega, 11
Iliad, 86, 88
Imaginative power, of animals and human beings, 192
Immortality of the soul, 196
Incas, 131–32, 133–34
India
    contempt for the pig, and veneration of the cow, 372–73
    silk culture, 166–67
Indian Mutiny of 1857, 372
Indians
    Brazilian, 134, 135–36
    Canadian, 142–45
Inez de la Cruz, Juana, 131
Inflation, in 16th century, 148
Infusiorians, 198
Inoculation, 254, 304–16
Insect Play (Capek), 89
Insemination, artificial, 348–49
Instinct, 320–22
Intelligence, see Thought
International Agricultural Institute, at Rome, 383
Irving, Washington, 361
Isabella, Queen of Spain, 181
Isis, 81
Islam, see Arabs
Italy
    menageries of the Medicis, 177
    technique of manège, 178–80
Ivan the Terrible, 145

Jacarés, 135
Jaguar, 135

Japan
    artificial silk industry, 354
    pearl culture, 367
    silk culture, 165–66, 169
Jardin d'Acclimation, in Paris, 285
Java, ape-men of (Pithecanthropus erectus), 42–43, 49
Jellyfish, 6
Jenner, Edward, 254, 262, 305
Jews
    tabu on camel-meat, 79
    tabu on pork, 78
Jockey Club, 279
Joinville, Jean de, 159
Jones, F. Wood, 45
Julius Caesar, see Caesar
Juno, 101
Jupiter, 101
Jurassic period, 17
Justinian, Emperor, 104–05, 165
Juvenal, 96, 104

Kadisiya, battle of, 112
Kangaroo, 232–34
Kangaroo Island, 234
Kansas, Ichthyornis discovery at, 20
Kant, Immanuel, 201, 204
Kassites, 83
Khnemu, 81
Kieser, D. G., 244
Klaatsch, Hermann, 45
Knights, of Middle Ages, 113–16
Koch, Robert, 304, 310, 312, 314, 317
Koehler, Wolfgang, 330
Krall, Karl, 327, 328
Krilov, 210
Krische, printer, 356
Kumiss, 110

La Fontaine, Jean de, 207–12
Lagoa Santa, discovery of human skulls at, 44
Lamarck, 5, 236, 293, 298, 300, 345
La Mettrie, Julien Offray de, 200–03, 230, 299
La Mouthe cave paintings, 63
Language, see Speech
Lapdogs, 120
La Plata, Gauchos of, 269

Lartet, Edouard, 38
Las Casas, Bartolomé, 130
Lascaux, cave paintings, 65, 77
Latifundia, of Europe, 373–75
Laveran, Alphonse, 313
Lavoisier, 245
Law of devitalization, 391–92
Lee, William, 168
Leeuwenhoeck, 198
Leibniz, 196–97, 201, 229, 295
Leicester, Thomas Coke, Earl of, 268
Lemurs, as ancestors of man, 45
Leo X, Pope, 177, 178, 196
Leonardo da Vinci, 154, 158, 161, 242, 251
Lepanto, battle, 175
Leprosy
    birds and cure of, 79
    potato as supposed cause, 149
Liber, 101
Lice, 314
Liebig, physiologist, 271
Linaria, 225
Lincoln sheep, 269
Linnaean Society, 295
Linnaeus, 41, 219–30, 231, 232, 235, 296
Linné, Carl von, see Linnaeus
Lions, 176, 177
Livestock, heavy slaughter in war-time, 370–72
Lizards, giant, 14–17
Llama, 30, 133
Locomotive, see Railway
Lods, Adolphe, 79
Loeffler, Friedrich, 310
Loesch, bacteriologist, 312
Longchamp, horse-racing at, 281, 282
Lorenzini, 245
Lorenzo the Magnificent, 177
Louis IX, King of France, 159
Louis XIII, King of France, 170
Louis XIV, King of France, 144, 171, 212, 255
Louis XVI, King of France, 117
Lucullus, Lucius Licinius, 97–98, 99, 106, 117, 365
Lund, university of, 219

Lund, Wilhelm, 44
Lungfish, 10
Luther, Martin, 196
Lyell, Charles, 12, 13, 295, 297, 300
Lyonet, Pierre, 249
Lyons
    silk and rayon manufacture, 354
    veterinary school, 257
Lysenko, T. D., 345–48

MacArthur, Captain, 269
MacCallum, bacteriologist, 313
Machine, men and animals as, 199–203
Madagascar, giant orchid of, 299
Madeira, 126, 127
Maeterlinck, Maurice, 320, 328
Magdalenian period, 63
Magnetism, animal, 243–45
Magnus, Olaus, 151
Maize, 148, 149
Malagoli, 325, 326
Malaria, 312–13
Malpighi, 197–98, 221, 242
Malthus, Thomas Robert, 13, 262–64, 267, 269, 270, 294, 380
Mammals
    egg-laying (monotremes), 234–37
    evolution, 22–23
    term coined by Linnaeus, 222
Mammary gland, 22
Mammoth, 379
Man
    ancestors of Homo sapiens, 44–47
    animals in the Ice Age and, 52–53
    anthropoids and ape men, 38–44
    breeding of animals and, 68–70
    cave art, 61–65
    classed by Linnaeus among pri-mates, 223–24
    domestication of animals and, 59–61, 65–70
    fear of animals and, 71–73
    hunter, 57–59
    independence, 392–94
    new attitude toward animals, 204–05
    physical and psychological rela-tionship to animals, 191–203

Man—*Cont'd*
  problems of animal population
    and preservation and, 382–94
  ritual of bull-fighting and, 186–
    88
  slow embryonic development, and
    late maturity, 383
  stature and brain of early man,
    49–52
  tool-maker, 47–49
  totem animal cult and, 75–78
Mana, 77
Mandeville, Bernard, 212–15, 216
Manège, technique of, 178–80
Manoel, King of Portugal, 178
Maoris, 239
Marcgraf, 217
Marco Polo, *see* Polo
Marconi, Marchese, 326
Margarine, 350–52
Marie Antoinette, 367
Marot, 208
Matadores, 183
Mathematics and heredity, 336–38
Maueranthropus, 43
Maupertius, 230
Mauritius, dodos in, 239
Mazolleni, Father, 249
Meat, *see also* Food
  decline in consumption, 390–91
  general shortage, 96–97
  heavy slaughter of livestock in
    war-time, 370–71
  high consumption, in ancient
    Rome, 97–101
  mediaeval Europe, in, 116–17
  refrigeration, 270–72
Mechanistic theory, *see* Machine
Meckel, J. F., 291
Medici, Catherine de', 156, 157,
    162
Medici family, menageries kept by,
    177–78
Medicines, from animals, 155–57
Méditations (Descartes), 194
Medusa, 85
Mège-Mouriés, Hyppolite, 351
Meister, Joseph, 308
Menageries, of the Medici family,
    177–78; *see also* Zoos

Mendel, Gregor Johann, 336–38, 343,
    346, 347, 361
Menelaus, 86
Merlins, 118
Mermen, 153
Mesmer, Franz Anton, 244
Mesopotamia, animal-drawn vehicles
    of, 83
Mesozoic Age, 14–17
Mesta, the, 172
Metamorphoses (Ovid), 76
Metazoa, 5
Metempsychosis, 73–75
Metric system, 273
Metullus, 107
Meudon, bowman of, 255
Mexico, 131–32
Meyer, Hermann von, 17, 20
Mice and frogs, war of, 87–89
Micro-organisms, *see* Bacteria
Microscope, animal psychology and,
    198–99
Migrations
  animals in Tertiary period, 24–31
  folk, of 4th century A.D., 108–09
Mikimoto, Kokichi, 366, 367
Milk
  ancient Rome, in, 100
  condensed and powdered, 376
  consumption, in U. S. A., 376–77
  kumiss of the Huns, 110
  textiles made from, 355–57
Mind, *see* Soul
Mithra, 188
Mithridates, 98
Mitshurin, Ivan Vladimirovitch, 346
Mitsukuri, Professor, 366
Mohammed, 78, 111–12
Mohammed, stallion, 328
Molecules, Buffon's theory of, 229–
    30
Monad theory, of Leibniz, 196–97,
    229–30
Mongols, horses of, 112–13
Monkey
  intelligence, 330–32
  literature in, 210
Monodelphia, 237
Monotremes (egg-laying mammals),
    234–37

Montagu, Lady Mary, 305
Montagu, Mrs., 168
Montaigne, 161, 191–92, 193
Montgolfier brothers, 252, 274
Montmartre, 319
Moors, the, 171, 185
Morgan, C. Lloyd, 329
Morgan, Thomas Hunt, 339, 343, 344, 345, 346, 347, 392
Morny, Duc de, 281
Mort, Thomas S., 271
Mosquitoes, 313–14, 382, 393
Mousterian culture, 52
Muenster, Sebastian, 150
Mule, 388
Multicellular animals, 5–6
Muscovy Company, 145
Music, horse-riding to accompaniment of, 180
Mussolini, Benito, 355
Mutations, 66, 291, 336–49

Naegli, botanist, 337
Naples, technique of manège and, 179
Napoleon I, 180–81
Napoleon III, 281, 351
Natural History (Aristotle), 94–95, 217–18
Natural History (Pliny), 101
Natural History of Strange Marine Fish (Belon), 158
Natural selection, 5, 293
Neanderthal Man, 38–41, 45, 47, 52
Neogaea, 241
Neolithic Age, see Stone Age
Neptune, planet, 300
Nero, Emperor, 106
Nervous system
  dinosaur, 16
  early man, 50
  training of animals and, 67
Netherlands, herring fisheries of, 140
Neural physiology, 243
New Leicester sheep, 268
New York, Bronx Zoo in, 285
New Zealand
  English cattle imported, 269
  moas of, 238, 239
Newfoundland, 139

Newmarket, horse-racing at, 280
Newton, Sir Isaac, 204, 295
Nietzsche, 203
Nika revolt, 104–05
Nixies, 153
Noah's Ark, 35, 262
Nobel Prize for medicine, 311
Noricum, 114
North America, see also United States
  explorers, 138–39
  prehistoric immigration of animals, 30–31
  zoo-geographical division, 137–39
North-west passage, 141
Notogaea, 240–41
Numa Pompilius, 101
Nylon, 354

Oaks, the, 282
Oinomaos, King, 85–86
Oken, zoologist, 290
Oligocene period, 29
Olympic Games, 280
Omar al-Khattab, 112
Orata, Sergius, 99
d'Orbigny, zoologist, 13
Orchid, giant, 299
Ordovician period, 8
Orientation, sense of, 322, 325
Origin of Species, (Darwin), 13, 17, 21, 41, 289–301, 337
Ornithodelphia, 237
Ornithogaea, 241
Orpheus, 207
Osbaldeston, rider, 276
Osten, Wilhelm von, 327
Ostracoderms, 9
Ostrich, 363–64
Oulton, R. T., 361
Ovid, 76, 160
Owen, Sir Richard, 20
Oysters
  ancient Rome, in, 99
  bred for pearl culture, 365–67
  spawn of, 266

Paintings, of animals, 205–07
Paix chez les bêtes (Colette), 320
Palaeolithic Age, see Stone Age

Palaeontology
  critics of Cuvier, 36–38
  Cuvier's ideas, 34–36
  18th century in, 33–36
  Renaissance interest in, 158–62
Paleotherium, 29
Palaeozoic period, 6, 11
Palissy, Bernard, 159, 160, 161–62
Pallas, naturalist, 315
Palm oil, 351
Panchatranta, 208
Panda, 288
Papua, 240
Paracelsus, 155
Paré, Ambroise, 157
Paris, Jardin d'Acclimation in, 285
Parkes, Alexander, 356
Parrots, 134
Pasly, animal bones at, 52
Pasteur, Louis, 230, 254, 304–09, 313
Pasteur Institute, 310
Patroclus, 86
Pavlov, I. P., 194
Peccary, 133
Pegasus, 85
Peking man (*Sinanthropus pekinensis*), 44, 47–49
Peleus, 85
Pellagra, 148
Pelops, 86
Peloria, 225
Pelsaert, 232
Perception and apperception, 195–97
Peregrine falcon, 118
Permian period, 11
Perrault, Charles, 319
Persiles and Sigismunda (Cervantes), 175
Peru, 132, 133
Petrestrelo, Bartolomeu, 127
Petty, Sir William, 261
Pfungst, Oscar, 327
Phaedrus, 212
Phenomenology, 329
Philip II, of Spain, 181
Philip the Good, 119
Phocylides, 91
Phoenix, 154, 155
Phosphate, 357

Picadors, 183
Picasso, 162
Pigeons, carrier, 322–26
Pignatelli, 180
Pigs
  attitude towards, of Jews, Syrians, Arabs, 78, 372
  heavy slaughter in war-time, 370
  Indian contempt for, 372
  introduced into New World by Columbus, 130, 149
  sacrificial animal, 101
  statistics, 383, 384
Pisanello, 206
Pithecanthropus, 42
Pithecanthropus erectus (ape-men of Java), 42–43, 49
Pius II, Pope, 177
Planck, Max, 335
Plastic, 356
Plato, 154
Platypus, 234–37
Plautus, 191
Pleistocene Ice Age, 29, 30, 52
Pliny, 101, 120, 154, 160–61, 197, 323
Pliocene period, 28
Plutarch, 88, 197
Polar bear, 141, 147
Police dogs, 322
Pollender, physician, 303
Polo, Marco, 113, 231
Polynesia, 240
Polyps, 6, 248
Pomponazzi, philosopher, 154, 196
Population
  decrease of, due to wars and epidemics, 262
  Malthusian doctrine, 262–64
  question of potency and fertility and, 264–67
Portugal
  bull-fighting in, 182
  fauna of Brazil and, 134
  Henry the Navigator's livestock experiments, 127–28
Poseidon, 85
Potassium, 357
Potato, 149
Potency and fertility, 264–67

Potter, Paulus, 205, 206–07
Pouilly-le-Fort, Pasteur at, 306
Powdered milk, 376
Preformation, 250
Prescott, W. H., 131
Primates, 41, 52, 223–24
Principles of Geology (Lyell), 13
Prjevalsky, Nikolai Mikhailovitch, 287
Property, origin, 68–70
Prophecy, in ancient Rome, 102
Prophylactic inoculation, 254, 304–16
Prometheus, 211
Protection of animals, *see* Conservation
Prussia, Crown Princess of, 300
Psycho-analysis, 329
Psychology, animal, 191–203, 320–22, 329–32
Puma, 133
Punic War, 107
Pyramids, built of fossil nummulites, 81–82
Pyrrhus, King of Epirus, 106
Pythagoras, 74

Quantum theory, 335
Quaternary period, chart, 51
Queensberry, Duke of, 276
Quintus Fulvius Lupinus, 99

Ra, 81
Rabbits
  farming, in ancient Rome, 99
  Porto Santo, 127–28
Rabelais, 208, 210
Rabies, 307–09
Radiation chemistry, 339–40
Radisson, Pierre, 144
Railway, introduction, 274–77
Rare animals, breeding, 358–67
Rats, 314–16
Ray, John, 218–19
Rayon, 354
Real, Corte, 138
Reason, age of, 199
Réaumur, René-Antoine de, 226, 248, 249–50
Recessives, 336

Red Cross dogs, 322
Redi, 245
Refrigeration, of meat, 270–72
Regeneration, 247–50
Rembrandt, 204
Renaissance
  animals as examples of beauty and, 175–78
  animal paintings, 206
  interest in fishes, 157–62
  luxuries of, 163
  superstitions regarding animals, 149–57
Reproduction
  artificial insemination, 348–49
  evolution and, 291–92
  factor of potency and fertility, 264–67
Reptiles
  Carboniferous Age, in, 10
  learn to fly, 17–22
  Mesozoic, 14–17
Respiration, Malpighi's works on, 197–98, 242
Reuter, newspaperman, 324
Reyer, bacteriologist, 303
Reynard the Fox, 121
Rhinoceros, 176
Rhodesian man, 49
Richard III (Shakespeare), 284
Richelieu, Cardinal, 170
Robber-Knight, 113
Roble Grotto, cave paintings, 64
Roman de Renart, 121
Romanes, George John, 329
Rome, ancient
  circuses, 103–06
  collapse of empire, 108, 110
  gourmandism and high consumption of meat, 99–101
  military use of elephants, 107
  organized elephant and dog fights, 106
  sacrifice of animals, 101–03
  use of silk, 164
Rome, International Agricultural Institute of, 383
Rosarius, Hieronymus, 192
Rosas, Juan Manuel de, 270
Ross, Sir Ronald, 313

Rostand, Edmond, 89
Rostand, Jean, 46
Rothschild, Nathan, 323–24
Rousseau, Jean-Jacques, 256
Roux, bacteriologist, 307, 310, 311
Royal Society, 156, 231
Rozier, Pilâtre de, 253
Rubens, 206
Rupert, Prince, 144
Russia
    Darwinism and work on heredity, 345–48
    fur trade, 145–47

Sable fur, 147
Saccharine, 352
Sacred cow of India, 372–73
Sacrifice, of animals
    ancient Greece, in, 101
    ancient Rome, in, 101–03
Sagres, geographic institute at, 127
Saint-Hilaire, Geoffroy, 236, 285
Salamander, 155
Salmon, 141
Salmon spawn, 266
Satire, use of animals in, 87–89, 212–16; see also Fables
Saurians, 14–17, 25
Sautuola, Don Marcelinos, 62
Scaliger, Julius Caesar, 155
Schaaffhauser, biologist, 40
Schaudinn, F., 312
Scheuchzer, biologist, 35
Schiller, 325
Schmerling, P. C., 36
Schopenhauer, Arthur, 203, 291–92
Schwann, bacteriologist, 305
Scipio Africanus, 99
Scorpions, 8
Sculptures, of animals, 205–06
Sea-cow, 147
Sea-serpent, 151–53
Sea-snakes, 152
Sea-spiders, 9
Sebek, 81
Semmelweiss, physician, 305
Semon, 66
Seneca, 197

Sept dialogues de bêtes (Colette), 320
Sericulture, see Milk
Serum therapy, 309–12
Sexual aspect, of Malthusianism, 263
Sexual classification of plants, 221
Shakespeare, William, 213, 284
Shaw, zoologist, 235
Sheep
    Australian and Argentine, 269
    cured of anthrax by Pasteur, 306
    domesticated in Stone Age, 68
    English breeds, 268, 269
    English woolen trade, 172–74
    introduced into Europe, 171–72
Shorthorned cattle, 68, 269
Siberia, settlement, 146–47
Si-Ling, Empress, 165, 169
Silk
    artificial, 353–54
    Chinese culture, 164–66
    introduction into Europe, 166–70
    Japanese, Indian and Arabian culture, 166–67
    used by Romans, 163–64
Silk Road, the, 164–66, 167
Silurian period, 9
Simond, bacteriologist, 314
Simonides of Amorgos, 90
Sinanthropus pekinensis (Peking man), 44, 47, 48, 49
Sirens, 153
Smallpox, 254
Snyders, 206
Soap, 351
Soares de Sousa, Gabriel, 153
Solnhofen, Archaeopteryx discovery at, 17–22
Solon, 92
Songbirds, 385
Soul, in animals, 192–203
South America
    introduction of vegetables into Europe, 148–49
    introduction of sugar cane, 149
    modern estancias of, 374
Southland, see Notogaea
Souvenirs entomologiques (Fabre), 329

Spain
  bull-fighting in, 181–88
  conquest of Mexico and Peru, 130–32
  discoveries of Columbus and, 128–30, 133, 148–49, 154, 175, 231, 264
  silk culture, 167
Spallanzi, Father, 249–50
Sparrow-hawk, 118
Specialization, in agricultural economy, 373–75
Species
  Hegel, Schopenhauer and Lamarck's theories, 289–93
  Ray, Linnaeus and Buffon's work on, 218–30
Speech, animals and, 194–95, 200–01
Spemann, 342
Spermatozoa, 198, 266–67
Sphynxotus, 164
Spinoza, 195, 204–05
Spirit theory, of Galen, 243
Splenic disease, *see* Anthrax
Sponges, 6
Spontaneous generation, 230
Spontini, musician, 284
Sport, *see* Circus
Steam power, harnessing, 273–74
Steinlen, Théophile-Alexandre, 319
Steller's sea-cow, 147
Stephenson, George, 275–76
Stock-breeding, *see* Breeding
Stone Age, 57–70
Strabo, geographer, 160
Strabo of Lampsacus, 160
Struggle for existence, 12, 293, 380, 394
Suessmilch, chaplain, 338
Suetonius, 105
Sugar
  cane introduced into New World, 149
  cane replaced by beet, 352
  made from wood, 352
  Roman medicinal use, 101
Superstition
  medieval, regarding animals, 121–22

Superstition—*Cont'd*
  rebirth, in the Renaissance, 148–62
Swammerdam, 198
Sweden, herring fisheries of, 140
Swift, Gustavus F., 376
Swift, Jonathan, 213, 215–16
Synthetic foods and materials, 350–57
Syphilis, 148
Syrians, tabu on pork and, 78

Tapir, 135
Tarsiers, as ancestor of man, 45
Tarsius spectrum, 45
Tasmania, 239
Taxonomic division, of Saint-Hilaire, 236
Teeth, evolution, 9–11
Tellier, Charles, 271
Tellurismus (Kieser), 244
Tennessee, legal action against teaching of evolution, 301
Tertiary period, 27–28
Thales of Miletus, 91
Theodora, Empress, 104–05, 165
Theogony (Hesiod), 85
Theological-Political Treatise (Spinoza), 205
Theophrastus of Lesbos, 160
Thevenot, zoologist, 249
Thiers, Adolphe, 276
Thirty Years' War, 261
Thought, nature of, in man and animals, 192–203, 320–22, 329–32
Tiberius, Emperor, 164
Tierleben (Brehm), 329
Tierra del Fuego, 297
Titanosaurus, 16
Titus, Emperor, 105, 164
Tool making, by early man, 47–49, 50
Toreros, 182, 184
Totem animal cult, 58, 75–78
Tournaments, of middle ages, 114–16
Transmigration of souls, 73–75
Transmutation theory, of Linnaeus, 225–27

Transport, in war, decline in use
of horse for, 388
Trapping, in Canada, 143–44
Tree kangaroo, 234
Trembley, Abraham, 247–48
Trilobites, 6, 9
Trypanosomes, 314
Tsetse fly, 314
Tuberculosis, 316
Tupi Indians, 58
Turbot spawn, 266
Turkey, Mexican, 148
Tyrannosaurus, 16

Unicellular animals, 3, 312
Unicorn, 120–21, 156
United Nations health organization,
313
United States
alligator-breeding in, 364–65
consumption of milk, 376–77
fur trade, 361
meat-processing in Chicago, 376
nylon manufacture, 354, 355
Uppsala, university of, 220
Urea, 356

Vaccines, 305–09
Valencia, Silk Exchange in, 167
Vampires, in Brazil, 135
Vegetables, from the New World,
148–49
Ventricle, 222
Veterinary science, 256–58
Vicente do Salvador, Frei, 153
Victoria, Queen, 300
Virchow, Rudolf, 40, 230
Virginia, silk culture in, 167
Visigoths, 110, 117, 181
Vitamins, 368
Vivisection, 242–53
conflict over, 253–55
Volta, Alessandro, 246–47
Voltaire, 210
Voyage of the Beagle (Darwin),
297
Vulgar Errors (Browne), 155
Vulture stele, in the Louvre, 83

Wagner, A., 17, 19

Wagner, Moritz, 128
Wales, Prince of, 272
Wallace, A. R., 137
War, animals in, see also Horse
carrier pigeons, 322–26
dogs, 322
elephants, 106–07
heavy slaughter of livestock, 370–
72
Wasps, The (Aristophanes), 89
Waste products, from meat, 375
Water
first living creatures dwellers in,
3–4
return of animals to, in Jurassic
period, 17
Watt, James, 273
Wax, 350
Weasel, 318
Wegener, geographer, 24
Weismann, August, 66, 346, 347
Wilberforce, Bishop, 299
Wild animal preserves, in ancient
Rome, 99
Wild ass, 68
Wild boar, 117
Wild fowl, 117
Wild horse, 287
William of Tyre, 114
Wilson, meat-packing firm, 376
Wolf-dog, Australian (dingo),
239
Wolf-fish, 141
Wolfhound, 119
Wood
sugar from, 352
textiles from, 353–55
Wool, artificial, 354, 355, 356
Wool-sorter's disease, see Anthrax
Worms, 248–49
Wotton, 158–59

Xanthos, Achilles' horse, 85
Xenophanes, 160
X-rays, 339, 341

Ye Yin Yang, 365, 366
Yellow fever, 313–14
Yermak, 146
Yersin, bacteriologist, 314

422 INDEX

Zebra, 176, 285
Zeus, 85, 86, 88
Zieberg, naturalist, 225
Zoo-geography, zone division of, 137, 240–41
Zoology
animal magnetism and electricity, 243–47
Aristotle's basic achievement, 93–95

Zoology—Cont'd
ecology, 380–82
fauna of Australia, and controversies over classification, 232–41
Ray, Linnaeus and Buffon's ideas, 218–30
regeneration, 247–50
Zoophytes, 159
Zoos, 285–88; see also Menageries

Set in Linotype Caledonia
Format by Robert Cheney
Manufactured by The Haddon Craftsmen, Inc.
Published by HARPER & BROTHERS, New York